*Inferno*

# Inferno, Alone

## AND OTHER WRITINGS

# August Strindberg

IN NEW TRANSLATIONS.
EDITED AND INTRODUCED
BY EVERT SPRINCHORN

*Anchor Books*
*Doubleday & Company, Inc.*
*Garden City, New York*
*1968*

The Anchor Books edition is the first publication
of *Inferno, Alone and Other Writings.*

Anchor Books edition: 1968

# Contents

Contents

# Introduction:

## Strindberg from 1892 to 1897

I don't hold any opinions, my views are impromptus. Life would be pretty monotonous if one thought and said the same things every day. We've got to keep it new and fresh. One's whole life, after all, is only a poem.

Strindberg,
*The Cloister* (1898)

Strindberg's autobiographical novels were written during two exceedingly productive periods in his life, 1886 to 1888 and 1897 to 1903. Strindberg did not set down his recollections in tranquillity; he wrote best when he had worked up a large head of steam. The writing of the first autobiographical series, consisting of *The Son of a Servant, Storm and Stress* (or *Time of Ferment*), *In the Red Room, The Author,* and *A Madman's Defense,* was a consequence of the emotional and financial crisis of 1884 and 1885, which aroused in Strindberg, then only in his mid-thirties, the fear that he was already bankrupt as a writer; the second series, a large selection of which is contained in the present volume, was inspired mainly by his experiences from 1893 to 1898, experiences that reached a climax in 1896 when Strindberg seemed to be on the verge of a mental collapse.

The self-portrait that emerges from the first series is that of a man who as an adolescent lost the faith of his childhood, and as a young rebel embraced Darwinism and socialism, and who finally succumbed somewhat reluctantly to the allurements of atheism. The second self-portrait reveals a man who abjures his brief flirtation with atheism and, under pressure of middle age and mysterious occurrences, acquires a belief in the beyond. Regarded superficially, these two self-portraits form a kind of Janus head, two disparate images that have nothing in common, except of course a common occiput—I mean the connecting years between 1888 and 1897. In order to see Strindberg whole it is necessary to understand what happened to him during these years, especially from 1892 to 1897, when he seemed to dry up as a writer but was actually only striking deeper roots. It was during this five-year period that he exiled himself from a Sweden that did not appreciate him and came in touch with an international group of artists and writers. Out of the shared experiences and ideas there came forth a new Strindberg. To borrow his own metaphor, the larval writer encased himself in a cocoon and seemed to die. But a metamorphosis was taking place, silently, secretly, and out of the chrysalis an artist was literally reborn.

## TO BERLIN

In 1888, writing the last pages of *A Madman's Defense*, Strindberg intimated that the husband in that novel (himself) was about to be driven insane by his wife and locked up. Life provided a less dramatic ending to the story. Strindberg and his wife Siri stuck together for a while longer before divorce proceedings were initiated in 1890. On March 24, 1891, an interlocutory decree was granted by a church council in Sweden. The three children of the marriage were placed in the care of Siri, and Strindberg was required to contribute 100 crowns a month for their support. In the wake of the divorce trial he was sued by his wife's close friend Marie David for slander and for assault and battery. Accusing her of being a lesbian and of breaking up his marriage, he had sought to gain possession of his children by arguing that entrusting them to his wife would be tantamount to placing them in a home of perverse women. So strong were his feelings that he once pushed Marie David off his porch when she tried to settle matters amicably. The court found against Strindberg on both counts. He was fined 498.80 crowns and threatened with imprisonment. (Some idea of what 400 crowns meant to Strindberg in labor hours may be gained from the fact that that was the sum paid him by the publisher for his play *Lucky Peter's Travels*.)

At this time Strindberg had virtually no income. After standing trial in 1884 for a blasphemous phrase in one of his short stories, Strindberg found that publishers were reluctant to print his work, in spite of the fact that he had been acquitted. It was, of course, his sexual frankness and socialistic inclinations that won him enemies. In 1887 the theologian J. W. Personne issued a pamphlet blaming Strindberg for the immorality that existed among school children in Sweden. Parents forbade their children to read him much as American parents a generation later would forbid their children to read Freud. Some parents vented their fury by spitting at Strindberg as he walked down the street, and naturally they thought *he* was quite mad.

The two greatest plays written in Sweden up to that time,

*The Father* and *Miss Julie*, were refused by the large publishing houses and printed by a small one-man firm in 1887 and 1888; and *Miss Julie* was not performed publicly in Sweden until 1906. In 1892, a bleak year for Strindberg, he seriously thought of giving up creative writing. He offered to translate Zola's *La faute de l'abbé Muret;* he tried to invent a method of color photography; he went back to painting and had an exhibit of his canvases in Stockholm, which brought him a few paltry crowns.

The more discouraged he grew, the more the south beckoned him. In Berlin the Freie Bühne (Free Stage) had given in 1890 a private performance of the censored play *The Father,* and in April 1892 they staged a production of *Miss Julie* that had to be taken off the boards after one performance because of the protests of the women subscribers. These two productions represented Strindberg's debut on the stage outside Scandinavia.

Living in Germany was the Swedish writer Ola Hansson who was at this time one of Strindberg's most ardent champions and a friend of the Berlin critics Otto Brahm and Paul Schlenther, the organizers of the Freie Bühne, who had done so much to further Ibsen's cause in Germany. A few years earlier, in 1888, Strindberg had endeavored to open a Scandinavian Experimental Theater modeled, as was the Freie Bühne, on Antoine's pioneering noncommercial theater, the Théâtre-Libre in Paris. Having written the long one-acts *Miss Julie* and *Creditors,* he was casting about for material for shorter plays, twenty to thirty minutes in length, of the type that Antoine had introduced at the Théâtre-Libre in opposition to the long, well-oiled machines that dominated the commercial theater. Hansson's short story "A Pariah" appealed to the dramatist and he wrote to the author, who was then still living in southern Sweden, suggesting that it would make a good twenty-minute play. During the next two years Hansson and Strindberg grew closer to one another. Both were interested in split personalities, abnormal psychology, especially in its sexual aspects, and in the relation of genius to insanity. Hansson regarded great criminals as similar to great artists in that both were profoundly ill. "All great artistic works are the product of an abnormality of the soul," he wrote to Strindberg. The insane person displays the same symptoms as the man who rises above the conventions of society. Hansson introduced Strindberg to the works of Poe, and Strindberg reciprocated by introducing Hansson to the works of Nietzsche.

Strindberg had just come out of the socialistic and utilitarian phase of his career when he met Hansson, and was in his brief Nietzschean phase. Both writers were rebelling against the strict naturalism of the 1880s which, they felt, emphasized the external forces of heredity and environment too much and slighted the mysterious inner drives. Hansson's volume of erotic case histories *Sensitiva Amorosa*, "studies in the anatomy of the soul," was denounced by the Swedish critics when it appeared in 1887, and those critics were no kinder to *Miss Julie* a year later. Hansson, however, wrote a piece for a Danish journal comparing *Miss Julie* with Ibsen's latest play *The Lady from the Sea* to the advantage of the former. Disgusted with the reception of his book in Sweden, Hansson quit his native country, moving first to Denmark and later to Berlin. In 1889, when Strindberg's marriage was breaking up, Hansson married a twenty-nine-year-old German journalist, Laura Mohr, who used the pen name Marholm and who had written a warm review of *Sensitiva Amorosa*. Thus by marriage and alliance the outsiders were consolidating their position against the Establishment.

Ola and Laura Hansson followed Strindberg's pecuniary and marital trials very closely and saw in him an ally against an unappreciative, ungrateful, and insensitive Sweden. In the fall of 1890 Strindberg complained to them, "My economic situation is desperate, and soon I'll try my hand at something entirely new." Four months later, at the time of his interlocutory divorce, some of his chattels were distrained by the sheriff for the payment of debts. In the summer of 1892, shortly before Strindberg's divorce became final, the sheriff seized some more of his property. The plays he had written during the previous year, *The Keys to the Kingdom of Heaven*, a play of fantasy, and five realistic one-act plays dealing with aspects of his marriage to Siri, represented so much wasted effort as far as income was concerned, for all had been rejected by theater producers.

To a French critic Strindberg wrote, "Subjected to a lock-out for some years now, I am about to die of misery, and I am casting my eyes outside my country to find a way of escape. You may consider me cowardly, but there is much that one will forgive a desperate man." A month later, at the very end of the summer, he wrote to Hansson, "To keep myself afloat, I've been painting pictures—at cut-rate prices, naturally. . . . Thought of becoming a photographer—to save my talent—as a writer. Can you think of any way of getting me out of here?"

Moved by this letter, Ola and Laura Hansson sent what money they could lay their hands on. Strindberg had said he needed 200 marks to get out of Sweden; the Hanssons sent 100; but actually 300 marks was needed since Strindberg had to pay the court costs before he would be allowed to leave the country. The Hanssons now set out to raise money for Strindberg in two ways: a loan from the Freie Bühne and an appeal to the public. After all, the board of the Freie Bühne had recently given the Norwegian author Garborg an "honorary" royalty of 2000 marks to keep him going as a writer. Why would they not do the same for Strindberg? The treasurer of the Freie Bühne was Semmy Fischer, the head of a small publishing house that was to grow into one of the largest in Germany. Although the Freie Bühne owed Strindberg royalties for the two plays of his that they had produced, Fischer handed out 400 marks as a loan (which Strindberg was foolish enough to repay later). Along with the money went the good news that the Lessing Theater was planning to produce *The Father*, if the theater could get the censor's approval.

On September 30 Strindberg left Stockholm and the years of exile began. Among the manuscripts he took with him was that of *The Bond*, a masterful one-act dramatization of his divorce from Siri. With that he had brought the story of his marriage up to date and ended a chapter in his life.

On hand to meet Strindberg at the Stettiner Station in Berlin were, in addition to the Hanssons, a young Finnish writer Adolph Paul and a young Polish writer Stanislaw Przybyszewski, who was to haunt Strindberg's mind for years. They watched the passengers stream out through the gates. At the end of the line, when the crowd had thinned out, came a figure of medium height, wearing a felt hat. Strindberg was now in his forty-third year. His luxuriant mane of hair was lightly streaked with gray; his face was furrowed; a small chin contrasted sharply with his expansive forehead. He had put on some weight in the past few years, and the extra pounds emphasized his measured movements. As he approached his friends and benefactors on the platform, he smiled that strange smile that always left an indelible impression on those who saw it, a smile partly inquisitive, partly shy, a smile which Paul described as that of "a child who is headed straight into the woods of fairy land."

The Hanssons whisked him off to their home in Friedrichshagen, a suburb of Berlin. At the Bahnhof Friedrichstrasse, Strindberg stood in the door of the train to say goodbye to Paul and Przybyszewski, and as he raised his hat, his long rumpled locks seemed to fly upward with his hat.

"Placenta!" whispered Przybyszewski to Paul. "Did you see the placenta? He's still holding on to the placenta! He'll never free himself from woman. He'll never cut himself loose from the womb."

That night a small party was held at the Hanssons' to welcome the Swedish writer. According to Przybyszewski's account,

> Strindberg seemed happy. He avowed that even as far as Hamburg he had been under surveillance by detectives and had not been able to catch his breath until he reached Berlin, where they had to give up following him. He spoke a great deal, and in bad German at first. But when he had been given something to drink (at the Hanssons' one drank only "toddy"—a mixture of hot water and cognac or whiskey), his tongue was loosened, and by the second glass he was expressing himself in pure literary German.
>
> He held forth the whole evening, startling us with astonishing paradoxes, and stunning us with his scientific theories which made havoc of all the accepted opinions. He had indeed a very extensive knowledge of the natural sciences. Literature he passed over with disdain. He recognized only one writer: Balzac—and a bit of Zola also. He told us of the pains and sorrows of his existence, and with such sincerity, with such absolute frankness that

we could not help looking at each other in embarrassment. Finally—morning was already approaching—he seized the guitar that had never been out of his reach and, standing with one leg on a chair, he sang the songs of the Swedish university students—disgracefully obscene and at the same time terribly sad.

To raise more money for Strindberg the Hanssons now resorted to their second method: public solicitation. The October first issue of a German magazine *Die Zukunft* carried without Strindberg's approval (he knew nothing of it until it appeared in print) part of his letter from Stockholm begging for some means by which to get away. The Hanssons were only trying to bring public attention to Strindberg's plight, but the humiliated Strindberg thought they were meddling unnecessarily in his affairs. The appeal did bring in over 1000 marks in October and November, however, and raised a small storm of controversy in Scandinavia when the Danes and Norwegians reproached the Swedes with neglect and inappreciativeness of their one authentic genius.

In Friedrichshagen, Strindberg stayed with the Hanssons a day or two before moving into a little hotel nearby. Here he was too cramped, and after a few days he moved into a flat at the back of the house the Hanssons occupied. This apartment consisted of three rooms and a large kitchen that Strindberg used for his experiments in color photography.

Now Laura Marholm—Strindberg called her Mara (nightmare or old witch in Swedish)—set out to manage his affairs as she managed her husband's. Fresh from his divorce trial, always sensitive to pressure, and doubly sensitive when the pressure came from a woman, Strindberg did not want to be managed. Furthermore, Laura's concern for Strindberg's career was far from altruistic. She was using Strindberg to promote Ola's career. The way Strindberg tells the story, the Hanssons were completely overshadowed by him as literary lights in Berlin; and it was this that led to quarrels between Laura and Strindberg. But our understanding of the situation is enlarged if we remember that Strindberg's cynicism and misogyny always asserted itself in the presence of any domineering woman, and he recognized Laura as a literary parasite without any talent of her own. "She's dangerous," he said.

"She steals the spermatozoa from men and passes them off as her own"—a rather fair assessment, to judge from her writings. To Strindberg a woman like that was really out to emasculate and destroy men, and especially a man like himself, a notorious woman-hater. Laura the Mortician—another of his epithets for her—would hold him in bondage, censor his works, and finally convince the world he was mad. "Bit by bit she'll box me up and put me away in the nuthouse."

Suddenly one night Strindberg left the Hansson house without a word of farewell and showed up at Przybyszewski's place. He informed the Pole that he was being spied on by Laura, that he had found his Green Sack, which served as his portable and expandable filing cabinet, spilled open, as if ransacked, and that his letters from Nietzsche were missing.

Later he remembered that he had deposited those letters with relations in Sweden. But in the meantime he had moved to Adolph Paul's pension in the center of Berlin, at Neue Wilhelmstrasse 2, near the Avenue des Tilleuls.

## THE BERLIN BOHEMIA

Some time before this, while out walking with Paul, Strindberg had passed a tavern whose sign consisted of three stuffed Arabian wine bags hanging on a rusty iron chain over the door. The wind blew, the chains squeaked, and Strindberg, glancing up, took the three bags to be a suckling pig.

"Hey," he said, "the pig is squealing a welcome to us. Let's go in."

Inside were over nine hundred kinds of liquor, gathered from all over the world, and including that poisonous brew known as Swedish punch. Bottles were everywhere, from floor to ceiling, even covering part of the windows, so that it was possible for those who drank through the night to see the sun rise through the colored bottles. Located at the corner of Neue Wilhelmstrasse and Unter den Linden, the tavern was usually known as Türke's *Probierstube* and officially as The Cloister. Strindberg christened it The Little Black Pig (*Zum schwarzen Ferkel*) and under that name it became famous in German and Scandinavian cultural history.

Making it his headquarters, Strindberg drew to it the bohemian avant-garde of Berlin. On the fringe of the group and serving to link it with more respectable circles were the popular satirist Otto Julius Bierbaum and the art critic Julius Meier-Gräfe. Together they founded in 1894 the art journal *Pan*, which became the unofficial organ of the Ferkel crowd. The inner circle consisted of a group of overstrung writers and neurotic painters, mostly in their thirties, all looking for new means of expression, and living as if *fin de siècle* meant the end of their lives. Here foregathered the writers Przybyszewski, Paul, and Dehmel, the doctors Asch and Schleich, and the Norwegian painter Krohg and his pupil Munch. All of them seemed to be driven by sex, art, and alcohol. Thin, tall Dr. Max Asch, the Mephisto of the group, was a friend of Przybyszewski, whom he had met at the University of Berlin a couple of years before when the Pole had been studying medicine there, and with whom he discussed the philosophies of Stirner and Nietzsche. Nicknamed "The Persian" for his looks and "Priapus" for other reasons, Asch was an eminent gynecologist by day and a notorious woman-hater by night. The painter Christian Krohg might appear to be happily married to his beautiful wife Oda but he tolerated and even seemed to encourage a *ménage à trois* with playwright and countryman Gunnar Heiberg, who was shortly to put what he learned from his triangular experiences into the plays *Artists* (1893) and *The Balcony* (1894). The poet Richard Dehmel might be a bowing and scraping official in an insurance company by day but at night he got drunk at The Black Pig, smashed bottles, and argued the philosophical aspects of sex with Przybyszewski—or learned about its biological and physical aspects from Dr. Ludwig Schleich, who had been at the University of Berlin with both Dehmel and the Pole. And Dr. Schleich might occupy himself during the day perfecting a method of administering local anesthesia, which he would be the first to introduce in 1894, but at night he would meet his mistress at Türke's and drink with Strindberg, whom he greatly admired, and not least when the Swede, after a long drinking session, looked for evidence that the earth was flat by lying down in the middle of a Berlin street to study the horizon.

In the absolute center of the circle was Strindberg, the

charged nucleus that kept the others in their orbits at various energy levels. Drinking enormous quantities of liquor and strumming his carefully untuned guitar, he was virtually a tourist attraction for the intelligentsia. About ten years older than most of the others and the only one apart from Krohg who had firmly established himself as a creative artist, he was their acknowledged leader. Przybyszewski got down on his knees before him, kissed his hands, and called him master. Dehmel wrote a poem extolling him as "a man for all time." Surrounded by this coil of artists, his brain became a generator of ideas. "When he is in good form," said Heiberg, who was no friend of his, "Strindberg squanders his wealth of ideas. . . . Whoever wants to can whenever he wants to pick up from Strindberg the plot of a play, completely worked out in his head. Or a novel. I know several who have done so without acknowledging the source." Strindberg said Heiberg did so.

Strindberg's own description of his role and function at The Black Pig is quite accurate and very typical in its choice of metaphor:

> He functions as a ferment, and his seed begins to sprout in the young brains prepared in advance by his disciple Hansson. He is hailed as master and father; they call themselves his apostles. He is tireless, rejuvenating himself each morning, while the apostles disperse and go forth to private circles where altars are erected to them and they are treated as gods. At the end of three months the members of the cluster feel themselves impregnated and begin to show a tendency to detach themselves from the mother stalk.

The Black Pig was a clearing-house of ideas, which changed hands faster than mistresses. All the writers and painters there shared a dislike for the naturalism and social realism of the 1880s. They all concerned themselves with the human being as a nonsocial creature, an animal of instincts and passions. "Skepticism had . . . crept into the movement," wrote Strindberg, "and everyone was preparing to rid himself of the naturalistic sourdough. So strangers found only feces where they had come for nourishment. Everyone was on the lookout for the new formula that would provide the key to the art and literature of the coming period."

After Strindberg the two most important writers in the Ferkel circle were Przybyszewski and Dehmel. Richard Dehmel (1863–1920) was called "the wild man" and looked the part. His face was marred by dueling scars received as a *Couleurstudent* at the University of Berlin. A boyhood injury had made him subject to fits, a malady that worked to his advantage in keeping him out of the army and allowing him to become a poet. He also suffered from hallucinations which provided him with material for some of his best poems. Paralleling Strindberg's career, he had written socialist poems in the 1880s, had read Nietzsche in 1890, and was now writing poems about sex. In 1889 he had married in return for favors received from a Jewish girl, Paula Oppenheimer, who had given him financial and moral support for some years. But Paula was asthmatic and aged rapidly. After the honeymoon in 1893 Dehmel abandoned her and fled to Hamburg, only to be fetched back again by the persistent Paula. During the period when Strindberg knew him best Dehmel was working on his second volume of poems, *What of Love* (*Aber die Liebe*), in which he sought to raise sexual love to the level of religious mysticism. The book contained a cycle of poems entitled "The Transformations of Venus," and in one of these metamorphoses the poet watches a nun masturbating. Ostensibly this scene provided a necessary link in the chain that led from sexual orgasm to religious ecstasy, but the public authorities thought the poem indecent and tried to suppress the whole book. The author was prosecuted and acquitted on the ground that the poems were too difficult to understand.

Stanislaw Przybyszewski (1868–1927) was the most sex-obsessed of the whole lot. As with so many of his generation, his pursuits had carried him from politics to psychology to sex. A socialist in his native Poland, he had come to Berlin in 1889 as a political exile. At the University of Berlin he studied architecture for a year before entering the school of medicine with the intention of becoming an alienist and distinguished himself as a brilliant student with a dissertation on the microscopic structure of the cortex cerebri. In May 1891, when he had just turned twenty-three, he took a nineteen-year-old

Jewish girl, Marthe Foerder, as his common-law wife. His first published works were two monographs, *Chopin and Nietzsche* and *Ola Hansson,* which were intended to be part of a series entitled "On the Psychology of the Individual." Hansson had sent these pamphlets to Strindberg in Sweden, and the playwright had had kind things to say about them; hence Przybyszewski was at the train station in Berlin to greet Strindberg on his arrival. The Pole's next work, *Totenmesse,* which was published on the same day as Dehmel's *What of Love,* May 20, 1893, showed the influence of both The Black Pig crowd and the decadent school in Paris, whose chief representative was Huysmans. Though some of Strindberg's personality may have percolated into the work, in the main it is Przybyszewski's voice that speaks. The hyperneurotic, alcoholic hero declares, "In the beginning was Sex," and goes on to spout a philosophy that mixes egoism and satanism in equal proportions.

> You still have an exterior world. I have none. I am only myself.
> I am I.
> I, the grand synthesis of Christ and Satan. I myself lead him from the Mount and bring him to Temptation. . . . I, the great synthesis of pure and devout Christianity and sneering, grinning disbelief, a mystical ecstatic and a satanic priest, who with a tongue that sanctifies utter at one and the same time the holiest of words and the obscenest of blasphemies.

The subjective writings of Przybyszewski in the 1890s bridged the gap between naturalism and expressionism. Man was still seen as a product of forces but the social environment began to recede as the individual moved into the foreground. The naturalist viewed the human psyche as the battlefield of many conflicting forces produced by his birth, upbringing and family inheritance. To the advanced artist of the 1890s man was subject primarily to larger, more pervasive, universal forces that antedated his birth. The difference was indicated by Strindberg when he distinguished great naturalism from little naturalism, the latter giving us a picture of nature complete in every detail including the spot of dust on the camera lens, whereas the former is highly selective, sees the woods and not just the trees, conveys the artist's temperament, and seeks out not moments of everyday life but life at its most intense. These views were set down by Strindberg in an essay, "On Modern Drama and Modern Theater," in 1889, although he had already exemplified them in *The Father* and *Miss Julie*. In the same year, which was also the year in which Nietzsche became widely known, Langbehn in his *Rembrandt als Erzieher*, a book that Strindberg esteemed highly, reacted against naturalistic psychology as Nietzsche had done and called for a larger view of life that would ignore naturalistic detail and give us a macrocosm in place of a microcosm.

The same shift of emphasis, the same effort to give greater meaning to naturalism can be traced in the work of Edvard Munch (1863–1944). His early drawings are conventionally realistic or impressionistic, but in the 1880s a new quality emerged. Paintings like *Sick Child*, *Morning After*, and *Puberty*, sometimes regarded as the first expressionistic paintings,[1] ostensibly concern themselves with disease, alcohol, and sex, typical naturalist subjects, but the viewer is immediately struck by a force at work behind the canvas.

In 1885 Munch had spent three weeks in Paris, acquainting himself with the latest trends in art, and in 1886, back in Norway, he had joined the coterie of social rebels who clustered around Hans Jæger, who scorned all morality and religion, believed that monogamy banishes happiness, and propagandized for the official recognition of prostitutes as providing a service more vital to the well-being of the community than priests and politicians. Jæger had become the hero of the young Norwegian rebels after his novel *From Christiania's Bohemia* had been confiscated by the authorities upon its publication in 1885. Found guilty of blasphemy, of offending public modesty, and of injuring social morality, Jæger was dismissed from his civil service position and sent to prison for sixty days. Among the early Jæger-ites was Christian Krohg, whose story *Albertine*, printed and con-

[1] Ingrid Langaard, *Edvard Munch, Modningsår. En studie i tidlig ekspresjonisme og symbolisme* (Oslo, 1960), argues that these works antedate Van Gogh's first expressionistic canvasses.

fiscated in 1886, defended the right of women, whatever their marital status, to love whomever they pleased. And Krohg was Munch's teacher.

In 1892 Munch moved to Berlin where in November he had a one-man show of fifty-five paintings. Sponsored by the Art Academy of Berlin, the show was closed after one week when a member of the association deliberately sowed the seeds of dissension by calling for a vote on the desirability of sponsoring such paintings. The closing provided a greater scandal than the show itself, which was exactly what the dissenters wanted, and Munch's name was made. He reopened his show on December 23. The following spring the Academy held another exhibit from which Munch's works were pointedly excluded. Munch and other rejected artists responded by arranging a *Salon des Refusés* in June, some paintings by Strindberg being included. The Norwegian painter and the Swedish playwright had met each other in November 1892, and Munch had immediately painted an oil portrait of Strindberg for inclusion in his December one-man show.

Perhaps it was at this time that Munch saw some of Strindberg's paintings. Said Strindberg, "I'm the greatest painter in Scandinavia." Replied Munch, "Sure, sure. And I'm the greatest poet in Scandinavia. Prosit!"

An early initiate in The Black Pig club, Munch brought on stage the femme fatale our drama requires. Her name was Dagny Juel. Her father and Munch's father were doctors in Norway. Munch had known her as a child, and now when Dagny came to Berlin to study piano he renewed his former acquaintance on a more intimate level. Dagny seemed to regard most men as a challenge to her seductive powers. She even chose to live on Karlstrasse, which was notorious for its prostitutes. She was not beautiful in the ordinary sense, but there can be no doubt that she was fascinating. To Munch she was the incarnation of female sexuality, and he immortalized this modern Norwegian Phryne in such oils as *Madonna* (which exists in more than one version, as do so many of Munch's paintings), *Woman in Love*, *Conception*, and *Woman in Three Stages* (the nude in the center of the canvas). She had excellent teeth, a classic profile, a forehead concealed by bangs, and the gestures of a world-weary woman, though she was only in her early twenties. Strindberg described her, in a malicious essay, as "tall, thin, haggard from liquor and late hours," and as speaking "with a drawling voice broken as if by swallowed tears."

As Strindberg's brain was the nucleus of the intellectual whirl at The Black Pig, so Dagny's body became the focus of the sexual activity. She passed from man to man. It was inevitable that she and Przybyszewski would eventually end up in each other's arms. Not only did they have a common passion for the piano and for Chopin (those who heard him said Przybyszewski's Chopin was more brilliant than any Chopin heard on the concert stage), they both seemed devoured by sex. Each time Dagny passed from one man to another her sexual attractiveness doubled in his eyes. She must have been the mistress of at least three men in The Black Pig before Przybyszewski won her.

One man Dagny did not go to bed with, through no fault of hers, was Bengt Lidforss, a skinny, brilliant student from the University of Lund in southern Sweden. Strindberg had met him through mutual friends in a radical, freethinking, drinking, and discussion group whose members called themselves The Young Old Boys. They spoke the language of Brandes, Nordau, and Nietzsche, but were also inclined toward socialism. Lidforss was very blond, very boyish, had small eyes and a bad stammer. Always dressed in shabby clothes, he did nothing to improve his appearance. In politics he was a left-winger, rebelling against his conservative father; in science he held orthodox Darwinist views; in sex he was rather heterodox. At the age of nineteen, he had tried to become engaged to a twelve-year-old girl, who, it must be said in his defense, looked and acted older. He also had homosexual tendencies that became increasingly apparent as he grew older.

Bengt had met Dagny in 1888 when she accompanied friends on a visit to the Lidforss family. Drinking, smoking, wearing excessive makeup and a tight-fitting dress, Dagny was a shocking cynosure to the strait-laced Lidforss parents. Bengt took one look and fell in love, and little more than that first sight was vouchsafed him. Dagny returned to Norway, leaving a frustrated Bengt behind.

It was perhaps because of his unfulfilled love for both Dagny and the twelve-year-old girl that Lidforss began in the following year to lead an exhausting double life, working hard in the botanical laboratory during the day and debauching himself at night. In his flight from frustration he became infected with syphilis. Regarding the disease with the dispassion of a true naturalist and laughing at the symptoms with the gallows humor of an utter cynic, Lidforss did not even bother to consult a doctor until it was much too late. He simply put blue vitriol on his sores and went on with his work.

Early in March 1893 he arrived in Berlin for a brief stay. He got a room next to Strindberg's in the Linden Hotel on Kleine Kirchstrasse. (Strindberg had moved from Paul's pension on Neue Wilhelmstrasse.) By sheer coincidence Dagny had arrived in Berlin at almost the same time. Lidforss heard that she was in town and was being escorted by Munch. On March 3 the three of them met at a restaurant, and Lidforss must have seen that Dagny was more interested in Munch and other men than in him. Six days later Munch introduced Dagny to the bohemians at The Black Pig, while Lidforss returned to Lund to defend his doctoral dissertation. He passed with distinction, was awarded a travel grant, and chose to return to Berlin, where he arrived at the end of March and was greeted by Strindberg and Dagny. Strindberg made it plain that he had finished with her and was turning her over to Lidforss. He left the two of them alone with several bottles of champagne and stuck half a dozen contraceptives in Lidforss' pocket as he said good-bye.

Lidforss embarked on a long drinking spree and plunged into debt. One might suppose he was trying to drown himself in liquor after finding out what sort of woman Dagny was. But the truth is more crude though almost as romantic. Out of regard for the woman he loved the syphilitic Lidforss chivalrously withheld himself from her and watched all the other men flock around her like drones around the queen bee on her fertilizing flight.

## A HASTY MARRIAGE

Now what was Strindberg doing during this welter of artistic and sexual activity? "Leading a life so rich and intensive," he said, "that I think at times I'll burst. But I shan't; I'm only being overhauled." Actually, apart from his nocturnal debauches, he was painting a little, sitting for his portrait often, experimenting in science constantly, and doing only a little writing. In the cross-pollination of ideas in The Black Pig, Strindberg does not seem to have received much in exchange for what he gave. His experiences were to bear literary fruit later on. There was patently no lack of material for a writer, but Strindberg was looking for a new point of view, a new vision that he could accept, at least for artistic purposes. This he had not yet found.

While he was looking, he too succumbed to the general sexual promiscuity. Shortly after fleeing from the Hanssons and settling in the center of Berlin, Strindberg got involved with a Miss Lund, a dark-eyed, black-haired Norwegian beauty who lived in the same pension with Paul, Munch, and Strindberg, and who was usually escorted by two admiring Norwegian lieutenants. Evidently embarrassed by the position in which he found himself, Strindberg abandoned the battlefield. He explained his behavior in a letter to Przybyszewski: "The tragic-comic husband has become the ridiculous lover, and since the role was quite insupportable for me, I escaped to The Black Pig in order to paralyze my raging spermatozoa with bad alcohol."

A day or two later, at the suggestion of Adolph Paul, he traveled to Weimar where he hoped to find the peace and quiet that would allow him to get on with his work. Instead he was "panicked" by his mounting hotel bill and wrote to Paul for 100 marks to pay his fare back to Berlin. Paul sent 125 marks, but by the time the money reached Strindberg his hotel bill had risen so much that not enough was left over to pay it, and he had to stay on. In the meantime the Finnish writer Karl August Tavaststjerna and his Swedish wife Gabrielle, who aspired to act on the German stage, passed through Weimar. Strindberg's spermatozoa began acting up again, and Gabrielle "completely wiped out the memory of Miss Lund." The brief December love affair was "two days of a storybook romance in reality. Incredibly pleasant and interesting. Battle of the brains and males! *Neue Liebe!* Complete declaration of love in the presence of the buck. —Jealousy. —Everything!" (Five and a half years later this episode was to provide the inspiration for the second scene of *To Damascus* —an excellent example of the way in which Strindberg hoarded material until the right moment came along.)

About December 10 Strindberg contrived to return to Berlin, and he moved into a two-room flat at Potzdamerstrasse 27A.

As far as his career was concerned, his prospects improved somewhat in January 1893, and toward the end of the month he spoke of it, prematurely, as a "turning point in my tragic-comic life" after the terrible year of 1892. *Miss Julie* was produced in Paris on January 16, and less than a week later, on January 22, his forty-third birthday, *Creditors* was staged in Berlin. Although both the producer, Sigmund Lautenburg, and the theater, the Residenztheater, were associated with French farce and comedy, Strindberg's tragicomedy proved to be an outstanding success and ran for about five weeks.

A more important series of events that were to have a lasting effect on August Strindberg's private life began auspiciously on his namesday, January 7. On that night he met Frida Uhl, the woman who was to become his second wife. The occasion was a supper party given by Julius Elias and his wife to celebrate the premiere of Sudermann's *Heimat*. In addition to being an art collector, literary critic, proponent of naturalism and realism, Elias was an Ibsen enthusiast and one of the founders of the Neue Freie Bühne. His friends called him Hassan because of his dark, almond-shaped eyes and his princely munificence. His wife was a fashion writer, and their home was the gathering place for the Berlin intelligentsia.

Frida Uhl hailed from Vienna. Her Catholic parents had separated after her birth, her mother having returned to her parents, rich landowners on the Danube, while her father, who was editor-in-chief of the *Amtlichen Kaiserliche und Königliche Wiener Zeitung*, the official court newspaper that virtually no one read, had moved into the royal palace in Vienna to be near his work. When Frida was nine, her older sister married, and Frida was placed in a convent, where she remained for the better part of ten years. Now she was twenty and she had come to Berlin to make a career for herself as a journalist and drama critic. As the protégée of Otto Neumann-Hofer, critic for the *Berliner Tageblatt* and editor of the *Magazin für Litteratür*, Frida had an entrée to the intellectual and artistic world of Berlin. Vivacious, independent-minded, and new to the scene, she was feted by dramatists like Hermann Sudermann and Ludwig Fulda and producers like Otto Brahm. Frida had as a matter of course attended the premiere of *Heimat* and had gone directly to the supper party at the Eliases'. Strindberg had seen the dress rehearsal the night before, and he and the controversial Edvard Munch, the two most talked-about personalities in Berlin at the moment, had been invited to the party as the Scandinavian contingent and as representatives of the avantgarde.

Frida was dying to meet Munch, but it was Strindberg who fascinated her. In his cape with the high collar, the one he is wearing in Krohg's portrait of him, he looked to Frida like the Flying Dutchman when he made his entrance. As he could often be, Strindberg was utterly charming. His stern exterior and his weak, pliable inner nature combined to arouse both the sex and protective instincts in many women, especially younger women who could respond to his quickly changing moods. Frida said she met three different Strindbergs in the course of an hour that night, and never had she met anyone who radiated such light and energy. They talked until after three in the morning.

They did not talk to each other again for nearly a month, although they did pass by each other on the street one windy night, and Frida did visit The Black Pig with Otto Neumann-Hofer in order to spy on Strindberg in his lair. Their second meeting took place on February 5 at the home of Neumann-Hofer and his young American wife. Strindberg did not even recognize Frida. To make certain she would not be forgotten again Frida invited him to her apartment on Courbière-strasse the following night. Her nosy landlady did not approve of gentlemen visiting the rooms of the ladies in her house, and the next week Frida moved to a more liberal boardinghouse. Shortly thereafter Frida and Strindberg were seen in public together, at the National Art Gallery. One of Strindberg's countrymen happened by, accosted the couple, and took note of Strindberg's clothes.

> Strindberg had jammed himself into the traditional apparel of an extreme Berlin dandy: suit of large-checkered design with large cuffs on the pants, a short yellowish-gray topcoat, a loud necktie, a cane of exaggerated size, and a well-polished silk hat which could hardly be induced to remain on Strindberg's fluffy lion's mane.

Within twenty-four hours the news got around that the notorious misogynist was in love, though the name of the woman was not mentioned.

A couple of days later Strindberg and Frida made an appointment to meet at the Deutsches Theater. They both showed up, but Strindberg, as reluctant to break his date as he was eager to avoid any deeper involvement with the girl, managed to hide himself in the crowd. Shortly after that Frida asked Neumann-Hofer to meet with her and Strindberg at the Café Bellevue to help arrange the dramatist's finances. On her way to the meeting Frida came across an epileptic having a fit in the street and never got to the restaurant. Yet, in spite of these contretemps, or perhaps because of them, Frida was getting under Strindberg's skin. To Adolph Paul he confided that she was "a completely new type for me— soft, plump, dark! And a thoroughgoing rogue!"

Matters reached a head in March. Strindberg had been sitting throughout all of February for Christian Krohg's magnificent portrait of him, the one that Ibsen bought in 1895 for a paltry $134, retitled *The Outbreak of Madness*, and hung over his desk that it might inspire him. The portrait was all but finished on March 2 when Krohg, his wife Oda, and her lover Gunnar Heiberg joined Strindberg and Munch at a gala party at The Black Pig. The guest of honor was the romantic Danish poet Holger Drachmann, who was in town on a brief visit. For some reason a series of petty quarrels broke out, and even Drachmann's bonhommie and talent for improvising clever speeches could not smooth the troubled waters. As a matter of fact the witty speech in which he pointed out that they were all avid artists with tender egos simply whipped the waters into a storm. Munch said he was too disgusted with such banter to deign to reply, and out he stalked. Strindberg and Oda got into a quarrel over what Drachmann had really said. Strindberg called her a stupid woman who did not know what she was talking about, ordered the waiter to bring paper and pencil, and challenged her to write down what she thought Drachmann had said. This "put-up-or-shut-up" attitude was most ungentlemanly and the consternated Oda responded in typical feminine fashion by crying. Her red-bearded husband consoled her by promising to take care of matters later, whereas her swarthy lover, Gunnar Heiberg, who had a real rival in Drachmann, tried to do the manly thing and take care of matters then and there. He got up, walked over to Strindberg, removed his pince-nez, stuck his paunch out and demanded that Strindberg apologize. Strindberg said he would not. Three times Gunnar uttered his demand, and three times Strindberg rebuffed him. Then Gunnar went back and sat down.

A good quarrel was as necessary for Strindberg's nervous system as exercise to an athlete's muscles. The next day he felt that he had got The Black Pig out of his system and declared himself madly in love with Frida. On the same day he received one thousand marks in advance royalties on the German edition of *A Madman's Defense,* which was scheduled for publication in May. Strindberg pocketed one hundred marks, sent five hundred to Finland to help catch up on the monthly subsistence payments for his children, and let Frida, who was manifestly seeking to install herself as Strindberg's literary agent and business manager, take charge of the remaining four hundred. Thereupon Frida extracted from him a promise not to frequent The Black Pig, and to stop drinking and carousing.

The next day Strindberg proposed to her. Frida answered him in a letter saying she honestly felt no deep passion or love. Just as she was about to mail her letter, they met again, and she handed it to him. But as she did to, she was suddenly frightened at the thought of what he might do upon reading

it; so she kissed him. Confused by the contradiction between
the contents of the letter and her kissing him, Strindberg
wrote a note asking for a less ambiguous response. The following evening, a Monday, Frida invited him to dine with her
and an editor friend of hers. He was a harmless married man,
but Strindberg did not know this. Eager for an answer to his
proposal, he was forced to spend an evening in small talk
with a man who might be his rival. That night he painted
one of his more impressive pictures, a somewhat Turneresque
storm at sea, the oils laid on thickly with a palette knife. He
called it *Night of Jealousy*.

Frida should have departed for Munich some days before
this. However, she felt she could not leave Berlin until her
affair with Strindberg had been settled one way or the other.
She telephoned his hotel but he refused to speak to her
until she had replied to his suggestion that he travel with
her to Munich. Finally she went in person to his hotel, and
she and Strindberg went for a walk together. In one of the
lanes of the Tiergarten they agreed to a secret betrothal. On
Wednesday afternoon, the day before Frida was definitely
to leave for Munich, Strindberg came to her apartment, carrying a large package which he carefully unwrapped. It was
*Night of Jealousy*, and he explained to her how he had come
to paint it. When night fell, Strindberg lit some wax candles,
which with all the foresight of a good stage manager he had
brought along. That night their love was consummated, probably after midnight, since Strindberg dated the painting
March 9, evidently taking that as the date on which his engagement to Frida was sealed.

She left for Munich in the morning, having made it clear
that she wanted no public announcement of their betrothal
for the time being. This reluctance on Frida's part caused
Strindberg to fear that he was losing her. He asked her good
friend Annie Bock, the American wife of Neumann-Hofer, to
intervene in his behalf and urge her to return. Frida replied
that it was "now impossible and useless." Two days later
Strindberg pleaded with her to come back and publicly announce their engagement, and threatened that unless she did
so, his disquietude would drive him back to The Black Pig.
By way of reply the level-headed Frida sent a long epistle,

more like a business letter, in which she asked Strindberg for full details on work in progress, income, translations, and so on, and made it plain that she would not announce her engagement until his economic status had improved.

In the meantime Strindberg had broken his promise to Frida and returned to The Black Pig to swill liquor and wallow in sex. Dagny Juel, who had been introduced to the tavern crowd only a few days before by Edvard Munch, now slipped from the painter's hands into the playwright's. The fact that Strindberg had so quickly betrayed his fiancée, that in less than three days the woman in his arms had changed from a convent-bred princess to a tavern whore left a deep scar on his conscience, to judge from future events; but the dramatic contrast would furnish material for his *To Damascus* trilogy.

About a week later Strindberg notified Frida that he planned to go to Vienna for the premiere of *Creditors*. This threw Frida into a panic because she knew that Strindberg who never went to premieres must have had some ulterior motive for going to this one, and what could that be but to talk to her father about the secret engagement? In spite of her efforts to keep the affair secret the news came out anyway through the intervention of the gods. The Austrian critic and dramatist Hermann Bahr met Strindberg by chance after a drinking party, and the Swede raved about the pretty Austrian girl he knew. Still a bit drunk, Bahr filed a report to Vienna in which as a prank he said that Strindberg was engaged to the daughter of the well-known editor Friedrich Uhl. Thus it was from the newspapers, more particularly, the March 22 issue of the Vienna *Deutsche Zeitung* that Frida learned of her official betrothal. Her father also heard about it for the first time.

Frida dashed back to Berlin, arriving there on April Fool's Day, a perfect occasion for the comic scene that was enacted. Not suspecting that a newspaper item could make Frida hasten back when all his letters had failed to do so, Strindberg had arranged another one of his regular meetings with Dagny. And at the same time came a letter from Gabrielle Tavaststjerna saying that she was arriving in Berlin from Italy. All three women converged on him. No French farce writer could have arranged things better. There was nothing to do but let life imitate farce in finding a way out of the difficulty. Strindberg pretended to fall sick and relied upon the good offices of Dr. Schleich to ward off the female horde. Gabrielle and Dagny did not call, but Frida appeared at his bedside with a bag of bonbons and the promise of 3400 marks which her father would be giving her for her trousseau, money with which Frida intended to pay Strindberg's most pressing debts.

On April 11, Frida and Strindberg exchanged rings. The very next day a quarrel broke out, occasioned by an outburst of jealousy on Strindberg's part. He accused Frida of having posed naked for some painter. Frida in a huff returned Strindberg's letters and broke off the engagement. A couple of days later she sent another letter in which among other things she discussed the physical aspects of marriage. Shocked and pained at first, Strindberg composed himself and sent a reply in which he expressed his admiration of the young girl's knowledge of human nature, congratulated her on displaying another one of her hidden charms, deigned to suggest that she had made a slight error in her remarks on the size of the male and female genitalia, and concluded his letter with the assurance that there was always a place reserved for her at The Black Pig.

The affair might have ended there but for Frida's older sister Marie who, coming to Berlin in the middle of April to help with the wedding, found herself faced with a broken engagement. Married to an eminently respectable Austrian sculptor, Professor Rudolf Weyr, Marie was baffled by the bohemians she met in Frida's company and utterly confounded by Strindberg. After having had a chance to observe Strindberg for a few days and correct her first impression of him, she wrote home to her husband:

> . . . You cannot possibly imagine, no more than I could before I got here, what sort of people Frida is living with. There is something unbalanced about them, unnatural, sickly, broken, completely intellectual and without a bit of common sense. —And Strindberg—he could drive people like us quite insane. I have never before in my life met such a person, no one like him exists among

us, thank heavens! I could not possibly endure him for long. He forms a leaden sheath around my nerves. Now he is so much recovered that he can go out, at least in the daytime. He looks much better and creates a much more favorable initial impression than in his photograph. Often looks much younger, too. But then suddenly his face changes to that of an old man when he suddenly, as often happens, begins to brood, and right in the middle of a sentence forgets that someone is with him, and for a quarter of an hour doesn't say a word and doesn't hear a thing that is said to him. When I am with him, I can't for one moment rid myself of the fear that at any instant he might go mad, but simultaneously I feel more and more that he is a true genius. . . . He paints fantasy pictures, symbolic pictures. Nearly every other day or every third day a new picture, astonishingly good when one considers that he has had no formal training. It is as if the talents within him did not know how they can best express themselves. But there is not a trace of a healthy, happy desire to create, rather a drive, an uncontrollable passion of the kind that forces a criminal to commit murder. Frightening, absolutely frightening! I cannot understand how Frida has the courage to entrust herself to such a person. But one can no longer keep the two of them apart; on the contrary, one must do everything to join them together. I am afraid that his love for her is mainly of a sensual nature, for intellectually and spiritually Frida cannot satisfy that man—no woman could, for that matter. Nor does he seem to expect it, since his opinion of women is the lowest possible. Generally speaking, he is rather shy and completely sufficient unto himself. . . . Her love for him is, in contrast, nothing but literary admiration and idolatry of his genius. I don't think she would dare to give him a hug if he didn't first allow it or command it. Heaven only knows how it will work out in the future. I have more fear for than confidence in a marriage under such conditions. Frida in her divine dotage sees heaven on earth in a life at his side. I can do nothing, absolutely nothing, except to give her some sensible advice on what to buy, and suggestions on her trousseau, and to support her in her wish to marry as soon as possible.

Marie had brought with her Frida's dowry of 4000 marks,

and the bride and groom had immediately gone out to buy
new clothes. Strindberg got himself a beige-colored suit cut
in the English fashion, and a silk cravat. Frida went to the
Wertheim, a new bargain department store which had just
opened in Berlin and which featured the latest Paris fashions.
The store was jammed with women and Frida ended up with
a sore toe, a torn hem, some black and blue marks, and two
new dresses for the honeymoon. As for the wedding dress itself, Frida's mother offered to send the linen underwear she
had worn when she was married thirty years before. It was
so starched it could stand by itself. Frida wanted something
soft, transparent, and frilly.

All these preparations would have been in vain if Marie,
whom Frida and Strindberg jestingly called "Mother-in-law"
for the duties she had taken on herself, had not managed to
patch up the quarrel. This she did, and the wedding plans
went ahead. The one remaining snag was that Strindberg had
not received his official divorce papers from Sweden, and
without these the banns could not be published. Strindberg
hit upon the idea of getting married on the island of Helgoland in the North Sea because of the peculiar legal situation
that prevailed there. Germany had acquired the island from
England in exchange for Zanzibar only three years before,
and the marriage laws in effect there were still the English
ones. Consequently no banns were necessary.

Frida and Strindberg decided to leave for Helgoland on
Thursday, April 27. Wednesday night they walked down to
the Lehrter Station to pick up their tickets. Suddenly Strindberg ran off, without a word of explanation, to accost two
men in the distance. After twenty or thirty minutes he returned, pale as a ghost. The man he had spoken to was Baron
Wrangel, the first husband of Strindberg's first wife Siri.
Strindberg naturally took the fortuitous meeting as an ill
omen, and back at his hotel he told Paul what had happened.
"And now, just like the last time, he wished me all the luck
in the world! This will never work out. I'm damned and
doomed again."

The next morning as the engaged couple boarded the nine
o'clock train for Hamburg, Adolph Paul and Bengt Lidforss
were there to wish them well, along with Gabrielle Tavast-

stjerna, who kept making snide remarks. Strindberg finally had to turn his back on her.

Paul and Lidforss handed the bride and groom two bouquets as they bid them bon voyage. "You boys are real gentlemen," said Strindberg, clapping them on the shoulders.

As the train pulled out, Frida asked worriedly, "You don't suppose those poor boys gave up their dinner money to buy us flowers?"

Strindberg smiled. "Well, they'd willingly have done so for you, Frida, but it's the end of the month; they haven't got a cent."

When Frida looked at him uncomprehendingly, he went on, "Don't worry about it. Lidforss knew how to handle the situation. He borrowed the money from me before I left the hotel this morning."

Arrived in Helgoland, Strindberg and Frida rented a three-room fisherman's cottage with a lawn and flower garden, and waited for the divorce papers to arrive. Five hundred marriage announcements had already been sent out, and since the divorce papers were delayed, congratulatory telegrams began arriving before the wedding, a situation that Strindberg thought worthy of a comedy, which, unfortunately, he never wrote.

Finally, on May 2, the ceremony took place. In the presence of two witnesses, the bride and groom were required to answer twenty-three questions put to them by the pastor. Nervous and tense, Strindberg mixed Swedish and German together.

The pastor absent-mindedly directed the wrong question at Strindberg: "Do you solemnly vow never to bear another man's child?"

With his left hand on the Bible and his right hand raised Strindberg replied in bad German, "I solemnly vow never to bear another man's child."

Frida broke into uncontrollable laughter. Strindberg and the pastor were appalled. Frida's sister tried to cover up by saying the bride was crying. She shoved a handkerchief against Frida's eyes, pinched her, and repeated over and over again, "Calm yourself, calm yourself."

After a three-week stay on Helgoland, the newlyweds

sailed for England where Frida hoped to promote her husband's career through the contacts she had there. They spent a short time in Gravesend and then moved into London around the first of June. Among Frida's contacts was J. T. Grein, who had founded the Independent Theater there in 1891, a theater modeled on Antoine's Théâtre-Libre and like it meant to provide a stage for the advanced drama. The theater had opened with Ibsen's *Ghosts* and in 1892 had staged *Widowers' Houses*, the first play by a red-bearded music critic, Ibsen champion, Fabian socialist, and soapbox orator named Bernard Shaw. Frida entertained hopes of either working with Grein or founding her own theater. It was Grein who turned over his two-room apartment on Eccleston Square to Frida and Strindberg while he was out of town for the summer.

Cut off from his friends and his chemical equipment, living on his wife's dowry, and suffering from the heat and humidity, Strindberg hated London and took his frustrations out on Frida. On June 10 he sailed for Hamburg, while Frida remained in London to find translators and publishers for his works. Strindberg spent more money on the ship than he had anticipated. What he had left was taken from him by a porter who overcharged him. In Hamburg the friends he had counted on meeting were out of town. In a way the Weimar situation was repeated: a rising hotel bill compelled him to write to Paul and others for money in order to leave. A few days later he was able to move on to Sellin on the island of Rügen, where he set to work in earnest on his chemical experiments and wrote two papers, "The Psychology of Sulfur" and "What Is Carbon?" material that would eventually be incorporated in a work called *Antibarbarus*.

Strindberg found nothing to like on Rügen, and the presence there of Tavaststjerna, whose wife he had seduced in Weimar, acted like a rasp on his tense nerves. Strindberg grew more convinced with every passing day that Tavaststjerna knew the truth and was playing cat and mouse with him. The fact that Tavaststjerna was stone-deaf only aggravated Strindberg's nervousness, for all oblique remarks and insinuations that should have gotten a rise out of the Finn were greeted with either a kind smile or a "I'm sorry, would you mind repeating that?" Convinced that Tavaststjerna was deliberately tormenting him, Strindberg finally screamed the supreme insult: "Skål, you Finn coward!" Tavaststjerna, who heard even less well when shouted at, smiled and replied, "Skål, my dear friend."

Strindberg was ready to explode. As soon as he had gotten a few yards away from the hotel, he ran madly through the woods.

In the meantime Strindberg's suspicions that Frida's associates in London were swindlers and shysters received confirmation from Frida herself. She wrote that Grein had proved to be a great disappointment and reported that he was quite unreliable. Not only was he virtually a confidence man, but he behaved despicably toward women, and his housemaid was a part-time prostitute. Even Grein's secretary had left him and had promised to work for Frida instead.

Strindberg now felt that he must either get Frida away from England or go there himself to protect her. First he wrote a begging letter to Frida's sister Marie.

> Frida is suffering, and I am half mad with anxiety. I am ashamed to die, but the situation is intolerable. Deliver me from this prison and let me go and find my lost lamb. If there are 500 marks in this world, find them for me, dear sister, and I swear never again to build my hopes on airy dreams.
>
> I admit we are both a little mad, but we are sincere, we love one another, and the future is going to be ours.

The following day, July 23, he wrote to Frida, offering to rejoin her in England on condition that she allow him his independence. "I allowed you more personal freedom than you allowed me. You wanted to run my life as a writer, and also acted as if you were trying to humiliate me (transform me into a money-grubbing farce writer)."

The next day Frida's mother, who must have heard from Marie, invited Strindberg to come to live at her home and entreated him to call her Mamma—"Mother-in-law has such a horrible sound." Desperately in need of a refuge, Strindberg accepted the offer and went to the Uhl summer home at Mondsee, Austria, at the end of July.

Not at all eager to join Strindberg there, Frida wrote her mother saying that he had really abandoned her in London. This prompted Strindberg to write a letter that sounded a bit like an ultimatum.

He told Frida that he was preparing to return to the shadows of Berlin where he had first met her and where he and she had lived like gypsies during the March storms and under the spring sun. "A savage love, a springtime love, sometimes grand, and sometimes sad. The sublime struggle of two souls who fought to avoid the inevitable, two cells that had to mix and mingle with each other to lose their individuality. And now it is at an end. Finished. Is it really possible?"

He accused Frida of longing for fame, of preferring the laurel to the rose, and reminded her that the laurel has the sharper thorns. At this point in his thoughts the specter of sex raised its phallic head. Strindberg felt that Frida had come to dislike him when he had refused to play the unhappy child in its mother's lap.

> You detested me when you scented the man, the male in me. Your flesh yearned for the male but your soul repulsed him—Amazon that you are! You sensed that I accommodated myself to your desires. It was as if I made myself, without knowing it, the woman, leaving you to play the role of the man. Why? Because unless I did so, you would not have loved me. And I had to have your love.

But now of course she despised him as a weakling, as an imbecile. He concluded his letter with a warning.

> Have you reckoned the consequences of a separation? Vengeance and revenge!
>
> And everything will collapse and crumble to pieces. Irreparably.
>
> Making up only to break up. One prostitutes oneself, offering a spectacle to the public impatient for another *Madman's Defense*. [The book had been published only three months before.]
>
> And the revelations and the recriminations. One dies of shame and comes back to life to avenge oneself.
>
> It's life itself that's at fault, beautiful life, cruel life.

The letter had the desired effect. Frida left London almost immediately, telegraphing Strindberg that she was on her way to him. Now the gods entered to play their predictable role. Strindberg sent his reply to Berlin, telling her to stay there until he arrived. Frida did not get the message and went on to Mondsee. Between Mondsee and Berlin the erratic paths of husband and wife crossed. Finally, about the middle of August, they were reunited and settled temporarily in two adjoining rooms in a pension on Albrechtstrasse.

After two months of relative calm there occurred a ludicrous episode that signaled the coming storm. During the weekend of October 14 a small row ended with either Frida or Strindberg locking the connecting door between their rooms. Strindberg went out to see friends. Frida decided to do the same and called on her girl friend Annie Neumann-Hofer, who had recently become a mother and was living in the country outside Berlin. Strindberg returned to find a note from Frida informing him that she had gone out for the day. Thereupon he went out once again and did not come back until shortly before ten in the evening. In the meantime Frida had returned and been informed by the maid that Strindberg had come and gone. Frida then stepped out to call on another friend, Bertha Doeppler, mistress of the composer Leoncavallo. She got back a few minutes after ten and was told by the maid that Strindberg had come in. But the doors to both rooms were still locked. Frida knocked on Strindberg's hall door. No answer. She knocked louder. Still no answer. The thought seized her that Strindberg might have taken some desperate measures against himself. Every key in the house was tried, as Frida continued to knock and pound on the door. At long last a firm voice was heard from inside the room, firm and strong enough to indicate that there was nothing wrong with Strindberg's health. Frida demanded the key to her room. Strindberg growled from inside that her key was in her door, that the door had been locked from the inside, and so had the connecting door.

Frida thought about that for a moment. If the doors were locked from inside that could only mean that someone was still in her room! Perplexed and a little frightened, she put her mouth against Strindberg's door and whispered her disturbing thought.

"Precisely!" exclaimed Strindberg as he opened the door, grabbed her and twisted her wrist. "The man you've spent the whole day with!"

And he shut his door again.

By this time the whole pension was in an uproar. The rumor that there was a thief in the house spread from floor to floor, from guest to guest. The police were called. Houselights, moonlight, pocket lamps, and lanterns played over the melodramatic scene as the building was searched inside and out. Someone saw a shadow move near the chimney, but the police refused to risk life and limb on the steep slate roof and said the fire department would have to be called. A fire engine arrived promptly, but the firemen said they would not undertake to spray the roof unless someone would sign a guarantee that they would be paid. Frida offered to sign, but the firemen would not accept a wife's signature and insisted that her husband had to sign. Strindberg, indigent as usual, grabbed Frida and hustled her from the room. The firemen's insult to her sex and Strindberg's insult to her person strengthened Frida's resolve to settle the matter, and with admirable sensibleness she called a locksmith, who quickly broke the lock to Frida's room. The key to the connecting door lay on the table in the center of the room.

Out in the street the comedy of errors continued as a young apprentice, who like a good citizen had joined in the search for the rumored thief, was himself mistakenly accused of being the elusive criminal. By midnight the crowd had had its fun, the excitement was over, and the police and firemen had dispersed.

Exhausted, torn between conflicting emotions, Frida undressed and prepared for bed. Strindberg approached her. In a voice conciliatory and seductive he murmured, "You've ruined the whole day for me, you witch. Do you want to ruin my night too?"[2]

[2] The details of the incident differ in the versions given by Frida Uhl and Strindberg. See Frida Strindberg, *Strindberg och hans andra hustru* (Stockholm, 1933–34), I, 126–129; and August Strindberg, *Klostret* (Stockholm, 1966), 119–122.

How the door came to be locked from inside was never explained. Strindberg accused his wife of having stuck something in the lock, a trick that she, the inveterate playgoer and aspiring drama critic might have learned, said he, from Octave Feuillet's play *The Gray Hair*.[3] It appears much more plausible that Strindberg, the confirmed playmaker in real life, remembered Feuillet's play and borrowed from it.

The next morning Frida left Strindberg for her sister's house in Vienna. She left a note saying she wanted a divorce and giving Strindberg the option of charging her with desertion or, if he had not applied for a divorce within four weeks, of being charged by her with physical cruelty. The main reason for Frida's behavior was the fact that she was pregnant, and the prospect of motherhood made her exceedingly nervous. Furthermore, her condition caused her to be easily nauseated by the chemicals Strindberg used in his experiments. Her sister Marie prevailed on her to go back to Strindberg, which she did on condition that he rid himself of his suspicions and jealous thoughts and not accuse her of intruding in his affairs.

At the end of October the couple set up housekeeping in Brün (Brno) in Moravia. However, their financial situation made living there impossible, and at the end of November they accepted the invitation of Frida's maternal grandparents, Judge Cornelius Reischl and his wife, to come and live with them.

The family estate of Dornach was located on the bank of the Danube about an hour's sleigh ride from Amstetten, the nearest train station. On a clear day the situation of the house afforded a magnificent prospect up the river to Castle Wallsee, and on an eminence across the river was the Kolmützberg church. However, during the winter months the mist rising from the Danube formed a veritable wall that cut off all views, and the isolation of the estate discouraged visi-

---

[3] Feuillet's one-act play *Le Cheveu blanc* (1860) consists of a dialogue between a man and his wife, he in his forties, she in her thirties. They have separate bedrooms. One night he finds himself unable to get into his room. After considerable banter about their possible affairs, his first gray hair, and so on, she confesses she put sand in the lock to his room to make him come to her.

tors. This could only please Strindberg, for the house had a good library where he spent all his time reading up on chemistry. But Frida found nothing to delight her, and much to irritate her. Her grandmother and her mother, who also resided there during the winter, were both very fond of children and were always hovering about the pregnant Frida, whereas Frida looked forward with misgiving and even trepidation to the coming birth. Moreover, Frida's mother was a religious fanatic of motley faiths whose prayers and preachments revived unhappy childhood memories in Frida. Her mother was afraid of the dark, kept most of the lights on in the large, dismal house, and spent her "sexless nights," as her daughter called them, absorbing the teachings of Judaism, Rosicrucianism, Buddhism, theosophy, Mohammedanism. When she was sufficiently worked up, she would on occasion come into Frida's bedroom to deliver a fire-and-brimstone sermon on the consequences of sin.

The behavior of Strindberg—engrossed in his scientific work —was as strange as that of his mother-in-law. When Judge Reischl, who was separated from his wife, came for the Christmas holidays, he was utterly bewildered by Strindberg's peculiar methods of reasoning. The tension between the two men grew noticeably from day to day. After one strange episode, in which Strindberg locked himself in his room for three days, Judge Reischl virtually ordered him out of the mansion. Early in 1894 Strindberg and Frida moved into a small cottage called Das Häusel on the estate.

While Frida was getting ready to become a mother, Strindberg was preparing to make his debut as a scientist. His conviction was that some of the so-called elements could be decomposed into other elements, and that any one element could be transmuted into another. He set forth his views in a work called *Antibarbarus*, which consisted of four parts or fascicles, dealing with the composition of sulfur, the transmutation of carbon, the composition of air and water, and the transmutation of the metallic elements. The turmoil in Strindberg's mind as he found himself torn between the claims and responsibilities of fatherhood and the glories of discovering nature's secrets, between domesticity and public fame, between the rose and the laurel, was given magnificent dramatic expression some years later in the second part of the *To Damascus* trilogy. As that play makes clear it was science and the prospect of fame and glory that won out. The very living arrangements in *Das Häusel* presaged the breakup of the marriage. Strindberg occupied the upstairs room and busied himself hours on end with his experiments, while Frida occupied the downstairs room and waited for her baby to be born. A further source of conflict lay in the separation of Frida from her relations. They, the Catholics, lived in the big house, while she and her mad husband, the Protestants, lived in the cottage.

On May 26 Strindberg became the father of a girl, Kerstin (1894–1956), and about the same time the first copies of *Antibarbarus* came off the press. He sent a copy to Friedrich Uhl in Vienna with the dedication, "To my good father-in-law, from the Prodigal Son . . . unlucky till now, but now perhaps lucky."

### THE DEMISE OF THE BLACK PIG

If Strindberg thought that 1894 would be his lucky year, he was mistaken. The year did get off to a good start with the publication in Sweden, after a delay of three years, of *A Book about Strindberg*, a collection of eulogies by twelve writers and critics, including Knut Hamsun, Georg Brandes, and J. H. MacCarthy. The object of all this praise was not very appreciative. He found that all twelve panegyrists had merely taken advantage of the opportunity to write about him in order to write about themselves and had put forward their own views, which were the direct opposite of Strindberg's.

The year also saw the publication of Dr. Wilhelm Hirsch's *Genie und Entartung*, in which the author analyzed Strindberg as a typical paranoiac suffering from pathological jealousy. Many writers might have been deeply offended by this kind of public examination, but Strindberg, who, it must always be remembered had to act as his own publicity agent, probably saw as much good as bad coming from the sale of such a book.

What really upset Strindberg was the critical reception of *Antibarbarus*. Though the renowned scientist Ernst Haeckel, an exponent of monism, treated it kindly, the supposed friend of Strindberg, Bengt Lidforss, who had helped to translate the work into German, wrote a scornful, malicious, ad homi-nem and unsigned review in the Stockholm *Dagens Nyheter,* a newspaper that had generally been well disposed to Strindberg.

Said Lidforss:

> The trained specialist will in most cases simply dismiss the book with a shrug and a few words about genius and insanity but without sensing what the attentive reader will probably discover beneath the surface. To the reader *sine ira et studio* who has followed Strindberg's career with psychological interest during the past decade *Anti-barbarus* proves one important point: Strindberg is nei-ther a reformer nor a philosopher but purely and simply a poet, the quintessential poet. In him the imaginative faculty has acquired such revolutionary violence that the boundaries between fact, hypothesis, and fantasy have been obliterated. A germ of a thought, driven past him by the winds of chance, is blown back, strikes root in his brain as a possibility and grows into an article of faith for which he will live and die. Strindberg is like the au-thor of "Die Elixir des Teufels," who became possessed eventually by the spectral beings he had at first delib-erately let his imagination conjure up. In such fertile soil monstrosities shoot up like mushrooms from the rich leaf-covered autumn soil. But a mushroom in fall does not prove that spring will never come.

The falling out of Lidforss and Strindberg was indicative of what had happened to The Black Pig since Strindberg left it to marry Frida. Those bohemians who had once been so close, picking each other's brains, feeding each other's egos, and stimulating each other's glands had broken into splinter groups and were now sniping at each other. The dissolution of the old gang was apparent to Strindberg when he returned to Berlin early in 1894 to help Lidforss with the translation of *Antibarbarus* and to press for its immediate publication.

Ola Hansson, who was more paranoiac than Strindberg and who had a wife who fired his hatred, began the backbit-ing with a novel, *Fru Esther Bruce,* that he published at the end of 1893. Among the secondary characters is the painter

Ödman (an evocative name that has suggestions about it of desolation, devastation, fate, and destiny), an easily recognizable caricature of Strindberg. He is described as belonging to the "earthworm group of animals. He lacks a governing brain. The spinal marrow gets longer and longer but no brain develops." That this is close to Hansson's own view is corroborated by remarks that he made in an essay in which Strindberg's mind is pictured as "a chaos where all thoughts are jammed together, scuffling, elbowing, somersaulting—an orgy of ideas, a carnival of contemporary thought, a battlefield where armed masses of notions fight without leaders."

Not long after the publication of Hansson's novel, Laura Marholm offered the world her opinion of Strindberg and proved to be a little more perceptive than her husband. She found that all Strindberg's works were directed to the solution of the riddle of his ego, and that the key to his personality lay in his suspiciousness, a suspiciousness that encompassed everything and everybody, including himself.

> In a conglomerate character like Strindberg's no unity has imposed itself beneath the threshold of consciousness. . . . In his work one finds no transitions, no coherence. . . . [He was] a boon companion whose good hours fell at the first cock-crowing, a humorist with a vague smile who played at chess with life, and cared less about the results of the game than its subtle tactics; a man of great foresight, unreliable, impulsive; a man whose intellect impressed you and who wanted you to be impressed; and who in addition to this possessed the cunning of a boy. [His personality is the product of] his inherited, restless, undomesticated Finnish-Lapp blood, . . . the blood of a race that remains always apart, that does not allow itself to be fathomed, but with true nomadic instinct seeks to wipe out all traces of its own existence, . . . the blood that scents the enemy everywhere, that dreads the enemy yet goes in search of him if only for the sake of the long, lonely raids that it remembers from the past. . . . [Strindberg] hates coherence as derogatory to himself; he is determined to be incomprehensible.

Strindberg had his innings in an essay he wrote in July 1894.

A lady—lady!!—has made an invaluable contribution to female psychology in a gossip-and-slander stew that she cooked up. She serves up a psychopathological diagnosis of herself in the belief that she is offering one of me.

From the very start she betrays her ignorance, and confirms it by building her whole argument, with that absolute self-confidence which is characteristic of the fair sex, on a false premise, namely, that my origin can be traced back to the Mongolian race. Now I know the lady personally. I replied to her, "Madame, Mongols are brachycephalic. I on the contrary am dolichocephalic. Consequently I can be of no service to you—as a Mongol."

No matter, nothing sufficed; to her I was a Mongol, since she herself was Negroid, a cross between a Livonian sailor and a Negress cook. [Laura Marholm's real name was Mohr, i.e., Moor.]

. . . At the end my female biographer revealed herself in all her inborn naïveté. After having knitted together 2000 lines of print about my personality, she admitted that the subject was too vast for her and renounced the task of unraveling a character as complex as mine. And this admission came after she had rolled up all the yarns that my enemies had spun about me, all, all to my honor. Charming, isn't it? And so like a woman!

During the summer of 1894 Adolph Paul also broke with The Black Pig coterie, caricaturing the Hanssons in a novel, *With False Eye and True Eye*, and denigrating Strindberg in a short story, "A Charlatan."

Paul was never much more than an errand boy for Strindberg, and the Hanssons had been much too eager to make Strindberg their front man for him to feel any great sense of loss when they turned their backs on him. But the rupture with the rest of The Black Pig circle, and especially with its sexual core—Dagny Juel, Przybyszewski, Munch, and Lidforss —was a significant event that marked the beginning of a new phase in Strindberg's career. He relied on Lidforss for aid and encouragement in his scientific researches, and he seems to have been genuinely fond of the brilliant young student who was the chief representative of the young rebels in southern Sweden. As for Dagny Juel, she was the embodiment of Strindberg's guilt feelings, for he had had a three-week affair with her just when he was wooing the supposedly chaste Frida. With Munch there was a double bond: Strindberg respected him as an original artist, and, further, the emotions he felt toward Dagny were cathected in Munch because the latter stood in the same relation to Dagny and Przybyszewski as Strindberg did. Now, since Lidforss was also involved with Dagny, it is clear that the interlocking set of love triangles, past and present, had as their center the blond Norwegian girl with the drawling voice and the blond Pole who drank his cognac from water tumblers.

It will be recalled that Munch introduced Dagny to The Black Pig in March 1893 and that shortly thereafter she had become Strindberg's mistress. In April he "donated" her to Lidforss, who had to abstain from enjoying her embraces and had to allow others to find satisfaction in the source of his frustration. He went on a month-long drinking spree and let his hotel bill grow to unpayable proportions. More serious than unpaid bills was the scandalous possibility that Lidforss would not return to Lund in time to have his doctoral degree conferred on him on May 27 at important ceremonies in which King Oscar II would participate. Strindberg, who by this time was on his honeymoon, was informed by Adolph Paul of Lidforss' situation and sent a message on May 9 to a good friend in Lund, with the result that two medical students were dispatched to Berlin to save Lidforss' career, while Dagny's sister also came down to the German capital to see if the stories about Dagny were true. Paul and Tavaststjerna, who evidently did not take a very serious view of the matter, decided to waylay the two-man rescue team by plying them with liquor at The Black Pig and sending to Lund for reinforcements. The plan backfired. Suddenly Lidforss became stark sober at the thought of the disgrace he might bring on his own head and that of his respectable father. He stalked out of the tavern to wander the streets alone. Fortunately he showed up at the train station in time to "rescue his rescuers," as Paul put it.

Back at The Black Pig, Przybyszewski and Dagny mournfully flayed the top hat Lidforss had left behind, and hung the skin beneath Strindberg's portrait. The devil had lost another good soul to the guardian of the moral order.

It was an odd role for Strindberg to be playing, as he himself realized, and it is apparent that his intervention was more malicious than moral, motivated as much by a desire to spoil Dagny's game as by any kindly wish to help Lidforss. Strindberg's hatred of Dagny was purely and simply the outward expression of his disgust with himself for having succumbed to a liaison with a woman who had nothing of the mother or the chaste wife in her and who therefore offended his deepest sensibilities. A night's orgy was one thing; a three-week affair quite another. He had slipped into the mud and now he blamed Dagny for having pushed him.

In Strindberg's version of the story he quickly grew tired of Dagny, who after the first days of enchantment appeared to him ugly, brazen, badly dressed and altogether lacking in taste, and he shoved her off on Dr. Schleich when Lidforss would not take her. After two weeks with her, Schleich showed up at The Black Pig with Dagny on his arm, and she was promptly hailed as a modern Aspasia. However, when she began to take seriously her role as the protectress of genius, Schleich also decided to pass her on, and arranged a rendezvous between the unsuspecting Dagny and Przybyszewski, which worked out perfectly.

As might be expected, everyone was furious with Strindberg for having attempted to rescue Lidforss from what were thought imaginary perils. Dagny's sister traveled all the way to Berlin to find nothing wrong with Dagny's way of life, and Lidforss returned to Lund the night before the commencement exercises to be slapped on the face by his offended father. Lidforss upbraided Strindberg for his interference, and Strindberg called Lidforss a "disgusting person" in a letter to Paul. Thus another link to The Black Pig was broken.

It was in May 1893, while Lidforss was still on his binge, that Dagny and Przybyszewski, who was a year younger than she, became steady lovers. He called her Ducha, a name suggesting soul in Polish, and everyone called him Stucha. He left his common-law wife and his three children to move into Dagny's apartment. In September, Ducha and Stucha were married. Munch resettled in Berlin a month or

so after that, and Lidforss returned from Lund. The complicated love polygon had now reduced itself to a simple square
with Lidforss in one corner and Munch in another. They
occupied the two best chairs in Dagny's shabbily furnished
one-and-a-half-room flat, silently drinking while Ducha
danced and Stucha played Chopin on a piano that in consideration of the neighbors had been damped with paper.

During the next couple of years Dagny inspired Przybyszewski's best works, and together they stimulated Strindberg's pen and Munch's brush. From 1893 to 1895 Munch
painted Dagny and Przybyszewski several times, and the
features of the Polish writer continued to haunt Munch for
years after. He had blond, short, curly hair, a pointed beard,
and a suffering expression that made him look a little like a
conventional Christ. Deep wrinkles in his face caused him to
look much older than his years. It is Stanislaw's face that
appears in the foreground of *Red Virginia Creeper,* an oil
done as late as 1900.

Though Munch had painted Dagny's portrait in 1892 and
even earlier, it was not until her alliance with Przybyszewski
that Munch found real inspiration in her. Together Dagny
and Przybyszewski appear in *Jealousy,* which shows a man
standing and looking at a naked woman. The green face in
the foreground is that of Przybyszewski. Munch said the
green represented Stanislaw's jealousy.

That jealousy was of a peculiar sort and requires a word
of explanation. Stanislaw seemed to take a masochistic delight in seeing his wife or mistress attracted to another man.
When he first became acquainted with Strindberg, the Pole
with Eskimo-like hospitality offered the Swede the keys to his
apartment so that Strindberg might sleep with Stanislaw's
mistress Maschka (Marthe Foerder). Later, when he was
married to Dagny, he attended an art exhibit with her at
which a bust of Strindberg was on display. Stucha went up
close to the bust and with a little-boy's smile distorted by
anguish or bitterness asked Ducha, "Is it like him? Does it
move you deeply to see him again? Is that the expression
you liked in him?" One could see that with each word he
stabbed himself. When he took to living with Dagny, Stucha
assigned the delicately handsome Munch with his Dresden-

doll features—"Pretty Boy," Strindberg calls him in *Inferno*—
the role of the Other Man.

Przybyszewski's sexual obsessions and subjective view of
the world undoubtedly gave Munch's works a nudge toward
expressionism. Munch's famous painting *The Cry* was interpreted by Przybyszewski as a sex-mad woman shrieking for a
new sacrifice. And Stanislaw retitled some of Munch's paintings to increase their allegorical content. *Woman in Three
Stages* was originally called *Sphinx*, and *The Vampire* was
first known as *Liebe und Schmerz* until Przybyszewski wrote
about them. In February 1894 there was published in Berlin the first brochure on the Norwegian painter, *Das Werk
Edvard Munch*, with appreciations by Przybyszewski, Franz
Servaes, Willy Pastor, and Julius Meier-Graefe. Munch was
hailed as a pioneer of symbolist art and of depth psychology.
In describing *Jealousy*, Przybyszewski did not recognize himself in the man with the green face but saw him as the embodiment of cultural boredom, of stupid, cowardly, brooding
resignation. *The Cry* he regarded as a literary work in color.
For him Munch's landscapes were visions of an inner world;
his images corresponded to sensations, not to surface appearances. Munch, he said, broke completely with the tradition
of painting the outer world and was the first to present states
of soul independent of cerebral activity. His paintings were
the result of a superabundance of psychic energy that over-
flowed the individual being and compelled an exteriorization
of the emotions.

Needless to say, these thoughts, representing as they did
the artistic vanguard of the 1890s, were bound to affect
Strindberg. He had helped to create the climate for them
but now the younger generation was building its own world.

So with the publication of Lidforss' snide review of his
chemical treatise, the praise of Munch as the prophet of the
future, and the stories and novels ridiculing him, Strindberg
felt increasingly that not only was he, the former high priest
of The Black Pig, going to be deposed in a temple revolution
but that his former disciples were bent on destroying him.
In characteristic fashion, he turned on them venomously.
The best attack is defense, and attack he did in a hail of
letters.

To Adolph Paul he wrote on May 15, when Paul was still his friend:

> I do believe you're afraid! But I tell you the Polack is
> *ganz* harmless; when he starts to lie, he ceases to be
> witty. This is his situation:
>
> That whore Aspasia hooked Bierbaum, editor of the
> *Freie Bühne* journal. So in its pages the Polack praised
> friend Munch's paintings in such an idiotic way—spinal
> marrow and neuroglia, uteruses and my old sunspots
> —that Bierbaum was sacked and the whole gang broke
> up. . . .
>
> That the Pole hates me for having had his Aspasia be-
> fore she got to know him, I can understand; but on the
> other hand I can't be expected to ponder his possible
> marriages every time I have intercourse.
>
> Not even Lidforss is dangerous. He's pathological, and
> after his latest exploit he's probably looking for a tree to
> hang himself in. Such deeds will give him no peace.
>
> He described his life with the Przybyszewskis when
> they lived in one room, Przybyszewski drunk asleep, and
> Bengt Lidforss and Aspasia sitting on the edge of the
> bed without crawling into it—.
>
> Then came Aspasia's brother with "Money-Bags." Ac-
> cused P, who defended himself by saying Aspasia had
> been to bed with four different men in a month. B looked
> up Lidforss and got it confirmed. And they thought they
> had finished me! Their hate has deeper grounds.
>
> And now I erase L from the number of the living. He
> no longer exists for me.
>
> His most recent exploit is absolutely nauseating.
> [Strindberg said Lidforss, disappointed because Strind-
> berg could not pay him much for the translation of
> *Antibarbarus,* had attempted to lay his hands on Strind-
> berg's luggage by telling the porter a lie.] I once called
> him a disgusting person, and I repeat it. . . .

A subsequent letter, mailed on May 26, shows that Strindberg regarded the Berlin episode in his life as over and that
he was burning his bridges and moving on to other fields.

> At first Lidforss astonished me, but now he interests me.
> And psychologically how can he explain his behavior to-
> ward me? If I were to publish in Lund his latest letter,
> written when he was translating *Antibarbarus* and in

which he says that he agrees with me on all points, "generally speaking," I wonder what he'd do. What did he say to you about the review he wrote for *Dagens Nyheter?* Do L. and the Polack really think they can eradicate me? They'll annihilate themselves. They know that whoever fools around with me dies. Like touching a powerful battery. And I don't have to raise a finger! Look how L. blew himself to pieces. They strike me down in Stockholm; I'm dead for a day, then I rise up in Karlstad. They kill me in Christiania and I rise up in Paris, where Pigeon has just published *Les Revoltés scandinaves,* and I'm the only Swede in it. I fell in Rome [*Miss Julie* was apparently a failure there], was hissed in Naples, rose like the sun in Copenhagen, was booed in Berlin by Aspasia and the cuckolds [*Playing with Fire* was a fiasco when staged at the Lessing Theater in December 1893], and popped up shortly after in Moscow last autumn. *Madman's Defense* was brought to trial in Berlin, pirated in Sweden, and again I was a dead man. —Pow! Cherbuliez, secretary of the French Academy, writes a whole essay about Aug. Sg. in *Revues des deux Mondes.* No, no, they can't eradicate me, not on your life! Paris is a ripe plum just waiting to be picked, and the next season is mine. I'm going there in the fall, when everything will be ready. *Dramatique,* vol. 2, is coming out any day now, *The Bond, Playing with Fire, Creditors* in it and my portrait on the jacket. *Le Figaro* has interviewed me about Zola's candidacy.[4] No, they won't eradicate me, but I can and will eradicate my enemies, and you just watch how meekly they'll curl up

---

[4] Strindberg was interviewed by mail by a French journalist in regard to Zola's candidacy for the French Academy. Strindberg's reply was published not in *Le Figaro* but in *L'Eclair*, May 30, 1894. He praised Zola as "the poet and master of our era" and saw him as both naturalist and symbolist. The extent to which Strindberg identified himself with Zola may be judged by comparing the letter given above with Strindberg's remarks in the interview: "Zola made the mistake of becoming too great. For twenty years one has had to put up with him. The young began by worshipping him; later his greatness became an embarrassment to them and they deposed him—how many times? They repudiated him, killed him, buried him, and still he lives! He was declared dead in Paris, and now at this moment he rises up in London. Truly, this man is immortal."

and die,—but fast this time. I've learned how to eliminate chance.

If you should meet anyone from the Bureau [the publisher of *A Madman's Defense* and other works by Strindberg], announce a new novel by me: *Everybody's Aspasia*. Set in Berlin. High-priced, and cash only. . . . Will you be the negotiator? My wife today presented me with a daughter.

Yours,

Aug. Sg.

On July 31 Strindberg severed his last link with The Black Pig. He posted a letter to Adolph Paul so filled with insults, defamations, and accusations that Paul declined to print it in his memoirs, except for one of the concluding phrases: "You shall never have another peaceful day as long as you live."

Paul insists that he never gave Strindberg the least occasion for this assault. However true that may or may not be, it is clear that Strindberg no longer had any use for him. Strindberg's eyes were now on Paris and Paul's place as advance agent and contact man was taken by Leopold Littmansson, a Swedish musician and friend of Strindberg since their student days, who had married into money and settled in Versailles. Strindberg's plan was to accept Littmansson's invitation to stay with him, and from Versailles lay siege to the City of Light.

À NOUS LA VIE

The Scandinavian invasion of Paris had begun with Ibsen. Before 1900 the man who was to be hailed as the father of modern drama was virtually unknown in France, although he was recognized as a major playwright in Germany. With Antoine's production of *Ghosts* at his Théâtre-Libre on May 30, 1890, the mists of the north began to obscure the clear lights of Paris, much to the chagrin of many French critics and writers. Antoine's production of *The Wild Duck* in April 1891 fell in with the aims of the Symbolists, who represented the avant-garde at that time, and made Ibsen's reputation. Later that year the commercial boulevard theater dared to take a chance on Ibsen by staging *Hedda Gabler*. In 1893 there

were productions of five different Ibsen plays. On the rec-
ommendation of a Danish writer of the decadent school, Herman Bang, Strindberg's plays came to the attention of Antoine, and on January 16, 1893, he produced *Miss Julie,*
which was the subject of much advance interest. It was the
first time in ninety years that a play by a Swedish dramatist
had been produced in the French capital. The Nordic horde,
which consisted of some seven or eight writers at most, scored
their greatest gains in the 1893–94 season when eleven Scandinavian plays were performed, and the most crucial battle
was fought on June 21, 1894, when Strindberg's *Creditors*
was acted by Lugné-Poe and the Théâtre de l'Oeuvre troupe
at the Comédie-Parisienne theater.

To fill out the evening Lugné-Poe included in the program
a lecture, another short play, and the reading of a Symbolist
poem to precede Strindberg's long one-act play. The lecturer
Lucien Muhlfeld attacked the critics in the house. The short
play by Herman Bang fell flat. The poem was greeted with
laughter. Furious, Lugné-Poe stepped forward to reproach
the critics in the audience for their insensitivity. The critics
answered back. After a stormy intermission, the curtain went
up on *Creditors* and came down seventy-five minutes later
to enthusiastic applause. Though none of the critics could
bring himself to praise the play wholeheartedly, all except
one found it a powerful work. Strindberg's youthful dream
of conquering Paris—the dream of any aspiring playwright in
the nineteenth century—had been realized.

The news of his success reached him in Dornach. To
Littmansson he conveyed his enthusiasm:

> Do you know Nietzsche? No? Ah—!
> The secret of life: the will to power—over minds.
> Happiness is to be free to grow and to rule.
> Unhappiness is not to be free to grow, and to be ruled
> over.
> This is happiness, this sense of power; to sit in a hut
> on the shores of the Danube among six women who re-
> gard me as a dimwit and know that right now in Paris,
> the brain center of the world, five hundred people are sit-
> ting as quiet as mice, stupidly exposing their brains to
> my hypnotic influence. Some rebel, but many go away

with my fungus-spores in their cortexes; they go home impregnated with the seed of my brain and they spawn my brood.

A half year from now I'll read a French book, a French paper, and recognize my children. Ah, those are my grains sprouting.

That is happiness!

Now as Strindberg prepared to go to France, *The Father* was scheduled for a Paris production, and *A Madman's Defense*, which was to be published shortly, had already been the subject of a couple of lengthy pieces. But Strindberg was never one to rest on his laurels. He was drawn to Paris not by the publication of novels and production of plays that he had written some years ago but by the prospect of launching a new career. In the spring of 1894 he began writing a series of essays in French intended for publication in Parisian journals; and through most of the summer he was busy painting oils to be sold in Paris; and when he was not writing and painting, he was carrying on his chemical experiments. *Antibarbarus* had not been received in Germany as the epoch-making book Strindberg thought it was, but the atmosphere in Paris was much more hospitable to alchemy and mysticism of one sort or another, and it was there that he thought his ideas might well bloom and flourish.

Now that The Black Pig coterie had deserted him what he needed first of all was disciples. Vacillating between amazing optimism and understandable despair, Strindberg regarded Littmansson, who was evidently in somewhat the same mood, as his first follower. In his letters to him Strindberg is constantly trying to encourage and stimulate him to dare to attempt something new and different. In writing to him Strindberg is really talking to himself.

Be skeptical, yes—toward the old! Have faith—in the new. Your skepticism is little more than a fear of being ridiculous, as mine is sometimes.

You flame up, die down. The flesh, the Chateaubriand steak entices you—wife and child—your violin.

And you always find obstacles. And you call for money.

Let's begin at the beginning. Then everything will come to us. But I've got to have someone who believes.

"Why not found a monastery?" suggested Strindberg, where artists could pursue their dreams without interference of wives and bill collectors. And when they had educated themselves as artists and rid themselves of the "tyranny of the mass," when they had so refined their souls that they represented "the highest type of humanity," then they would reveal themselves to the world.

> —Like the Salvation Army! We'll build a white dragon ship, gold and other colors, dress ourselves in white robes, and row down the Aisne on a pilgrimage, and when the wind is right, glide with blue silk sails down the Seine; go through Paris without disembarking, playing new instruments which I'll invent, new melodies which I'll let nature (chance) compose, singing songs in scales with quarter tones and eighth tones, music never heard before, and then we'll sail into the Marne and up to Aisne where we'll live.
>
> But before that—self-education! And a seeking out, a reckless, daring search, without fears of any kind.

"Be serious," replied the domesticated Littmansson. But beneath his wild impromptu thoughts Strindberg was serious, serious in his longing to be free to pursue his thoughts wherever they led, free to open his mind and tap its depths. Germany and Austria, home and family had now become prisons for him.

The flesh was "your tragic aspect," he wrote to Littmansson, "and the family mine. But one has to go through everything—and put everything behind. Forward!"

> I am always ready to fly off as soon as I feel someone stroking my wings. And I'm always ready to pull up my tent pegs when the air begins to suffocate me. And that it does now.
>
> Léon Daudet may not be wrong when he says . . . that man goes through his ontogeny (like sulfur) not only in the oviduct but also later in life. Like this: the young man up to thirty is the image of his mother and has a woman's hysteria, vanity, lustfulness, and everything else disgusting. Between thirty and forty he takes after his father and has a man's ambition, strength,

insensitivity. Only after forty does the true self appear, propagated by these mother and father doubles.

So, *à nous la vie* (as Zola said when he turned fifty and began to ride the velocipede!)

At the station in Linz, Austria, on August 17, 1894, at three in the morning, Strindberg caught the train for Paris. He arrived there thirty-eight hours later.

## GETTING RID OF BALLAST

Strindberg spent the first few weeks in Versailles with the Littmanssons, who helped him revise some of his essays. Frequently he would take the trip into Paris to meet publishers and reporters, but the big city discouraged and depressed him.

"The air must be poisoned," he wrote to Frida. "What am I doing here? In the long run I'll lose my wits, and there are moments when I feel like running away from it all. Where to? Sweden! . . . Paris is so boring, as boring as London. And what I came to do, I've done. A business trip, that's all it was, and a successful one."

Early in September, Strindberg met Albert Langen and Willy Grétor, who helped make his business trip successful at first. Langen was a young millionaire from Cologne who had inherited a fortune made in the sugar beet industry and who had married the daughter of Norwegian playwright, novelist, poet, orator, politician Bjørnstjerne Bjørnson. A connoisseur and patron of the arts, Langen collected paintings and authors. He had just established a publishing house in Paris and had signed up such writers as Anatole France, Henry Becque, Paul Hervieu, Georg Brandes, and Knut Hamsun. On his spring list were Strindberg's *A Madman's Defense* and *Lucky Peter's Travels*.

Grétor was Langen's right-hand man and advisor. He was a young Danish painter of twenty-five or thereabouts who seemed to have connections in the art and literary worlds, had a good nose for the coming thing in literature, and a marvelous knack for laying his hands on old masterpieces that Langen could not resist buying. Strindberg showed him his paintings. Grétor glowed, and immediately disposed of four of them for 900 francs. He spoke enthusiastically of organizing a one-man Strindberg show and guaranteed the hard-pressed Swede an income of 400 marks a month if Strindberg could keep on turning out the canvasses. When the Littmanssons moved from Versailles to a seaside resort and Strindberg needed a new place to lay his head, Grétor promptly invited him to live rent free until October first in his Paris apartment in the Passy district. Would not Strindberg be inconveniencing Grétor? Not at all. Grétor had another more sumptuous apartment on the Boulevard Malesherbes; the Passy apartment was only for his mistress, who was living in the country for the time being. Strindberg took advantage of the offer and found himself in possession of an elegant and spacious ground-floor apartment at 51 Rue de Ranelagh consisting of five rooms plus a kitchen. There were gilt mirrors, crystal chandeliers, Persian carpets, cordovan chairs, and on the walls hung a Boucher, a Rubens, a Leonardo, and a Cézanne (bought from Gauguin).

Yet, alas, Strindberg was not happy in these surroundings and tried to dissuade Frida from coming to Paris, where she hoped to resume her career as journalist and critic.

> I have everything I could wish for, and I wish—to drop everything and go away, just to be near you, and fight with you like cat and dog. Remember what I once said to you: a bad marriage is better than none at all. It's too peaceful here. No one to rile me or torture me. I yearn for an honest-to-goodness quarrel, in which you unquestionably will remain master. . . .
>
> Frida, you're still living on teen-age memories and dreams of Paris as the golden city. But remember, you're a mother, and our child will prevent you from living an active life here. And to be locked up *à deux* in a wasteland of people is worse than being in the country.
>
> In Paris there's autumn weather, and noise, envy, *blague*, and bluff. Which doesn't mean that my career is closed—far from it, since I can serve certain interests. But how unpleasant it is.
>
> In a week you'd be wishing you were back at the cottage. If you have talent, it will find a way of expressing itself without your having to be here. . . .

I've painted five pictures. Well enough, but there's no money to show for it. Money. If we ran out of that, we'd be lost. It's a new age we're living in, and I feel myself a stranger in this world of money. I'm losing my personality, my very being, and I want to get out.

I sit here alone, painting, visiting no one, as usual.

If this keeps up, I don't know what I'll do. Alone morning, noon, and night. In five rooms and a kitchen. . . . I could cry when I think of my fields by the Danube.

The very magnificence of the Passy apartment made Strindberg suspicious of Grétor. "Frida, I smell something rotten here. . . . Just between us, Grétor is no true art lover. And no chump like me."

And how right Strindberg was. Though Langen did not know it at first, Grétor displayed his true artistry as a swindler and confidence man. His real name was Willy Pedersen; he had taken the name Grétor from Greta, a Swedish mistress of his. Using a subsequent German mistress as a stepping stone, Grétor arrived at an Austrian mistress, a baroness, who had inherited 250,000 gulden. Grétor installed himself as her kept man and set to work spending the money. The Passy apartment actually belonged to the baroness, whose fortune and patience were now nearly exhausted. The luxurious duplex apartment on Boulevard Malesherbes to which Grétor also laid claim belonged to Langen, who was out of town until September 12. Grétor may be said to have some interest in it, however, for he had been responsible for the decor, skillfully mixing fake and genuine masterpieces. His present mistress, an Italian girl who had cost him 40,000 francs out of the baroness' fortune, also lived there, temporarily.

Using one mistress to maintain another was typical of Grétor's whole way of life. His brilliant conversation consisted of bon mots picked up at one party and dropped at the next. The apartments he lived in were borrowed apartments. His creative ideas were got by picking brains. He bought Strindberg's paintings, signed his own name to them, and sold them in Cologne. His real talent lay in imitating the masters; he faked Michelangelos, Mantegnas, Piero de Cosimas, and Luca della Robbias. When Langen found out that Grétor had foisted some fake nymphs on him, he pursued the fleeing swindler and demanded his money back. The irrepressible Grétor settled accounts by selling Langen the idea for a satirical journal to be called *Simplicissimus*. The idea had originated with Strindberg. Not that that bothered Langen. The only difference between Langen and Grétor was that the former had money and the latter had to use other people's. Strindberg had them pegged from the beginning as philistines and businessmen, cunning beyond their twenty-five years.

To help keep tabs on his various enterprises Grétor hired at the beginning of September a secretary, a young, struggling, desperately poor playwright from Germany, who like Grétor had a game leg. His name was Frank Wedekind. Grétor did much to help Wedekind, lending him money, and perhaps even revising Wedekind's sex play *Erdgeist* for publication by Langen's firm in 1895. When *Simplicissimus* began publication in 1896, Wedekind became one of its chief contributors. A few years later he gave Grétor a measure of immortality by writing a whole play about him, *The Marquis of Keith*. Keith's ethics are summed up in his definition: Sin is a mythological designation for bad business.

Grétor wanted to use Strindberg as a front man to occupy the Passy apartment and pose as a friend of his mistress. Strindberg was pained by the suggestion, but the cynical Becque said he should feel honored. "Mais vous voilà installé en parisien tout à fait."

When Frida Uhl, unable to resist the glamorous life, arrived in Paris—without her baby—Grétor and Langen gave her the red-carpet treatment. Langen's liveried butler was at the station to meet her and present her with a bouquet of roses.

To create publicity Grétor and Langen contrived a meeting between Bernhardt, the Divine Sarah, and Strindberg, the outlandish woman-hater who had just written a somewhat critical piece[5] on Dumas' misogynistic play *La femme de Claude*, in which Bernhardt was playing the part of the treasonous wife who is shot by her husband. The plan was to

[5] "Césarine," *Le Figaro*, September 30, 1894.

have Strindberg come on stage during the intermission and meet the Divine Sarah while reporters commemorated the event. Before the theater Langen gave a splendid dinner at his Malesherbes apartment, for Becque, Hervieu, the Strindbergs, and others. After dinner a servant escorted the Strindbergs to the street and hailed a cab for them. Strindberg grabbed Frida by the arm and steered her away from the cab —away from the theater, away from the Divine Sarah, away from the hucksters Langen and Grétor. They walked in silence until Frida moaned, "J'ai soif." They spent the rest of the evening in cafés.

The next day Langen called on them. "If one of you isn't dead or dying," he said, "I'll never forgive you."

When Grétor's Austrian baroness did not keep up the payments on the Passy flat, Strindberg and Frida, who were in no position to do it for her, moved across the Seine to more modest rooms in the Latin Quarter, at 14 Rue de l'Abbé de l'Epée near the Luxembourg Gardens. For a while they carried on an intensive social life through Langen and his circle of writers and through the Swedish painters and journalists that Strindberg knew. But Frida and Langen found time to spend long hours together in the apartment ostensibly discussing translations and inevitably arousing Strindberg's suspicions.

In November, Frida was suddenly called back to Austria because her baby had become ill. A kiss in the street near the Gare du Nord, and Strindberg and Frida never saw each other again. It is at this point that Strindberg begins *Inferno*, the autobiographical novel that recounts his experiences during the period 1894 to 1897.

With Frida out of town he was free to devote himself once again to his alchemical experiments and to the writing of what was intended to be the second part of *Antibarbarus*. But his behavior toward Frida suggests that behind his interest in the occult sciences lay an ulterior motive that is scarcely discernible until 1895. It is a desire to discover new worlds, to begin a new life, and to be reborn as an artist. This motive had been lurking in the background ever since Strindberg divorced Siri von Essen, even before that, but now it came to the fore. Once again, here in Paris, as he had in Berlin, he threw overboard whatever ballast might keep his spirit from soaring. The Black Pig was only a stopover for his restive creative nature, and though he certainly felt bitter toward his former friends there, he expressed no sense of regret at their disaffection. In Paris too he was quick enough to cut himself free from Langen and Grétor and the world of cheap publicity and shoddy philistinism. Strindberg was eager to have his former works published in order that he might be free to pursue his own highly individual course, not because he wanted to be known as the author of *The Father* or *Miss Julie* or *A Madman's Defense*. And when Frida returned to Austria, Strindberg seemed almost relieved—relieved of a burden that was holding him back on the unknown path he was about to take.

To a Swedish painter Strindberg wrote at the end of November:

> I don't really know much about my marriage. I never took it very seriously, as you must have noticed in Berlin, and it's probably headed for a breakup—though I can't be certain. Now and then it was a lot of fun, and sometimes a good marriage, but language, race, bad habits, our notions of right and wrong created tensions at times.

This is cool and dispassionate enough, but the letter he wrote to Frida at about the same time reveals a Strindberg who has decided to force the issue. He accuses her of sullying his name, of casting doubt on his being the father of Kerstin, of conspiring with art forgers in Paris, and even of having been the mistress of Langen. And he warns her that if she returns to Paris she would be treated as a prostitute; she might even be locked up.

> It's no skin off my nose since I can prove my innocence, and a bit of prison means nothing to me.
> But what about you? Is your conscience clean? Can you clear yourself of the charge of being an accomplice in this crime? Give me something to go on and I'll take care of things, not as a grand gesture nor out of gen-

erosity, but for the pure, simple, and humane reason that
my child needs its mother.

But one word of advice, no matter what the situation
is:—wipe out *immediately* all traces you've left behind,
if any, and prepare your defense.

Though the vague accusations he hurls at Frida are not
without some substantial foundation (more substantial than
may be apparent), his way of handling them is, let us say,
dramatic. He makes a few inferences and recklessly builds a
whole plot on them, a plot with a purpose, and that purpose
to get rid of Frida while keeping his own hands relatively
clean.

She could not remain indifferent to this letter, and in December she did what Strindberg no doubt wanted her to do:
she initiated divorce proceedings. Now the Catholic Church
in Austria could not divorce couples who had been legitimately married. However, since Strindberg had been married previously, a Catholic girl could not legitimately have
married him. "Ergo," concluded Frida's lawyer, "your marriage was not and is not a legitimate marriage here in
Austria!"

In the ensuing correspondence Strindberg refused to withdraw his charges, but he did invite her to come back to Paris
to live with him on certain conditions, which amounted to a
humiliating demand that she reform her ways. In January,
at the request of Frida's lawyer, Strindberg sent to Austria
certain legal documents necessary for the separation. For all
practical purposes the marriage was over.

## MADAME CHARLOTTE'S MILK BAR

In the meantime Strindberg was building a reputation in
Paris as the oddest of the odd Scandinavian writers and forming new alliances and friendships among the bohemians and
"decadents."

Part of his essay "Sensations détraquées," a milestone in
Strindberg's development, was published in November[6] and
admired by the small clique that gathered at his café.

[6] It appeared in three parts in *Le Figaro littéraire*, November
17, 1894, January 26, 1895, and February 9, 1895.

At the Café Napolitain, which is my Dionysius' Ear 6
to 7 in the evenings—silence. [My essay] was received as
something new, extraordinary but crazy. Since my talent
is not questioned, nor the originality, the craziness served
simply as spice, and now I'm addressed as *Cher Maître*.

In December, when Strindberg was easing Frida out of
his life, he called on Ida Molard, a Scandinavian sculptress
who had married a Frenchman and settled in Paris. Very
masculine in appearance, she dressed like a man and smoked
cigars. She and her handsome composer husband William
held open house at their flat on Rue Vercingétorix for such
personages as the composer Delius and the painter Gauguin.
Strindberg found their company much more congenial than
that of Langen, Grétor, and the fashionable writers whom
they entertained.

Gauguin and Strindberg had much in common. The French
painter was only a year older, and they were both rebels to
whom artistic and intellectual creativity meant more than
anything else. But in complete contrast to Strindberg, Gauguin was an extrovert and a showoff, and while Strindberg
was a bit of a prig, Gauguin had the morals of a rabbit.
Gauguin at this time was in mid-career. He had married a
Danish girl (hence his connection with the Molards) and
had left her when he sailed off to Tahiti in 1891 to discover
his new world. He had returned to France, on money his
wife sent him, in 1893, visited her in Copenhagen, moved on
to le Pouldu and Pont Aven, and come back to his Paris
studio early in December. Here he was to reside only until
the following March when he re-embarked for the South Seas
never to return. His best friends in Paris were the Symbolist
writers and painters Mallarmé, Moréas, Redon, and Saint-
Paul Roux.

Once Strindberg had overcome his shyness the two of them
got along very well, and Gauguin introduced him to his favorite eating place, a small crémerie on the Rue de la
Grande Chaumière just off the Boulevard du Montparnasse.
It was owned and run by Mme. Charlotte Coutterer, an Alsa-
tian woman in her forties. With plain tables and a floor of
large square red tiles, the place was a favorite hangout for
unknown artists who frequently ate on credit and paid their

bills with paintings. In time the little unassuming restaurant was adorned with works by Gauguin, Slewinsky, and at least three by Strindberg. It is this *petit restaurant* that provides the principal setting for Strindberg's comedy *Crimes and Crimes*.

To the hungry artists in a strange city Madame Charlotte's well-stocked counter and ample bosom meant home and mother, a combination that Strindberg could never resist. Madame Charlotte seems to have been genuinely fond of the enigmatic Swede, who could often play the little boy hiding his face in his mother's apron, whether out of pain and loneliness or in sheer mischief is hard to say. At seven o'clock one morning Madame Charlotte came in to her restaurant and found all her pots and pans piled in a heap in the middle of the floor. Gyrating around them was Strindberg, dressed only in his shirt and underwear, doing a dance of exorcism to drive out the evil spirits that might poison the food. The narrator of this anecdote (the sculptor Carl Milles) leaves us unenlightened as to whether Madame Charlotte was pleased by Strindberg's apotropaic offices or affronted by this lurking insult to the cleanliness of her kitchen.

After leaving Paris, Strindberg kept up a correspondence with Madame Charlotte and about the turn of the century he asked for her photograph. She thought this was the preliminary to a marriage proposal. Her high expectations were defeated when she heard that Strindberg had married a young actress in Sweden. Shortly thereafter she closed up her restaurant and returned to the Alsace.

During December and January, Strindberg was one of the most talked-about personages in Paris. First of all there was a great deal of publicity attendant upon the premier of *The Father*. Strindberg knew that the reception of this play would make him or break him. When Lugné-Poe cut the Captain's death scene as being too strong for Parisian stomachs, Strindberg raised no objection, preferring to trust Lugné-Poe's sense for the right thing. He said he gave Lugné-Poe and the adaptor of the play permission to change the end. "And why not? In exchange for that M. Poe will play it for a whole week. That's the way things are, and that's how certain they are of success." The premier was scheduled for Friday, December 14, but had to be moved ahead to December 13 in order not to conflict with the celebration of the one thousandth performance of *Faust* at the Paris Opéra. "Who has the persecution complex," joked Strindberg, "I or the Opéra?" *Le Figaro* interviewed him and gave the following "snapshot" portrait: "A majestic forehead crowned by anarchic locks; pale blue eyes; taciturn, tall, and lanky[!]; acts as if he were on an apostolic mission; completes the Nordic Trinity, in which Ibsen is the Father and Bjørnson the Son."

*Tout Paris* gathered at the large Nouveau-Théâtre on the Rue Blanche for the premiere. Dressed in his astrakhan hat and a long robe, Gauguin was the cynosure of the occasion while Strindberg as usual absented himself and waited nervously at home. Though the audience was enthusiastic, the reviews were mixed, the negative ones disparaging the play for its melodrama and its echoes of Dumas *fils,* the positive ones praising Strindberg's power and originality. All in all, the impact of the play was the greatest made by any Scandinavian drama up to that time. The papers were filled with comments and notices, most of which were colored by xenophobia and a few by its opposite. In Germany the word had gone out that in the drama "the light today comes to us from the North." In a Paris magazine those words provided the gag line to a cartoon that pictured the Act II climax of *The Father:* the Captain, looking very much like Strindberg, throwing a burning kerosene lamp at his wife.

Further publicity came Strindberg's way from his contribution to the woman question. He did not initiate the discussion; a series of misogynistic articles had appeared in French magazines from 1892 through 1894. But Strindberg took advantage of the trend and republished with a few additional paragraphs a longish essay "The Inferiority of Women," which he had written and published in 1890 and which utilized the arguments of Lombroso and Spencer, Darwin and Hartmann, Haeckel and Nietzsche. This appeared in the January issue of the *Revue Blanche* and immediately stirred up so much interest that the editors of *Gil Blas* sent out a reporter to obtain the opinions of fifteen celebrities on Strindberg's article. Some, such as Alphonse Daudet, were disgusted: "To me woman is Mother. Strindberg's paradox is therefore monstrous." Most preferred to use the occasion to display their wit. Said the aging Dumas *fils:* "It is conceivable that man produces more; it is certain that woman is worth more." Said Octave Mirbeau, sensing that some woman must have caused Strindberg great suffering, "In former times those who were disillusioned with women threw themselves into the Seine. Today they throw themselves into anthropology. That is to go from bad to worse."

For once being on the receiving end of witty remarks did not bother Strindberg. To Frida he wrote, "The way the woman question is discussed here is unbelievable. They used to say, 'In Paris they kill with ridicule.' Not true at all if one has talent."

Actually, he concerned himself less with the woman question than with chemistry. When the reporter came to interview him in January about *The Father,* Strindberg insisted on talking about the composition of sulfur.

## NEW WORLDS

That interview took place in a hospital. Strindberg's experiments had precipitated a severe attack of psoriasis, a disease from which he suffered all his life (and which accounts for a character such as the lawyer with the bleeding hands in *A Dream Play*). When Frida had first seen the thick growths, like boils, under his thumb and on his index finger, she had turned pale. Strindberg dismissed it as "a completely harmless case of eczema. But I have had it since I was a child and I can't get rid of it. When something bad happens to me, the sores open up—probably bad blood from my parents—and start to bleed. The doctors can't make heads or tails of it. For that matter they can't make heads or tails of anything at all about me."

In January 1895 the sores became so large and painful that he was unable to button his clothes. Realizing that Strindberg was penniless—*The Father* brought him only about one hundred francs after the actors, the producer, and the translator had taken their shares[7]—Ida Molard noti-

[7] On December 13, the day of the premiere of *The Father,* Strindberg informed a friend in Sweden that he had sold paintings for

fied Nathan Söderblom, the Swedish pastor in Paris, of his condition, and it was he who provided money for hospital treatment. Strindberg went to the Saint-Louis Hospital on January 7 for a diagnosis, was sent home for a few days, and was registered as an inpatient from January 11 to January 31.

Strindberg preferred to keep his illness as mysterious as possible, and no doubt viewed his bleeding sores as stigmata. His secretiveness encouraged two rumors to be bruited about among his friends and enemies. In the nineteenth century psoriasis was often thought to be either a symptom or a side effect of venereal disease, a view not shared, however, by Strindberg's dermatologist at the Saint-Louis Hospital. But Strindberg certainly feared that he might have contracted syphilis at some time or other; his companions seemed willing to believe it; and Dagny Juel apparently spread stories to that effect. Munch drew a crude lithograph *At the Clinic,* about 1896, showing syphilitic patients undergoing examination, and in the middle sits a haggard Strindberg-like figure.

The other rumor implied that Strindberg was an anarchist whose attempt to improvise homemade bombs had burned his hands. In the 1880s Strindberg had been a vociferous parlor anarchist, and Paris in the 1890s was the scene of a scarifying series of anarchist bombings. When Strindberg entered the hospital, one newspaper reported that "August Strindberg, zealous amateur chemist, has suffered blood poisoning through his experiments with explosives."

After reading that, Strindberg wrote to Frida, "That sounds just marvelous in this tin-can-anarchist-assassin era."

Gauguin, who was readying a one-man show at the Hôtel Drouot to raise money for his trip to the South Seas, sought to capitalize on this publicity by having Strindberg write an appreciation for the catalogue. Strindberg must have seen Gauguin's work on several occasions during the previous seven or eight weeks, but he paid another visit to his studio on January 31, evidently to refresh his mind before writing the requested letter, which is dated February 1. The bright light of the Tahitian paintings, falling on "trees that no bota-

---

400 francs. "I'm painting small decorative panels on cardboard. Have 10 ready. Price $10–$11 each with gilt frames. . . . Designed to be hung in door panels with tacks."

nist would recognize" and "animals that Cuvier never dreamt of" seared his mind, and his sleep was filled with Gauguin's visions. As might be expected, the letter tells us much more about its author than about its subject. Strindberg is not reluctant to say he does not like Gauguin's paintings because he knows that "being hated only strengthens you. Your personality takes pleasure in the antipathy it arouses, eager to be left in peace. Admired, you would have followers who would systematize you, pigeonhole you, attach to your art a label, which in five years would become for a younger generation the empty name of an outmoded form that their every effort would make still more outmoded."

To help put Gauguin's work in perspective Strindberg went to look at the works of the popular muralist Puvis de Chavannes, whom he once admired warmly. He stood before *Le pauvre Pêcheur*, lost in sympathetic contemplation of it until he saw the symbolic crown of thorns. This repelled him.

> I hate Christ and the crown of thorns, my dear Gauguin. I tell you I detest them. I want to be rid of this wretched, miserable God who turns the other cheek. I'd rather have as my god Vitsliputsli, who stands in the full light of the sun as he eats the heart of man. . . . Who is Gauguin but a savage who hates a burdensome civilization, something of a Titan, who, jealous of the Creator, makes in his leisure hours his own little creation, the child who breaks his toys in order to make new ones out of the pieces. He is the man who denies and dares and challenges, preferring to see the heavens red than to see them blue as the hoi-polloi does.

By the time Strindberg reached the end of his letter he had done a nearly complete about-face with respect to this new art.

> Having gotten myself warmed up, I now begin to have a clearer understanding of Gauguin's art.
>
> A certain contemporary author has been reproached for not having portrayed real human beings but having *simply* constructed his own beings. Simply!!
>
> Bon voyage, maître. But do come back to us, and look me up again. Possibly by that time I shall have learned to understand your art more, and that will put me in a

position to write a real preface to a new catalogue for a new Hôtel Drouot exhibit. For now I too begin to feel an irresistible drive to become a primitive and to create a new world.

From this point on the desire to be reborn begins to dominate Strindberg's thoughts and imagination. He had always wanted to be in the vanguard but now, approaching middle age, surrounded by younger writers who were exploring new paths, he realized that one had to have young eyes and a youthful curiosity in order to see the world afresh. Gauguin, who was a year older than Strindberg, had left his wife and family and at the age of forty-one sailed to Tahiti to discover his new world. And now, less than two years after his return to France, he was about to embark again for the South Seas. Certainly Gauguin's reckless search for a fuller life encouraged the more timorous Strindberg to cut himself loose from the old moorings of traditional thought and conventional behavior and like Baudelaire, whom Strindberg may well have been reading at this time, set forth on a voyage of the human spirit that might plunge him "to the bottom of the pit—be it heaven or hell, no matter—to the bottom of the Unknown in order to find the New."

While it cannot be said that he was bored with life, as Baudelaire was, for Strindberg was immersed in his chemical experiments, it is true that creative writing bored him. To write well he needed the stimulus of new experiences that would produce new points of view and called for original techniques of expression. Most authors would have found enough material in the Berlin experiences and in the marriage to Frida, but they had not affected Strindberg deeply. Looking back from our vantage point, we can see that they did actually furnish a vast storehouse of material on which he was to draw for a long time, but they lacked at this time the emotional resonance and moral meaning without which they were useless to Strindberg. They were mere jottings, filed away in his Green Sack, without real significance or order. Only some new vision would serve as a magnet to pull all these filings into some pattern both beautiful and meaningful.

What he required was a sense of perspective over the recent past and at the same time an intensely personal attachment to it. We can see how he strives to fulfill both opposed needs in the letters he writes to Frida at this time.

Very often I ask myself if you were consciously my enemy. And I answer, "What if you were!" You were a happy, pleasant enemy whom I liked very much, even if I gradually trained myself to conceal that.

I feel now that I shall not see you again, the same feeling I had when we parted on the island of paving stones, surrounded by darkness and the roar of the wagons.

But whatever happens, drop me a line or two about you and the child. Why part like enemies? Let's be modern. Treat me like a discarded lover, always less harmful than a legitimate husband, and believe me when I say I am gallant enough to let my lady partner play the glorious part of victor. . . .

My God!—"Happy New Year"! That's what we wished each other in Dornach once upon a time. What a disgusting world! It's enough to make me cry. Weep, if you can. Unfortunately, I still can, I can!

. . .

You took pity on me, and you wanted to comfort me in the depths of my greatest misery. As thanks I slapped you in the face. You had to suffer. I know that because I suffer, suffer terribly—without any pangs of conscience.

You took pity! Can one take pity on an enemy?

It's all over—so we think! But as long as the child is around, there will always be points of contact, always that invisible bond that brings us together through our memories. There's the ineluctable hell, the eternal punishment by which we shall torture each other to death, because we tried to deceive nature. Think a bit about your life, about your unconscious behavior, which will drag you down to ruin.

How can you explain the following simple facts? I introduced you into my circle of friends in Berlin. I have lost them all, and you still have them. Same thing in London. And again in Paris! Don't I have good reason for running away from you? . . .

You see the world belongs to the mean and cruel. The art of cruelty is a divine gift, one that has not been vouchsafed me, and cast out into the desert like the son of Hagar the handmaiden, I am born for the desert, where I shall perish alone. Or else I shall have to create my own god who will protect me against the evil spirits.

It has been four months, a third of a year, since I last saw you . . . and a half year since I saw our child. I have acquired a horror of life and people. I have been on the verge of becoming an utter wretch. I have been exposed to all human temptations, and I have resisted them— thanks be to God, perhaps? "I know" is a phrase that no longer exists for me. I no longer know anything, for during these past few months a life of anguish and triviality has revived in me my old yearning for a life lived on the heights.

Do not be my enemy. Just leave me in peace. Leave me in peace, alone with my sorrows.

And tell me that you are no longer suffering, tell me that I haven't hurt you.

## THE ALCHEMIST AT WORK

After leaving the Saint-Louis Hospital, Strindberg may possibly have been in better physical condition but his financial condition was worse than ever. He lacked clothes and had to wear his summer suit through the Paris winter. When he sat down, he tried to cover up the holes on his knees by placing his hat over them. Knut Hamsun, who had starved and shivered in Christiania, was shocked to see Sweden's most famous author in this deplorable condition. He invited Strindberg to a good restaurant, but Strindberg took one look and turned away. "It's too bright for me. And too expensive."

Hamsun promptly got in touch with his colleague and countryman Jonas Lie and also with the Swedish etcher and painter Anders Zorn to organize an appeal for money to be given to Strindberg. An advertisement signed by them and three others was published in the liberal Copenhagen daily *Politiken* in March. According to Frida Uhl, the Swedish papers refused to print the appeal. Contributors were advised to send what they could directly to Strindberg. In *Inferno* Strindberg writes of money flying unexpectedly into his hands without explaining where it came from.

The publicity understandably embarrassed Strindberg. Money also came to him from another source and in a less humiliating way. Pastor Söderblom of the Swedish congregation in Paris collected money from his parishioners and passed it on to Strindberg as discreetly as possible. Strindberg never forgot Söderblom's tact and kindness. Two months before his death in 1912 Strindberg sent the pastor one thousand crowns to be forwarded to a Paris agency for Swedes who might be temporarily short of funds.

Much of the money that Strindberg received was spent on material for his chemical experiments, designed to prove through qualitative analysis that sulfur was not a simple element. The incentive for these experiments had come from his reading an old chemistry textbook by Mateo Orfila, dating from the 1830s, from which he learned that though sulfur had been classified among the simple elements, the ingenious experiments of Sir Humphry Davy and Berthollet *fils* appeared to indicate that it contained hydrogen, oxygen, and a special base that had so far not been isolated. First Strindberg burned sulfur and attempted to separate the constituents of the flame from the burning sulfur. Then, following Berthollet's method of producing acetylene from ether, Strindberg tried to achieve a partial combustion of the sulfur by means of cuprous ammonium chloride in a glass tube. The third and for him decisive experiment was carried out with two ovens. In one oven a clay retort for the sulfur was placed. The second oven had a tube to collect the carbon. He inserted the retort neck in the tube, using putty to seal the joint. Professor Troost of the Sorbonne had attributed the finding of foreign elements in attempts to obtain pure sulfur to water deriving from the cork used in the retorts. Strindberg hoped to avoid this by using putty instead. He heated the second oven until red-hot, driving out all the water; then he lit the sulfur retort. In this way he determined the presence of hydrogen sulfide. After letting it cool awhile, he broke the retort and found carbon in the form of powder, which he concluded could not have come from the carbon bits in the tube but must have come from the sulfur. Ergo, sulfur contained carbon.

The experiments were more complicated and the results

less clear than this indicates, and Strindberg spent a year trying to improve both. Obviously the use of ridiculously primitive equipment, which allowed minute traces of other elements to insinuate themselves, had led him to make the same errors that many another chemist had made in the nineteenth century in analyzing the elements. Even the renowned Lockyer had been led a few years before Strindberg's experiments to doubt that phosphorus was a simple element. In a paper "Experiments Tending to Show the Non-Elementary Character of Phosphorus," submitted to the Académie des Sciences in Paris in 1879, a paper that Strindberg read, Lockyer deemed phosphorus to be a compound on basis of spectral analysis. If spectroscopy could result in such errors, one can imagine that the possibilities for incorrect analysis were increased tenfold by using crude equipment. Strindberg was quite familiar with spectral analysis, of course, but in rebelling against the conclusions reached by modern scientists he disdained to use their methods and deliberately resorted to the older techniques of the alchemists.

Experiments continued to engage nearly all of Strindberg's energies during the spring when he worked at the Sorbonne laboratory seeking to decompose not only sulfur but also iodine. On May 11 he left the Sorbonne, having discovered, he said, the true formula for iodine as well as a method of manufacturing it from coal-tar derivatives.

"I'm going to preserve the starched shirt cuff on which I jotted down the reaction, so crucial. If I were a businessman I'd take out a patent, but I'm not going to. Instead I'm writing an article for *La Science Française*, where I am co-editor and have followers. Here's how iodine looks from the inside, even though it's been thought to be an element up to now: $C_6H_4O_2 + H_2O$ or $C_6H_6O_3 = C_6H_6O_3$ or $C_6H_6(OH)^2$."

He now moved out to Rouen for a brief stay with an engineer named André Dubosc, who was interested in the possibility of manufacturing sulfur using Strindberg's formula, although that formula, if it was the same as the one Strindberg wrote on his shirt cuff, would strike any modern chemist as utterly absurd.

The first six months of 1895 constituted the most successful phase of Strindberg's abortive career as chemist. For a while he seemed on the verge of making some real contribution to science; at least, some quite respectable and even distinguished engineers, scientists, and manufacturers were willing to listen to him. Writing to his Austrian translator, Strindberg outlined the sequence of events that had brought him a certain amount of fame and notoriety as a chemist.

In January 1895 I had to enter the Saint-Louis Hospital to have my hands treated, since I couldn't even dress myself. Certain people who feared my presence in Paris spread the rumor that I had carelessly burned my hands in working with explosives (anarchist) in order to get me expelled from the country. Then came the reporters from *Le Matin* and *Le Temps* to question me. I took advantage of my illness to tell them about my chemical experiments, as well as to write in *Le Temps* on the composition of sulfur [January 30, 1895]. On his own initiative the editor (Perrau) sent a clipping of my piece [it was not written by Strindberg; it was a newspaper report on his experiments] to Berthelot. I felt compelled to write to Berthelot, who answered with a polite and nondeprecatory letter. This was the signal for any number of scientists to make themselves heard, and all the timorous ones who had shared my thoughts in silence now stepped forward. Obalski in *La Science française* [February 8], Gautier in *Le Figaro* (February 15), Dubosc in *Le Traivailleur Normand,* all wrote pieces that were printed in the papers.

I expanded my thoughts on the subject in an essay to Berthelot and in an article in *Le Figaro* [February 12], and in yet another in *Science française* [March 15]. Thereupon I went to the laboratory at the Sorbonne and by carrying out experiments with carbon bisulfide I obtained complete proof of the composition of sulfur, which had already by means of analysis been shown to contain carbon. In May I wrote about iodine in *Le Temps* [May 14; this article, "L'iode comme un dérivé de houilles," was reprinted in *Le Moniteur Industriel,* June 8, 1895]. This won a great deal of attention and even caused a tremor on the Paris bourse because a cartel that had cornered the iodine market (for fourteen million marks) feared a crash. An agent ran to see me and

asked to buy my secret for an incredible sum. But since
there was no secret I advised him to make his own
iodine. He called in a chemist and asked Naquet to
manage things, at which point I left for Sweden.[8]

I then made a compilation or abstract of all my findings and speculations, which I called an Introduction
[to a Unified Chemistry]. This is only a kind of catalogue,
so to speak, and incomprehensible to anyone who has
not read *Antibarbarus* and my other pieces.

## PROJECTIONS AND IDENTIFICATIONS

However encouraging the first six months may have been,
by the end of the year it must have become apparent to
Strindberg that his gamble on science and alchemy was not
going to pay off immediately if at all. He had abandoned
his wife and child to seek fame in Paris; he had given up
writing in order to pursue his experiments; and all he had
gained was some respectful notices in a few journals and considerable notoriety in the newspapers as an eccentric Scandinavian.

It was now four or five years since he had written a major
work. Poverty and failure began to erode what faith he had
in himself. He still sought to unveil the secrets of Mother
Nature; he still yearned for new worlds to discover; he still
longed, almost obsessively, for some mystic way by which he
might shed the husk of middle age and be reborn; but accompanying these hopes and desires was a mounting sense
of despair. Paradoxically, this despair, if it can be called that,
for it seemed more like a desire to taste the dregs of defeat,
was the source of his fulfillment as an artist.

It was in 1896 that he plunged, willfully, into that pit, be
it heaven or hell, that Baudelaire wrote of. "I was living in

---

[8] In June, Strindberg went to southern Sweden for a three-week
visit, returning in July to Paris, where he lived for a brief time
with the journalist Julien Leclercq, a friend of Gauguin. Possibly
at Leclercq's suggestion Strindberg wrote two articles, "Misogynie
et gynolatrie," printed in *Gil Blas*, July 24, and "Le Barbare à
Paris," printed in the same periodical August 8, which seemed intended to preserve Strindberg's image as playwright and woman-
hater.

a strange country, forgetting the past and forgotten by my friends, devoting myself completely to science after having abandoned creative writing, when in the year 1896 I entered that phase of my life which I call Inferno, and it was under that title that there appeared in 1897 the book which represents a turning point in my life."

In contrast to the events in Strindberg's life that I have been chronicling so far, the events of 1896 are extremely difficult to verify. The reason for this is that he deliberately cut himself off from most of his former friends and went into his cocoon. Consequently the year that is most crucial to Strindberg's life and career, the year of his greatest metamorphosis, is the year we know least about.

What we can be certain of is that a kind of creative process was going on. As always with Strindberg, this involved identifying with people and projecting onto them part of his own conflicts. The major part of Strindberg's creative work was done away from his desk. In 1896 there were three writers and artists who served as batteries for Strindberg's psychic energy, out of which would flow the current that would produce some of his finest work. Part of this energy took the form of sexual jealousy and centered on Edvard Munch and Przybyszewski, both of whom had, along with Strindberg, been lovers of Dagny Juel.

Munch arrived in Paris in June to prepare a one-man show for Bing's *L'Art nouveau* gallery. Pursued by adoring women, as later Strindberg was to be pursued by the Furies, the Norwegian painter began to suffer from a severe persecution complex that caused him to drink excessively. (Or was the causal relationship the reverse of this?) By 1896 he was virtually an alcoholic. The villain in the plot his mind conjured up was a certain woman he had broken with and who now sought vengeance. In turn Munch sought revenge against all those who had kept him from glory. In 1902 the pursuing woman shot off one of Munch's fingers, and a few years later Munch suffered a severe breakdown. Symptoms of Munch's paranoia must have been apparent to Strindberg in 1896 or even earlier. Needless to say, Strindberg could identify with Munch in some respects and could also use him as a kind of model. And Munch could do the same with Strindberg. His

famous lithograph of Strindberg shows the playwright framed
by women and by thunderbolts and lightning.

In his review of Munch's exhibit[9] Strindberg wrote apropos
the painting *Jealousy:*

> Jealousy, sacred feeling of cleanliness of the soul which
> abhors mingling with another through the intermediary
> of woman. Jealousy, legitimate form of selfishness, born
> from the instinct to preserve self and race. . . . He who
> is jealous says to his rival, "Go, imperfect one, you fan
> the fires I have lit. From her mouth you shall breathe my
> breath and drink my blood. You will remain my slave for
> my spirit shall rule you through this woman who has
> become your master."

This sounds as if it might have been borrowed from Przybyszewski's appreciation on Munch's Berlin paintings; yet
Przybyszewski may have got some of his thoughts from
Strindberg who painted his *Night of Jealousy* before Munch's
painting on the same subject was done.

When Munch came to Paris he brought along with his
canvasses some news about Przybyszewski that obviously had
a profound effect on Strindberg. In order to understand why
the news should have been so disturbing it is necessary to
describe Strindberg's situation at this time. He had been carrying on a flirtation with an English sculptress named Mme.
Lecain, a woman whom Gauguin, who did not lack for experience, called "a demon, a man-eater." Strindberg let his
conscience bother him. He felt he was betraying Frida, to
whom he was still legally married, just as in Berlin he had
been unfaithful to her with Dagny when he was merely engaged. Previous to this Strindberg had sought to test Frida's
love by employing somewhat devious or, to say the least,
circuitous methods. Her love would be manifest if she asked
him to return. To bring about such a request Strindberg attempted by means of black magic to cast a spell on Kerstin,
his daughter by Frida, on the assumption that the illness of
the child would raise a call from the anguished mother and
bring about the reunion of husband and wife. The hand of

9 "L'Exposition d'Edvard Munch," *Revue Blanche,* X (June
1896), 525–26.

fate was, however, not to be forced so easily, and instead of striking Kerstin the black powers caused one of the children of Strindberg's first marriage to fall ill.

On May 26 Strindberg met Mme. Lecain once more, and the following day he received a call from Frida's lawyer regarding her divorce. Three weeks later Munch brought Strindberg the news that Przybyszewski had been arrested for the murder of his common-law wife Marthe Foerder and their children. A month later Strindberg's persecution feelings reached a peak.

I am setting these details down as if they were hard facts, and that is how they are generally accepted. But what we are confronted with is a mixture of fact and fancy. We have only Strindberg's word for the black magic; and as for Przybyszewski's murdering his wife, the truth is that Marthe killed herself, the three children were not harmed, and Przybyszewski, overwhelmed by guilt feelings, turned himself over to the police. Either Munch or Strindberg embroidered the story with dramatic detail. Munch was more intimately involved with Przybyszewski, and it was Munch who entered into the Stucha-Ducha ménage, encouraged by Stucha's strange attitude toward rivals. Przybyszewski's motives may be divined from a short novel he wrote in 1893, *The Vigils*, in which the hero, Stanislaw's alter ego, gives his wife to an artist and luxuriates in the feeling of hate and jealousy he has aroused in himself. After leaving the two of them together for a while, he returns and abases himself before his wife. For the publication of this story Munch prepared another version of *Madonna*, with Dagny as model; and Przybyszewski presented him with an inscribed copy of the book.

If we take a disinterested view of the information we possess, we see that the effect of the news about Przybyszewski on Strindberg was not so much that it pricked his conscience as that it spurred the artist in him. He had no strong reason to feel remorse for his behavior to Frida; his remorse has its roots in his treatment of his first wife Siri—the black powers knew this when they struck the "wrong" child—and in his behavior toward others in the earlier part of his career. However, what remorse he does feel at this juncture can be colored dramatically by overlaying it with the remorse of others, and the general spiritual malaise that affects him in the mid-1890s can be given a focus. When he observes Munch and hears about Przybyszewski, his own confused emotions and thoughts begin to sort themselves out. He is like an actor who finds a great role for himself, and then is able to cure or alleviate his own ills by a kind of homeopathy. He invests himself with the robes of the repentant Pole and the persecuted Norwegian, steps into their shoes, and then proceeds to act out his own drama.

The psychological process is traced in *The Vigils*, the philosophical concerns of which are sex and artistic creation. Taking his cue from Schopenhauer, Przybyszewski divides his hero in two, one part representing Brain, the other Sex. These are in opposition to one another, but having derived from the same original unity, they are also attracted to one another. The Brain is that of the artist contemplating his own misery; Sex is embodied in the loved one, who is merely a projection of the hero's Unconscious. Przybyszewski attempts to bring about the original harmonious, androgynous unity of Sex and Brain, of Will and Idea, of Ego and Id, by submitting his brain to her sex. If Przybyszewski engineered this process in real life, and the evidence is that he did, he did so by splitting himself into Dagny and Munch and observing them.

The same process took place in Strindberg in 1896, but in a much less obvious way. With his characteristic distrust of metaphysics (his constant retort to Przybyszewski in their Black Pig talks was, "That's metaphysics. I'm not interested."), Strindberg began with human beings rather than with a philosophy. His comedy *Crimes and Crimes*, written in 1899, reveals much more clearly than *Inferno* how his artistic imagination worked. Instead of writing pure autobiography Strindberg here created composite figures and experiences out of the people he met and the things that happened to them. The rapacious sculptress in the play is compounded out of Mme. Lecain and Dagny Juel, while the devoted mistress owes nearly all of her being to Przybyszewski's common-law wife and virtually nothing to Frida Uhl. Maurice, the playwright-hero, is half Strindberg and half Przybyszewski. Like the latter, Maurice abandons his mis-

tress for a glamorous femme fatale and with her seems about
to attain the pinnacle of success. Mere delusion, of course,
for on the eve of his triumph his child (not his wife) dies,
and Maurice is sought by the police as the possible murderer.
Thereafter follow the scenes of remorse and mutual anguish
as playwright and glamour girl incriminate and torture each
other. This may appear to be the purely Strindbergian element in the drama, yet it could have come directly from
Przybyszewski's life. When he and Dagny returned from
Scandinavia to Berlin in May 1896, they had their eight-
month-old baby with them. Seeing the child made Marthe
realize that her dear Stucha would never come back to her,
and she committed suicide. As we have seen, Przybyszewski
felt so guilty that he turned himself in to the police for questioning, and was held for two weeks. After that he seems to
have suffered from fits of depression and to have declined to
his old drinking habits, which he had shaken off in Scandinavia or perhaps before leaving Berlin. Eventually he turned
violently against Dagny, locking her out of his house and
taking up with other women. When in 1901 Dagny was killed
in Tiflis by another one of her lovers, who first blew out her
brains and then his own, Przybyszewski—far from mourning
the woman who inspired the only works for which he is remembered—sought to expunge her presence from his life (at
least the literary part of it) by denying she had influenced
him at all. And as a final insult he remarked that even to
Strindberg, who had dubbed her Aspasia, she was nothing
more than "an episode." Henriette in Strindberg's comedy is
treated with much more sympathy, but the two girls are like
enough to be sisters.

As for Munch's part in *Crimes and Crimes*, the humble
painter Adolph who achieves overnight success but loses his
girl, the femme fatale, to Maurice, was probably inspired by
him, though Strindberg once again put much of himself into
the role.

If Przybyszewski and Munch provided two objects of
cathexis for Strindberg in 1896, an artist named Paul Herrmann provided a third, though much less important one. Like
Strindberg, Herrmann was poor and rejected. Like Strindberg, Herrmann had in his youth written a blasphemous pam-

phlet that brought the law upon him. (I have not been able to confirm this and suspect it was invented by Strindberg to increase the element of identification.) Strindberg met him at Madame Charlotte's crémerie, probably through Edvard Munch.[10] Born in Munich, Herrmann was the nephew of the German poet and novelist Paul Heyse. During the early 1890s he lived in the United States and contributed to the art exhibit at the Chicago World's Fair in 1893. In 1895 he settled in Paris and took the professional name Henri Héran to avoid confusion with an artist named Herman Paul. He lived in Paris for eleven years, associating with Strindberg, Munch, and Oscar Wilde, among others, and he was one of the pallbearers at Wilde's funeral in 1900. Strindberg may have met Wilde in 1897 through Herrmann. He may also have met the German symbolist poet Stefan George, whom Herrmann etched in 1897. And it must have been at Herrmann's flat that Strindberg met Yeats. The Irish poet mentions the writer of a pamphlet "Strindberg and the Wolves" —this must have been the Swedish theater producer Gustav Uddgren—whom he met in

> the rooms of an American artist [so Strindberg refers to Herrmann in *Inferno*] who was of Strindberg's Paris circle, and it was probably there that I had heard for the first time of stage scenery that might decorate a stage and suggest a scene while attempting nothing that an easel painting can do better. I am pleased to imagine that the news of it may have come from Strindberg, whom I seem to remember as big and silent.

No doubt Herrmann and Strindberg shared many thoughts, for Herrmann was one of Strindberg's most regular café companions during this shadowy period in the Swede's life. One of Herrmann's etchings from this period is called *Jealousy*, apparently the most popular subject among the pre-expressionists. From about the same year, 1896–97, is Herrmann's etching of Christ, drawn as an evil-looking man with Mongoloid features, thick lips and a huge nose, more like a Judas than a Jesus. There may be some connection between this

[10] Munch painted him in the double portrait *Paul Herrmann and Paul Coutard*, 1897.

etching and the satanism that lurks behind part of *Inferno*. The incident in the "Purgatory" chapter involving a painting by Herrmann and thirty pieces of silver may have had a basis in real life.

## THE SHOEMAKER AND HIS LAST

In the summer of 1896 the Uhl family invited the destitute Strindberg to Klamm, Austria, to visit his two-year-old daughter. He arrived there to find that Frida had left. Nor did she show up during the four months that Strindberg was in Austria, alternately accepting the hospitality of his sister-in-law and his mother-in-law. The letter that Frida wrote to him in September made clear that she was not coming back to him. Frida was much too young and much too bedazzled by the bohemian life to remain down on the farm. In 1895 she had joined the Munich bohemia, and it was there about a year later that she met a friend from her Paris days, Frank Wedekind, who had been appointed editor of the satiric journal *Simplicissimus* that Langen had established. In her schoolgirl version of her marriage with Strindberg (*Marriage with Genius*) Frida Uhl says not one word about her life with Wedekind, and by omissions of one sort or another makes herself appear as a young girl who lost her innocence when she married Strindberg, an impression he sustains in the first part of the *To Damascus* trilogy. However, his letters to her during their engagement reveal how well he understood her polygamous nature from the start. In the second part of the *Damascus* trilogy, at the end of which the hero walks out on the Lady, Strindberg gives a more accurate portrait of her. His marriage to her was not one of great love or passion as was his first marriage; and its dissolution had practically no bearing on his *Inferno* crisis; he merely used it for dramatic material.

By 1897 Frida, pregnant with Wedekind's child, was pressing Strindberg for a quick divorce. A few months later he divined through dreams and "hunches" that Frida was "a deserted mother with a babe on her hands." The dreams and hunches probably had their origin in the gossip of friends, for the Scandinavian community had learned in 1896 through

Knut Hamsun that Wedekind and Frida were lovers; and when they moved to Berlin, the whole world knew it. A son, Friedrich Strindberg, was born to them in August 1897, but the affair was already over by that time; and the parents had acquired other partners.

To return to 1896. Having spent the autumn with his daughter Kerstin in Austria, living off the bounty of his in-laws, the nomadic Strindberg left on November 27 for southern Sweden. He went from Malmö to Lund, lived for a while in a hotel room there, then took over two rooms from a bachelor friend who had a three-room flat, and two weeks later moved again to a two-room flat of his own on a quiet street, Grönegatan, where the only sound he could hear was the beating of his heart.

To mark his return to Sweden, Strindberg decided to present his public with a new image. He exchanged his dark Flying Dutchman cape for a flashy belted jacket. "Your old daddy," he wrote to his Austrian in-laws through the intermediary of his daughter, "has become a young sport. Got himself some new, painless teeth, a new outfit with knickerbockers and bicycle stockings, yellow shoes and gloves. No longer a black chimney sweep, but a bright vision of spring."

The impression that Sweden's most controversial figure made with this outfit on the students at Lund University can be imagined. Years later one of them wrote of his first sight of Strindberg at a popular restaurant in the city hotel.

> Even if I had not known who he was, his dress and appearance would have attracted my notice. He was clad in sporting costume, not so common then as now, at any rate in a dining room, with yellow shoes, check stockings, knickerbockers and a jacket fastened by a belt. The color of the suit resembled the plumage of a sparrow hawk, that is to say, it was black-grey with white dots. You have only to substitute a pair of boots for the yellow shoes and you have him precisely as in the photograph he had taken of himself in Switzerland, when he was full of Russian nihilism. . . .
>
> More peculiar, however, even than his costume was the look of the man. Once you had seen his face, you could not forget it, it was so striking. His hair, rich, brushed up,

black—even if already sprinkled with silver threads—fell in soft, moist locks round his head and over his enormous, beautifully shaped forehead, which dominated his whole face. It was like the mountain in a landscape. Everything sunny and dark was reflected on those heights. . . . The big, light-grey eyes with their black irises, almost like a horse's, looked round timidly and with an expression of dejection. Weary, sorrowful eyes, as if washed in tears.

Everything, moreover, in Strindberg's manner testified to his shyness. His tread was noiseless, and with down-cast eyes he took a seat at the table which stood nearest the door, turning his back on the company which had been sitting in the room before him. After he had, in an inaudible voice, ordered something of the waiter who had bustled up to him, he provided his plate with something from the common sideboard, had some soup ladled out to him, and, after this enterprising performance, withdrew timidly to his table.

With this new costume he hoped to embark on a career as a newspaper reporter, touring southern Sweden on a bicycle and writing nature pieces. However, the slushy roads proved too treacherous, and the middle-aged Strindberg soon abandoned the "acrobatics." He also abandoned the newspaper project when he realized that "an old author can't write reports; he writes essays and descriptive pieces."

His friends and associates in the evenings were mostly from that radical group of writers, journalists, professors, and graduate students at the University of Lund who called themselves The Young Old Boys. With them Strindberg could relax, fire off his paradoxes, and drink till early morning. His insomnia continued to plague him, and only drugs or drink seemed to alleviate it. When he took sulfonal to sleep, he had pleasant dreams but felt terrible the next day. When he did not drink, he had nightmares, and when he drank, he found it difficult to write. "Sick at my desk, fit as a fiddle at the bar!"

However, the years of heavy drinking and smoking had taken their toll, as Strindberg found out. Consulting a physician for palpitations of the heart, Strindberg learned he had emphysema. But the old habits were not easy to break. A brief spell of abstinence and a diet of tea, milk, and tea-cakes would be followed by a champagne dinner and a six-hour drinking spree. Fired up by liquor and lively discussion, Strindberg would be the life of the party.

Among the Young Old Boys was Bengt Lidforss, whom he had not seen in three years. One day Lidforss called on Strindberg with a copy of Swedenborg's *Arcana Cœlestia*—Lidforss' mother was a Swedenborgian—under one arm and a young student and poet under the other. The book was to exert a great influence on Strindberg; the young poet Emil Kleen became one of his closest friends for a few brief years. They shared an interest in the occult, for Kleen too had had his share of strange experiences, some of which surpassed Strindberg's. According to Strindberg, "He had once thought himself dead and kept looking in the papers for his obituary." Which was perhaps not so unusual in view of the fact that Kleen was to die less than three years later of tuberculosis. Strindberg spent many hours at his bedside during his last months.

By the time he arrived in Lund, Strindberg had largely recovered from the crisis of mid-1896. In February he could write of the experience as something that had been lived through. "I have fought with God and fate. Looked for the good God and found the evil Fiend." Six weeks later he was anticipating a new phase in his life, "a change of situation, of my whole existence."

It might seem, and Strindberg would have us believe, that *Inferno* was merely a compilation and expansion of diary entries. Actually it was the result of careful planning and a couple of false starts. He could not at first find the right form for thoughts that were certain to be greeted with jeers in Sweden, for the notorious naturalist and materialist who had mocked Christianity in the 1880s was now to reveal himself to the reading public as a religious mystic. Plans for the book are mentioned as early as March 28, 1896, but it was the summer crisis that provided the major impulse. To his fellow occultist, the Swedish theosophist Hedlund, who provided him with funds and who published some of his scientific pamphlets, Strindberg wrote on August 18, "The last crisis of my life I haven't described to you, but I shall in a book—a novel, you might call it. . . . So I am giving up my scientific studies, on a trial basis."

A week later he was a little more explicit about his planned book.

You said recently that we are looking for—

A Zola of the Occult.

I feel the call. But something on a sublime level. A prose poem—called *Inferno*.

Same theme as [my novel] *By the Open Sea*. The decline of the individual when he isolates himself. Salvation through: work without thought of reward, honor, or gold; deity, the family, and consequently woman—mother and child. Resignation after discovering that each and everyone has a task assigned by Providence.

In September he wrote to Hedlund that he wanted to illustrate the book himself in an occult manner. "It's pointless to think of finding a publisher for my *Inferno* in Sweden. I'll have to write it in French in order to find readers—perhaps only in manuscript. But copies would be so expensive."

By January 1897 nothing concrete had developed from these plans. "Shall I tell the story of my checkered career during the last five years since I left Stockholm in 1892?" he asked. "Rather not, at least, not for now. That I've still got my health and strength is more than wondrous. My plans? Have none. Only waiting for the winds to blow me whither they will."

However, less than a month later Strindberg declared that *Inferno* would be his most beautiful work, and on March 1 he wrote to his fanatically religious mother-in-law, "My *Inferno* has been completely outlined; I've found the form for it and now I want to write it all out. *Ad majorem Dei gloriam.*" Ten days later he began to fill in the outline. "To amuse myself I have today begun to write my *Inferno;* and it is not true that this book will be insincere in its feeling." But his thoughts would not flow; the work died aborning, as his letters in April testify. Finally, at the beginning of May his thoughts began to stream in orderly fashion, and the sheets of expensive Lessebo paper began to fill with lines of black Antoine ink. By June 4 he had written 250 pages and was beginning the "Beatrice" chapter, and on June 25 the work was completed.

## STRINDBERG'S WORKSHOP

Strindberg began with a large collection of notes, notes on whatever had caught his attention, all filed away in his precious Green Sack. Like the Dadaists and surrealists after him, he worked with *objets trouvées*. But the trick in creating an art work out of such heterogeneous material was to find a balance between the apparent randomness of the material and a deliberate arrangement of it, between spontaneity and premeditation.

"The artist works unconsciously," said Strindberg, "creating like nature herself by trial and error, with incredible waste, but in that moment that he, *post festum*, attempts to think over what he has done and analyze it, he wakes from his half-sleep and falls to the ground like a sleepwalker."

> When I create, I lose contact with my surroundings. I fall back to the level of instinctual life. But for my undeveloped brain the effort is too great. It hesitates; it draws back. The messages I receive are much too often left at the threshold of my unconscious without being arranged according to the laws of time and place. And as for what lies on the other side of that threshold, it has been stamped in our time with the cheap label Madness.

Looking back over Strindberg's career from 1890 to 1896, we can see that he was making every effort to tap the unconscious and accommodate it to the exterior life around him, or to make the two one, living his life as if it were a "happening." He strove to become the alert spectator watching the birth of his own works.

Perhaps because he had had no academic training as a painter, it was easier at times for him to receive messages from his unconscious while standing at the easel than sitting at his desk. Whether he turned to painting for this reason or for the more mundane one that his literary market had dried up, the fact is that he did a great deal of painting in 1892, when some of his works were put on sale in Stockholm, Lund, and Berlin; in 1893 when he exhibited works alongside those of Munch at the Salon of Independent Artists in Berlin; and in 1894 when he painted a number of pictures before and after coming to Versailles. It was in the summer of 1894 that he wrote his essay "The New Arts, or, The Role of Chance in Artistic Creation"—printed below—a landmark in art history. Here for the first time chance is recognized as the basis of a certain kind of art; and although automatic art was appreciated in the Renaissance, and is indeed as old as art itself, Strindberg was the first to exalt it and thus lay the foundation for much of twentieth-century art. The theory behind Strindberg's automatic art was that by working without any predetermined goal, by following caprice and instinct, the artist would create as nature creates—purely by chance. The result would be an "extraordinary confusion of the conscious and the unconscious," and this would be the basis of the art of the future.

Strindberg did not limit the application of this theory to easel works or even to art itself. He lived much of his life in the 'nineties according to it. "I act by improvising," he says in *Inferno*. "Life is more fun that way." His errant existence, his strange outbursts, his illogical behavior had their origin in his desire to escape the bonds of social order and traditional thinking, to de-brainwash himself, and to submit himself to chance; that is, to follow the dictates of his unconscious.

As with Gauguin, Strindberg's paintings expressed an inner state, not the external world. Gauguin felt he had to go to the South Seas to find a world untrammeled by conventions, artistic and social. Strindberg went on a similar journey, confining himself to Europe but alienating himself from former friends and old traditions. In the summer of 1894 he wrote from Austria to his new disciple in Versailles that he was ready to make the leap into the future. He stood at a parting of the ways and had to make a choice.

A painting of himself in a raincoat and facing a three-masted ship probably dates from this time. Strindberg's best oils are of storms and barren, windswept landscapes that expressed his inner turmoil. Sea, wind, and sky merge into a turbulence of black, white, and gray that provides no point of rest for the eye. These are visions of nature rather than nature itself. The brush was for Strindberg too delicate an instrument, and in his best oils he applied the colors thickly with knife and thumb, building up impastos and using pigment as a sculptor uses clay.

In Strindberg's opinion, these landscapes and seascapes represented something new in art—"nature symbolism," a step beyond the allegorical figure symbolism of Puvis de Chavannes. The claim is too large, for Munch and Gauguin were pursuing parallel paths at this time and Van Gogh was probably running a bit ahead. But Strindberg was certainly not influenced by them at first, and it is entirely likely that he may have exerted some influence on Munch. Munch's technique of letting nature put the finishing touches to his canvasses by exposing them to the chance play of wind and rain was apparently suggested by Strindberg.

Strindberg's oil *Night of Jealousy,* which he gave to Frida Uhl in 1893, is regarded by critic Gunnel Sylvan as a watershed in his development. From this time on the symbolic content is greater than before and is intellectually determined. Here possibly Strindberg was influenced by Munch's work (as interpreted by Przybyszewski) or, more likely, by the whole Symbolist school of writing and painting. On the back of the canvas Strindberg wrote, "To Fräulein Frida Uhl from the (Symbolist) painter August Strindberg. The painting represents the sea (below to the right), clouds (above), a cliff (left), a juniper tree (above to the left), and symbolizes A Night of Jealousy." This kind of explicitness is unusual in Strindberg; it sounds as if he were delivering an art lecture to an ignorant Frida. What he is actually doing is allowing his conscious mind to devise a meaning for what his unconscious has created. The spectator Strindberg contemplates what the artist Strindberg has wrought.

In the summer of 1894 he described to Littmansson some of his paintings, which he said represents

> *l'art fortuite,* the most subjective of all arts, which means that only the painter himself enjoys (suffers) the work since he knows what is meant, and also the chosen few who know the painter's inner (outer) life a little bit (very much). Each picture is, so to speak, double-bottomed; has an exotic aspect that anyone can make out, and an esoteric aspect for the painter and the chosen few.

However, the meaning reveals itself only in the act of contemplating the picture, not in the act of creating it. The picture of the man in the raincoat, with a three-masted stranded ship on the horizon, acquires an esoteric meaning only when Strindberg inspects it more closely. The man is seen to have a slouch hat like Wodan or Buddha.

> The crests of the waves resemble monsters, the clouds demons, and right in the center of the sky is a superb portrait of Rembrandt. The three masts with their yard-arms straight across ††† (three daggers) look like Golgotha, or three cemetery stones, and may be the Trimurti, but this depends on one's taste (subjective).

Another picture shows exoterically "a shit-green landscape with shit-red cliffs, a shit-yellow sky, and shit-green spruce trees." Its esoteric meaning? "Sweden!"

In his nonwriting years Strindberg's other great pursuit besides painting was science, and he treated scientific "fact" and theory with the same sovereign ease that he handled the pigments on his palette. They were for him only materials with which to create a vision. "Here is my universe," he proclaimed in one of his botanical essays, "as I have created it, as it has revealed itself to me." As a scientist, Strindberg was a superb poet. Cosmology and astronomy were to him like a new set of blocks to a child. Accepting the classic idea of an empyrean realm of pure light, he saw the stars as holes in the great eggshell called heaven. His universe was neither geocentric nor heliocentric. Taking his cue from a Catholic apologist, he regarded the universe as theocentric: the sun and earth had a common gravitational center. The earth to him was no tedious spheroid. He chose to see it as shaped like a doughnut, or rather like a hollow rolling pin, with the polar regions in the center, so that one could, theoretically, sail from the North Pole directly to the South Pole. (Bernard Shaw would have been delighted with Strindberg's world. When caught in the crossfire between an advocate of the flat earth theory and an advocate of the round earth, Shaw offered to arbitrate their differences by proposing a theory of a cylindrical earth—not hollow, however.)

When Strindberg visited Lidforss in 1891, the young

botanist took him and a mutual friend to the observatory at Lund University. Strindberg looked at the moon through the telescope, turned around, and declared that the moon was a slice of quartz which had been torn from the earth and hurled into space, that a moonscape of valleys and craters was a myth, that the man in the moon was—America, reflected in the sheet of quartz. The friend demurred and politely raised the objection that in looking at the moon from Europe one should see the reflection of Europe, not America.

"Humph," answered Strindberg with that strange smile of his, "when one is advancing new theories, one can't be finicky."

Later that night they went to a science laboratory where they were shown a new Abbe microscope. Strindberg listened intently to the technician who demonstrated the improvements over the older type. Then Strindberg asked to borrow it and disappeared into another room. After some minutes the others went to see what had become of him. They found him kneeling in front of a window sill on which the microscope had been placed. The tube had been reversed and was aimed at the stars.

Along with these intellectual hijinks went a more serious study of the physical world, especially in chemistry and botany. Beginning about 1889 and continuing through 1896 Strindberg developed a monistic and hylozoistic view of the universe. For him all the elements and all forces derived or emanated from one unity. "They arise through condensation and dilution, through copulation and crossbreeding, through heredity and transformation, through selection and struggle, addition and subtraction, and through whatever else may be necessary," wrote Strindberg in 1894, refusing at this time to accept the necessity for any teleological principle but allowing for its possibility. In *Antibarbarus* he sought to apply the Darwinian principle of evolution that derived all animal life from a common source to the field of chemistry. If the material world is essentially one, then the chemical elements too should be condensations of one basic substance. Mendeleyev's periodic system of the elements was a step in the right direction, but its implications had not been fully explored. The work of the Swedish chemist Blomstrand in the 1870s and

1880s determined Strindberg's thoughts. However, he too did not go far enough, and Strindberg felt that a revolutionary approach was required. "A generation that had the courage to get rid of God, and to crush the state and the church, and to overthrow society and morality, still bowed down before Science. And in Science, where freedom ought to reign, the order of the day was 'believe in the authorities or off with your head.'"

In chemistry the elements were deemed to be the irreducible building blocks of the universe. Strindberg's monistic belief, on the other hand, had as necessary corollary the theory that elements could be transmuted into one another. After reading Berthellot's history of medieval chemistry Strindberg buttressed his views and rebelled against nineteenth-century science by harking back to ancient doctrines. In evaluating Strindberg's theories we must remember that they were advanced before the discovery of the electron. He had to work exclusively with atomic weights and with the physical and chemical properties of the given elements. Arguing with those facts, he concluded, for example, that sulfur was not an element but was a compound whose formula was $CH_4O$, the weight of which, 31.98, corresponded to the atomic weight of sulfur.

Strindberg's approach to transmutation was, as it turned out, less absurd than the approach of respectable scientists to the problem of radioactivity. Since the elements were held to be irreducible, the traditional view would not allow any explanation that involved subatomic transformation. Therefore radioactive decay was explained by saying that external rays were absorbed and then reradiated. The transformation of the elements, a basic principle of alchemy and the tenet that distinguished alchemy from chemistry, became an accepted fact only after the 1902 publication of the findings of Rutherford and Soddy, whose experiments proved that the elements were indeed transmuted in certain forms of radioactive decay. But so firmly lodged in the minds of the scientists was the principle that one element could not be changed into another that Rutherford and Soddy had to be very careful not to use the word transmutation. "Don't call it transmutation," Rutherford warned his partner; "they'll have our heads off as alchemists." Once it was presented to the scientific community, however, the new theory was quickly accepted. Strindberg was instinctively right and about a decade ahead of his time, but his reasoning was unscientific and his experiments were carried out with the primitive tools of the alchemists. On the other hand, scientific developments had reached the point where a bold leap forward was required, and the poet could take it more easily than the scientist.

Even more in harmony with the modern theories of subatomic physics was Strindberg's view that a better understanding of nature could be achieved by thinking in terms of force instead of weight and resistance instead of matter.

In 1895 he drew up plans for putting all his scientific observations into a large work to be called *Sylva Sylvarum,* an exploration of the entire universe, including earth, sea, and space, plants, animals, and minerals. It was to deal in rather haphazard fashion with a universe of "great chaos and infinite coherence." A year later he was still synthesizing his thoughts and contributing regularly to the alchemical journals in Paris. And through that channel he came into close contact with the French occultists.

For it was only a short step from a hylozoistic universe in which stones had life and plants had brains, a universe governed by chance, inspirited by mysterious forces emanating from a primeval unity and operating on the principle of simultaneity, to a universe in which there was a god behind every tree, a spirit behind every gesture and every thought, a providence behind every chance event, and an astral plane that bridged space and time. The interpreter between the material world and the spirit world was not the scientist but the poet, the high priest in an age of skepticism; and the common ground between naturalism and occultism was symbolism.

During the years Strindberg spent in Berlin and Paris the Symbolist movement, that reflowering of Romanticism, was at its height, having been launched in 1886 with the publication of Rimbaud's *Illuminations,* René Ghil's "Treatise on the Word," and Jean Moréas' "Manifesto of Symbolism." At precisely the time when the naturalists were creating their greatest works, the Symbolists stepped in to restore to art the mystic or religious element that had virtually been eliminated by the triumphs of experimental science and the exclusive recognition of the law of cause and effect. The poets and artists had always tried to cling to whatever clouds of mysticism remained in a sky swept by telescopes. Delacroix declared that the material world was "a dictionary of hieroglyphics," and Baudelaire avowed that the poet's task was to decipher the divine hieroglyphics. Influenced by the Illuminist Joseph de Maistre and by the visionary from Stockholm, Emanuel Swedenborg, Baudelaire saw in everything the impress of God.

Looking for new worlds and oppressed by the heavy air of materialism, Strindberg found in the realm of Symbolism the heady air his congested lungs needed. He was reborn in his natural element, and life was once again filled with surprises. Being "enough of a child in spirit and sufficiently poor and miserable to extract poetry from the commonest and most natural incidents," he found significance in the fall of a flake of soot, augury in the sound of a distant piece of music, and hell in a water closet. In contrast to the French poets, who as Symbolists though not as Decadents, put everyday life and the creative life into separate compartments, Strindberg lived his life as though it were a Symbolist poem.

The precocious Rimbaud declared that the poet makes himself a seer and arrives at the unknown by a "deliberate derangement of all the senses." He tried to simulate insanity by corrupting his mind and body. Baudelaire used hashish to produce his artificial paradise, and the Symbolists of the 1890s sought by means of alcohol, ether, and drugs to enter that other world whose gates now swing open to some users of mescaline. The fin de siècle regarded the "détraquée," the disturbed mind, as the more sensitive mind. Upon his arrival at Versailles in 1894 Strindberg promptly entered into the French spirit by writing one of his most charming, free-association essays, "Disordered Sensations," in which he describes his agoraphobic journey across the Place d'Armes at Versailles, being stranded on the island of lampposts in the center, and sailing across the rest of that vast sea of paving stones by jumping on a cloud shadow that happily passes by.

Later, lying in reverse position in bed, his senses excruciatingly sharpened, he detects the flow of ether and realizes he is riding backward through the universe. Strindberg regarded this essay as a "Symbolistic, détraqué-ish compromise with science, poetry, and madness. I think it's crazy enough to be thought modern and sane enough not to be."

Along with "Graveyard Reveries"—printed below—this essay serves as a preliminary sketch for *Inferno*. But Strindberg had to plunge much deeper into the sea of strange sensations before the Other World, the submerged self, would reveal itself to him. The question was how to accomplish it? Nerval went completely insane and descended to a hell of hallucinations. Rimbaud tried debauchery and perversion but implied in *A Season in Hell* that to pursue his poetic genius any further in real life would be madness. The hero of Przybyszewski's *Totenmesse* induced strange sensations by drinking alcohol and going without sleep. This regimen opened up his unconscious, enabled him to "see" music, gave his thoughts a grotesque allure, and stimulated complete free association. Earlier, in 1890, the starving hero of Hamsun's *Hunger* suffered delusions from lack of food; his mind became a sensitive plate recording the sights and sounds of a drab Christiania. So there was no lack of precedent in the nineteenth century and especially in the early 1890s for what Strindberg attempted. Absinthe, combined with lack of food and lack of sleep, honed his nerves, sharpened his senses, and in bad physical condition this explorer of the human spirit entered a new world, the world of the unconscious, of the unpremeditated and the irrational. Those who knew him best testified to the physical influences at work during the Inferno period. Dr. Schleich, friend from The Black Pig days, said Strindberg confessed to him that too much absinthe played a major part in the Inferno experiences. Munch said it was gastritis, insomnia, and the terrors of the night, originating in the Berlin orgies, that completely altered Strindberg's view of things. And Marcel Réja, former medical student turned poet, who revised *Inferno* for publication, averred that Strindberg deliberately constructed a typical textbook delirium on the basis of contemporary psychological knowledge.

The impression the book makes on the average reader is that of a man torturing himself as penance for his misdeeds. Even the narrator himself raises the possibility that it is his imagination that has "created these chastising spirits in order to punish" himself. But after having visited Strindberg's workshop and seen how, like an artist with his sketchbook, Strindberg has all along been preparing himself for a major creative effort, we know that he is inflicting the punishment on himself to stimulate his unconscious. It is the artist who sets the wheels rolling, not the moralist. It is the middle-aged fabulist who has "arrived at the midpoint of life," and who feels he is temporarily written out, who finds the days monotonous and the world a bore—it is he who seeks a new and different world in which he can be reborn. The anguish he feels is the very real anguish of a man who is forty-six and a failure, a man who has lost his wife and children and who is very much alone. But the anguish is transmuted first into adventure and then into art. And out of his souvenirs from hell he creates a collection of gems: *Inferno, Jacob Wrestles, To Damascus, Crimes and Crimes, Erik XIV, Charles XII,* and *A Dream Play,* to name only some of the splendid and original works written during an amazingly productive five-year period.

## THE FIRST MODERN NOVEL?

Outside Scandinavia *Inferno* is generally understood to be the factual record of a diseased mind. In Scandinavia, however, *Inferno* is now regarded as a literary work, a work of fiction that was created essentially in those moments when Strindberg lived the experiences.[11] Employing Coleridge's terms, we can say that Strindberg's fancy worked to create the experiences in real life and that his imagination carried on the shaping and refining process at his desk. In my introduction to *A Madman's Defense* I have shown how similar Strindberg's creative methods are to those of an actor who lives his role.

[11] See Gunnar Brandell, *Strindbergs Infernokris* (Stockholm, 1950), p. 226. Brandell's book, a classic of Swedish scholarship, is a detailed study of the Inferno phase of Strindberg's career.

Frequently Strindberg's letters provide a rehearsal of the finished performance. They comprise the artistic feelers by which he tentatively surveys the ground he is about to invade. Never is this more true than in the long letters he wrote to theosophist Thorsten Hedlund from 1894 to 1896. These, and the diary he began to keep in 1896, "A Diary of Strange Occurrences," constitute a rough first draft for *Inferno*. When Hedlund had served his purpose as rehearsal partner, Strindberg abruptly and rudely broke off the correspondence and proceeded to the next stage in the creation of his role, rejecting what he finds unsatisfactory, polishing what seems promising. Naturally, then, there are discrepancies between the letters and the final work, discrepancies that would not exist if Strindberg were not fibbing. In July 1896 he dips at random into the Bible and reads words of encouragement; so say the letters. But at the same point in *Inferno* the same bit of rhabdomancy discourages him from continuing his alchemical experiments.

With the writing of the letters the real experiences have already been modified somewhat, of course. And when we put aside the letters and compare the events of *Inferno* with what can be verified by actual witnesses, the discrepancies are often much greater. For example, Dr. Eliasson, who gave financial aid to Strindberg and with whom Strindberg stayed on two occasions in Southern Sweden (this is the source of all those completely untrue stories that Strindberg was confined briefly in a mental institution), was deeply hurt by the lies and distortions relating to him in *Inferno* and never wrote to the author of them again. Sheer fabrication is the story about the disappearance of the artist Paul Herrmann, whom Strindberg associated with during this period. Strindberg would have us believe that Herrmann was a doppelgänger who vanished about Easter time 1896. Yet the portrait of Strindberg that adorns the first French edition was drawn by Herrmann in August 1897. And Strindberg resurrects him to play a part in *Jacob Wrestles*.

One of the more amusing discrepancies between mundane fact and Strindberg's fiction has to do with the poisonous gas that his "enemies" were subjecting him to, often pumping it through the walls to get at him. We can appreciate how unnerving the smell of gas can be, especially when there is no gas outlet and no gas stove, as was the case in Strindberg's room at the Hotel Orfila. When Herrmann visited Strindberg one day—Strindberg rarely let anyone into his room—he did indeed smell something rather like a noxious gas. We can imagine the quiet triumph that Strindberg might have felt at this moment, and understand why he chose to let someone into his room at this particular time. But the intrepid Herrmann spoiled the performance. He traced the odor to the area under Strindberg's bed, which he pulled away from the wall. There lay a rat in an advanced stage of putrefaction. Herrmann neglects to say what Strindberg's response was.

Since he deliberately isolated himself, there are not many witnesses to the Strindberg of 1896. But whenever his story can be checked against that of witnesses, the two virtually never agree. Sometimes he does not even bother to employ a factual basis but creates a lie out of whole cloth. In *Legends,* the sequel to *Inferno* which tells of the occult and mystic experiences of others, he quite shamelessly used as models his cronies among the freethinking Young Old Veterans in Lund. For one of them, Waldemar Bülow, Strindberg conjured up a marvelous vision: five devils in the shape of monkeys sitting on the edge of Bülow's bed, waving their tails. When Bülow rebuked Strindberg for this flagrant untruth, the irrepressible fabulist replied, "Oh, come on! You know well enough that as soon as I get a pen in my hand, I feel full of the devil." And in 1897, evidently when he was still writing *Inferno* (this is truly extraordinary, for when creating his roles, his whole personality seemed to be absorbed by the character), he told a friend, "With three-fourths of my being I believe in the reality of these configurations, but with the remaining one-fourth I ask myself if, in the final analysis, all this isn't just my own imagination playing games."[12]

As the publication date approached, Strindberg began to have trepidations, knowing that many readers, especially those who were close to him, would greet it with skepticism.

[12] For more information on the discrepancies between *Inferno* and Strindberg's life, see Walter A. Berendsohn, *Strindbergsproblem* (Stockholm, 1946), 85–92.

"In a week my *Inferno* will be published in Sweden, and then I'll be called 'charlatan' or 'fool.'"

The fact that psychoanalysts have, with charming naïveté, accepted it as a perfectly trustworthy account of a certain type of madness (on which they cannot agree) and that other writers have used it as a guide and handbook for picturing insanity[13] is testimony not for Strindberg's madness but for the efficacy of his methods.

Therefore, however effective it may be as a psychological and autobiographical document, it is best to read it as a novel, a symbolic novel in which poetry is created out of life's trivia, in much the same way as the surrealists made art out of *objets trouvées.* Strindberg abstracted poetry out of incidents that usually pass by unnoticed. He began to pay strict attention to his every word and action. "Insignificant occurrences drew my attention, my dreams at night assumed the form of omens. I considered myself as having died and gone on to live my life in another sphere." More than superstition is involved here, for the superstitious person knows what it means to walk under a ladder or spill salt and is consequently disturbed. But Strindberg is disturbed because he does not know what the trivial event means, or why it should disturb him. He is like Jerome Cardan, the Renaissance mathematician, who had to find out why the smallest mishaps could at times breed enormous fears. Awaking one morning to find his foot entangled in the bedclothes, Cardan was afraid to leave his house, and was troubled for days about the meaning of the portent, until the next calamity that befell him revealed the source of his anxiety.

By rendering for us the psychopathology of everyday life (before Freud), Strindberg could speak of himself as a naturalist of the occult. He united the naturalist's interest in science with the occultist's interest in magic, and found himself on the threshold of the unconscious. His world is a very tactile one, with no ghosts and no drunken boats. Nothing that happens to him would seem strange to the outside observer, for

[13] Lawrence Durrell, for instance, in his Alexandria quartet, modeled Nessim on the narrator of *Inferno,* often down to the smallest details. See Stellan Ahlström, "Lawrence Durrell och Strindberg," *Svenska Dagbladet* (Stockholm), September 28, 1964.

everything has a natural explanation. The strangeness is introduced by Strindberg as he enters a world where "no one can follow" him. The Symbolists also made poetry out of petty details, but generally their poetry was too internalized and too abstract. They presupposed a Platonic and ordered world of ideas shrouding the material world. If one does not share their premise, their world is vacuous or unconvincing. Strindberg, in contrast, is a realist who initiates us into this other world gradually. If at the end we do not share his conclusions, we can at least understand how he arrived at them and respond to the consequences flowing from them. And he offers us a variety of alternative explanations, whereas the Symbolists are not so liberal. Once the ear has tired of their echolalic effects and the inner eye of their dreamscapes, there is little left to satisfy the mind.

Finding a form for this new kind of poetry proved difficult for Strindberg. A solution of sorts was provided by a description of an oriental vase he encountered in a travel book by André Chevrillon. The fine lines forming the design present a seeming chaos to the eye. Little by little, however, forms emerge, gods, fishes, flowers, not grouped according to some motif but thrown together helter-skelter. Each line by itself is clear and precise, yet the finished design is of infinite complexity and offers continual surprises.

Like the oriental vase, *Inferno* does not reveal all its delights at a first casual reading. The shifting points of view, the variety of detail, and the apparent lack of plot or overall design, however disconcerting they may be, are part of a deliberate procedure.

The tone, too, may baffle readers, unless they accept *Inferno* for what it is, a modern version of mock epic, very dry, very detached, and relying for many of its artistic beauties on correspondences between the present-day, deflated hero and the giants of legend or history. *Inferno* inaugurates, as a matter of fact, the whole line of twentieth-century novels, most famous of which is Joyce's *Ulysses*, which are constructed largely on mythic foundations and embellished by details that exploit legend for character and plot similes.

To appreciate *Inferno* it is much more helpful to compare it with the new novel of mid-twentieth century than with the nineteenth-century confessional novel. Like the new novel, *Inferno* is visionary in its technique, presenting a seemingly familiar world as a place of mysteries and puzzles, in which material things acquire the same importance as people. For Strindberg as for the new novelists the ready-made, hand-me-down explanations no longer suffice. Like the new novel, *Inferno* is characterized by abrupt changes in point of view, in tone, in the accents of the narration. The story does not comprise a finished product; the action is left unresolved. The book examines things around us, confronts us with opposing impressions. Expectations are not aroused in order to be satisfied, as in the traditional forms of storytelling. The reader is not allowed to take anything for granted, and he cannot determine in advance what is important and what is not. He must always be on the alert, and in a sense a participant in the action.

## PRAISE TO THE PRAISEWORTHY

Strindberg has been dead for over half a century, but unfortunately the tendency persists to emphasize his eccentric personality and to see his works as faulted because of his psychological quirks. It is time we recognise that his best works are masterpieces which achieve near perfection precisely because of his personality. It is time that we recognize in him both the researcher who used the methods of experimental science and the fabulist whose best lies were artistic truths, both the scientist whose greatest experiments were carried out on himself and the artist who made his own life into a poem.

# The New Arts,

## or The Role of Chance in Artistic Creation

*(Des arts nouveaux!*
*où Le hasard dans la production artistique)*

Translated by Albert Bermel

"Des arts nouveaux! où Le hasard dans la production artistique" was written in the summer of 1894 and intended to form part of a planned volume of essays, *Vivisections II*. It was first printed in *Revue des Revues*, November 5, 1894. The essay is remarkable for its enunciation of principles that dominate much of twentieth-century art and writing. In Strindberg's career the essay represents a kind of watershed. From this point on chance and the unconscious were to be allowed a major share in his writing.

THEY SAY that the Malays make holes in bamboo stems that grow in the forests. The wind comes, and the savages stretch out on the ground to listen to the symphonies executed by these gigantic aeolian harps. Remarkable thing: each man hears his own melody and harmony, depending on how the wind blows.

It is known that the weavers use the kaleidoscope to discover new designs, leaving it to blind chance to mix the bits of colored glass.

On arriving at Marlotte, a well-known artists' colony, I go into the dining room to look at the very famous painted panels. There I see: portrait of a woman, a) young b) old, etc. Three crows on a branch. Very well done. Later I see what it is about. Moonlight. A rather bright moon; six trees, stagnant water with reflections. Moonlight, then.

But what is it? This very question leads to the first excitement. It is necessary to search, conquer; and nothing is more delightful than fantasy in movement.

What is it? The painters call it "palette scrapings," which means: When he has finished, the artist scrapes together the remaining pigments and, if his heart tells him to, makes any kind of a drawing out of them. I stood overjoyed in front of this panel at Marlotte. The colors had a harmony—very understandable, since they had belonged together in a painting. Freed from the pain of finding the right colors, the artist's soul spends all its forces in seeking shapes; and as his hand manipulates the spatula at random—still keeping nature's model in mind without trying to copy it—the result reveals itself as a charming mixture of the unconscious and the conscious. This is natural art: the artist works like capricious nature, without predetermined aim.

I have seen those scraped panels a number of times since, and I always find something new in them, according to my psychic condition.

I wanted a melody for a one-act of mine called *Simoom*, which takes place in Arabia. I began to strum my guitar at random, tightening and loosening the strings haphazardly, until I found a tune which struck me as being something extraordinarily bizarre without overstepping the boundaries of beauty.

The air was accepted by the actor who was playing the part; but the director, an excessive realist, learned that it was not a real melody and asked me for an authentic one. I hunted up a collection of Arab songs and performed them for the director. He rejected them all, finally choosing my little song because it was more like an Arab song than the Arab songs.

The melody was sung and had a certain small success when our fashionable composer came to ask if I would let him base all the music for my playlet on my "Arab" melody, which had impressed him . . .

I knew a musician who amused himself by thumping away at his piano without any sequence or sense. Then he played Beethoven's Pathétique by heart. It was an incredible joy to hear an old work come to new life. I had heard him play that sonata for twenty years, always the same way, without hope of seeing it develop—fixed, incapable of evolving.

Since then, I have done the same on my guitar with stale old tunes. And other guitarists envy me, envy me to the point of asking me where I got this music from, and I tell them I don't know. They take me for a composer.

An idea for the manufacturers of those modern, portable organs [Strindberg probably means street organs]: Pierce the music drum at random, anywhere, and you will have a musical kaleidoscope.

In his *Life of Animals,* Brehm claims that the starling imitates all the sounds it happens to hear: the noise of a closing door, the knife-grinder's wheel, the millstone, the turning weathervane, etc. There is more to it than that. I have heard starlings in most European countries and they all sing the same jumble of sound, consisting of memories of the jay, the blackbird, and other birds of the species, so that each listener can hear what he wants in the song. The starling, in effect, possesses a musical kaleidoscope.

The same with parrots. Why are gray parrots with scarlet tails called Jacob? Because their natural sound, their call, is "Yako." And the owner thinks he has taught his parrot to talk by starting with his name!

And the ones called Kakadou! And Ara! It's funny to listen to the old lady who imagines she is teaching her parakeet. The animal lets out its incoherent cries; the lady looks for the nearest approximation, translates or rather adds a lyric to this horrible music. Then, a visitor finds it impossible to hear what the bird is "saying" until he hears the words from the owner's mouth.

I had the idea of making a clay model of a young lover, like those of antiquity. He stood there, his arms raised. But he displeased me and in a moment of despair I let my hand fall on the poor creature's head. Well! A metamorphosis that Ovid never dreamed of. Under my blow, his Greek hair-cut flattens into a Scottish tam-o-shanter which comes down over his face; his head is pushed down with the neck between the shoulders; his arms drop with the hands still at the height of his eyes, which are hidden by the bonnet; his legs bend; the knees come together—and the whole thing is transformed into a boy of nine crying and hiding his tears with his hands. With a little refinishing the statuette was perfect; in other words, the onlooker gets from it the desired impression.

Later, in some friends' studios, I improvised a post-hoc theory of automatic art.

—You all remember the story of the young man strolling through the forest when he comes upon "The Lady of the Woods." She's as beautiful as the dawn, with emerald hair, and so forth. He goes toward her. She turns away and suddenly looks like a tree.

Obviously the young fellow saw nothing but a tree and his fantasy put it into poetic movement.

Which has often happened to me.

One fine morning as I walked through the woods I came to an uncultivated field. My thoughts were far away, but I noticed a bizarre, unfamiliar object stretched out on the grass.

For an instant it was a cow; then two peasants kissing; then a tree trunk; next . . . This oscillation of visions pleased me . . . an act of the will and I no longer wanted to know what it was . . . I felt the curtain of my conscious mind about to lift . . . but I didn't want it to . . . Now it is a lunch in the open air . . . and people are eating . . . But the figures are still, as in a frieze . . . Ah . . . that's it . . . It's an abandoned plow on which the laborer has flung his jacket and hung his satchel (probably with his lunch inside). All is known. Nothing more to see. A lost pleasure!

Doesn't that offer an analogy with modernistic paintings which to philistines are so incomprehensible? At first you see in them only a chaos of colors, then it begins to seem, it resembles—but no; it resembles nothing. All at once a point is established, like a nucleus of a cell; it grows, the colors group themselves around it, accumulate; it forms spokes which sprout branches, and then twigs, as ice crystals do on windows . . . And the image is presented to the spectator who has witnessed the act of procreation of the picture. And even better: the painting keeps renewing itself, changes according to the light, never wears out, is rejuvenated by the gift of life.

I paint at leisure. In order to dominate the material I choose a medium-sized canvas, or better, a piece of cardboard on which I can complete the painting in two or three hours, while my inclination lasts. A vague intention rules me. I plan a shadowy wood through which the ocean is visible at sunset.

Good: with the palette knife I use for the job—I don't own any brushes—I distribute the colors on the cardboard and mix them so that I have a roughed-out design. The opening in the center represents the horizon of sea and sky. Now the interior of the wood, the tracery of boughs and twigs is extended in a group of colors, fourteen, fifteen, pell-mell but always in harmony. The surface is covered; I stand back and look. Damn! I can't find the ocean; the lit-up opening shows a perspective to infinity; pink and bluish light or vaporous shapes, without definition or body, float like fairies behind clouds. The wood has become a dark underground cavern subdivided by brambles; and the foreground—let's see what it is—rocks covered with unidentifiable lichens—and there, on the right, the knife has smoothed over the colors too much until they look like reflections in water—Well, well, it's a pool. Perfect.

Now, above the pool is a patch of white and pink. I can't explain its origin or meaning. One moment!—a rose!—The knife goes to work and in two seconds the pool is framed in roses, roses, so many roses . . .

A touch with the finger here and there to bring together the warring colors, blend and dispel the crude tones, refine, melt and—there's the picture.

My wife, friendly for the time being, comes up, looks, gets ecstatic over the "Cavern from Tannhäuser" from which a great serpent (meaning my flying fairies) crawls out into fairyland; and the hollyhocks (my roses!) are mirrored in the river of sulfur (my pond!), and so on. For the whole week she admires the masterpiece, values it in thousands of francs, guarantees it a place in a museum, and so on . . .

After that week, we're back in a period of fierce antipathy and in my "masterpiece" she sees nothing but filth!

And they say that art exists as a thing in itself . . .


Have you made rhymes? I'll bet. You've noticed that it is detestable work. Rhymes tie up the spirit; but they untie it, too. Sounds become intermediaries between notions, images, ideas.

This Maeterlinck, what does he do? He puts rhymes in the middle of his prose.

And that degenerate beast of a critic[1] who suggests that he is out of his mind and gives this sickness the scientific title of Echolallée.

Every true poet since the creation of the world has been an Echolallist. Exception: Max Nordau who rhymes without being a poet. *Hinc illae lacrimae!*

The art to come (and go, like all the others!): Imitating nature almost; above all, imitating nature's way of creating!

[1] Max Nordau in *Degeneration.*—EDITOR.

# Graveyard Reveries

(Études funèbres)

Translated by Albert Bermel

This essay, probably written in the autumn of 1895, was first printed in *Revue des Revues*, July 15, 1896. It was included as a chapter in the French edition of *Inferno* and omitted, at Strindberg's instruction, from the Swedish translation. "Graveyard Reveries" may be seen as a preliminary study for *Inferno* and *Jacob Wrestles*. This and other essays of this period show Strindberg acquiring and inventing new techniques designed to explore the frontiers of the mind through free association and the avoidance of the ordinary channels of logic. Here, too, are the themes of rebirth and suffering; but that of guilt, which was to become so vital in Strindberg's post-*Inferno* writings, is not dwelt on. Readers familiar with Strindberg's plays will recognize the opening scene of *Crimes and Crimes* (1899) in the pages of this essay.

# I

A YEAR HAS RUN its course since my first morning walk
to the Montparnasse Cemetery. I have seen the leaves
fall from the elms and lindens, seen everything become green
again, the wistaria and roses flowering on the grave of Théo-
dore de Banville; I have heard the blackbird begin his seductive song beneath the cypresses, and the pigeons usher in
the mating season on the graves.

Now the lindens are turning yellow, the roses decay and
the blackbird no longer sings; he only emits a sneering laugh
at his springtime loves which have gone in order to return.
And the dirty autumn and slushy winter will come and go
like everything else.

On entering the cemetery I leave behind me the rather
commonplace and noisy quarter of Montparnasse. The night's
unhealthy dreams are still in pursuit, but I shake them off at
the main gate. The din from the streets dies away and the
peace of the dead supersedes it.

I am always alone at this time of the morning, and so
accustomed to regarding this place of refuge as my pleasure
garden that I look on the occasional visitor as an intruder . . .
The dead and I!

All through this year I have not taken one friend, man or
woman, to this place; no one who might have left some
memory behind to intrude on my personal impressions.
Greeting my favorites, Orfila, Thierry and Dumont d'Urville,
I go up the Allée Lenoir, all decorated with cypresses like
the Allée Raffet. It gives one a sense of extreme power to
pass between these lines of straight trees, like grenadier
guards in green fur shakos, presenting arms. When the wind
blows a little they bend, the two lines bowing toward me,
and I march, proud as a marshal, to the end of the avenue.
There I read and read over on a facing tombstone: "Boulay
was indeed a brave and honest man." (Napoleon.)

I don't know Boulay, have no desire to know him, but for

Napoleon to address me every morning from beyond the grave—that warms my heart, and I seem to be one of his intimates.

Between the cypresses: these thousands of graves, covered with flowers that have sprung out of hard rocks, nourished by corpses and watered by sincere or half-sincere tears. In this immense garden the ornate little chapels, like doll houses, strewn with crosses that raise their arms to heaven in protest, cry aloud: *O Crux, ave spes unica!* That is the universal creed, it seems, of suffering mankind. And from the midst of the foliage, here, there, everywhere, in shortened form: *Spes unica!* In vain do the busts of the little capitalists, with or without their cross of honor, rear up to demonstrate that there is hope after death.

I was warned that these frequent visits were dangerous because of the miasmas that pervade the place. Indeed, I still noticed a certain after-taste of verdigris in my mouth two hours after I got back to the house. The souls, I mean the dematerialized bodies, remain floating in the air; that is what led me to try to trap some and analyze them. Armed with a small flask filled with liquid lead acetate, I go off on this hunt for souls, I mean bodies, and shaking the corked-up phial in my closed hand, I walk about like a bird-catcher who has been freed of the hard work of snaring his prey.

At home, I filter out the plentiful precipitate and place it under the microscope.

Poor Gringoire! Did these little crystals really constitute the brain-machine which, when I was young, awoke my precocious sympathies for the poet who was desperately poor, yet capable of winning the love of a pretty girl? Brave and honest Boulay (who drew up the Napoleonic Code, as I have now learned), is it really you that I've captured with my fly-catcher? Or you, d'Urville, you who took me on my first trip around the world during those long winter evenings, far from here, under the aurora borealis in Sweden, between spells of rod and homework?

Instead of answering, I pour a drop of acid onto the slide. The dead matter swells up, it quivers, begins to live, gives off a smell of rotting, subsides and dies.

Yes, I know how to revive the dead, but I don't try it again, because the dead have foul breath, like that of debauchees who have been carousing all night. Is it really possible that they don't sleep very well down there while waiting for the resurrection?

Ten years ago I converted to atheism. Why? I don't exactly know. I was bored with life, had to do something, especially something new. Now it's old and I'd like to be ignorant of everything, to leave questions hanging, and wait. . . .

Nothing happens in this enclosure of death, the days are all alike, and the tranquil life is disturbed only by the mating of the birds. An isle flourishing in the middle of the sea: from afar you hear something like the murmuring of waves. The Isle of the Blessed—an enormous field where children have gathered flowers, toys—plaited wreaths and set them with pearls collected at the shore; lit candles, decorated them with ribbons, baubles . . .

But the children have fled, the grounds are deserted . . .

One morning in June I saw a girl walking along the central avenue. She was not in mourning and seemed to be waiting for someone, looking nervously in the direction of the main gate, through which so many people enter, never to go out again.

"Her lover hasn't come," I told myself; "rather dismal place for a meeting." And I left the cemetery.

Next morning she was there, staring down the avenue. It was heartbreaking. She walked, stopped, listened, watched.

Every morning she was there, paler than before; sorrow gave nobility to her common face. She was waiting for the wretch!

I went to a distant country for five weeks. Back again, having forgotten it all, I walked into my cemetery and noticed the woman standing forlorn in the middle of the avenue. Her emaciated body was outlined against a cross in the background as if she had been crucified. Above her, the inscription: *O Crux, ave spes unica!*

I drew closer and saw how this short lapse of time had ravaged her face. I seemed to be looking at a cremated figure under its white asbestos veil. Everything was there still, a simulation of the human form but incinerated, lifeless.

She was sublime. Believe me, suffering is not in the least banal! The sun, the rain, had washed out the colors of her cloak; the flowers on her hat had yellowed like the lindens. Even her hair had faded . . . She waited all day, every day. A mad woman? Yes, struck by the madness of love! She would die while waiting for the act that creates life and prolongs suffering!

Prolongs it? For life? If I admit that, then why not "forever"? Since matter is eternal?

I would like to become a believer again, but I cannot because I demand a miracle. Yet I came very close a few days ago. A storm was building up; the clouds gathered, the cypresses shook their heads threateningly, persisted in bowing down to me. Napoleon again declared that Boulay was a brave and honest man; the pigeons coupled on a stone cross; the corpses exhaled sulfurous smells and the miasmas left the taste of verdigris in my mouth.

The clouds, at first horizontal, suddenly reared up and became vertical, assuming the shape of the Lion of Belfort, which stands on its hind legs.[1] I have never seen anything like it except in pictures of the Last Judgment. The lines of the black figures dissolved and the sky took the shape of Moses' tablet, immense but finely etched. And on this gray slate of steel the lightning, as it cracked the firmament, carved out a complete, legible word: *Jehovah*, that is to say: *God of Vengeance!*

The atmospheric pressure made me bend my knees; but hearing no heavenly voice other than the rumble of thunder, I continued on my way home.

[1] *Lion of Belfort:* a massive statue executed by Bartholdi to commemorate the siege withstood by the fortress of Belfort during the the Franco-Prussian War 1870–71.—EDITOR.

## II

Fall has come again. The lindens turn brown and the heart-shaped leaves tumble down, touch the earth with a small dry blow, rustle under my boots as I go on with my triumphal march over these arid, crackling hearts.

Above my head, high up, scraping the clouds—strange and yet familiar sounds, recalling the huntsman's horn, irregular, panting, plaintive, awakening in me the memory of an old Swedish song, as foolish and charming as a child's tale:

> Does my linden play?
> Does my nightingale sing?
> Does my son weep?
> Does my husband ever feel happy?
> Your linden doesn't play,
> Your nightingale doesn't sing,
> Your son weeps night and day,
> Your husband never, never feels happy.

It is the wild geese who are emigrating from the north, greeting me on their flight to warmer countries and wider horizons.

The night breeze has shaken the lindens and—my miracle! —the buds meant for next year have opened, so that the black skeletons turn green again like Aaron's rod. The lindens of the cemetery, then, are becoming *semper virens,* immortal as the eternal ones, thanks to the mortals who nourish them from below with their bodies and souls.

"An organism never stops absorbing from whatever surrounds it new molecules which pass from the state of death into life . . . If one of these molecules wanted to tell us its history, 'Since the earth came into being,' it might say, 'I can assure you I have been on some extraordinary journeys. I was a blade of grass, then, cut free, I was sucked in by the roots of a powerful oak, I became acorn, and then, alas, I was eaten, by whom? . . . I was salted for a long trip overseas;

a sailor digested me; then I became lion, tiger, whale; after that I was injected into a sick young pair of lungs, and so on.'"

So writes J. Rambosson in his *Légendes des plantes,* thereby confirming my own speculations on transmutation. And in passing Banville's grave, I wonder why the friends of the dead man have planted roses and jasmins there. If it was the wish of the deceased, did he know that the cadavers give off the smells of rose, jasmin, and musk? I don't think so, but I am inclined to believe that we are most knowledgeable in our beautiful moments of greatest ignorance.

Besides, why all these flowers on the graves? Flowers, those living-deaths which lead a sedentary existence, put up no resistance to attack, suffer evil rather than inflicting it, imitate carnal love, multiply without fighting, and die without complaining. Superior beings, they have realized the dream of Buddha: to desire nothing, to tolerate everything, to be absorbed in oneself to the depths of the unconscious will.

Is this why the Hindu sages imitate the passive existence of the plant, abstaining from any relationship with the outside world, whether by a glance, a sign, a single word?

A child once asked me: "How is it that flowers, which are so pretty, don't sing like birds?"

"They do sing," I replied, "but we don't know how to hear them."

I stop in front of Banville's medallion.

Is there a trace of rose or jasmin in this capitalist's face, with its thick cheeks, its lips swollen as if after a succulent meal, and its miser's eyes? No, this is not the poet of Gringoire. It is someone else. Who?

I recall the bust of Boulay. This cannot be the brave and honest Boulay, this face with a gnome's nose, a wicked witch's mouth, a cunning peasant's features.

And Dumont d'Urville, the great naturalist, linguist, bold and prudent explorer! What the artist gives me is a common stockbroker. What does it mean? Is it a mark that man bears, this screen of flesh and skin pierced by five holes, five communication routes, and the great drain . . . I call up the images of our leading contemporaries: Darwin, an ape;

Dostoevsky, a completely criminal type; Tolstoy, highway robber; Taine, financial speculator . . . Enough!

Yet there are two faces, at least two, under the more or less hairy skin. A Roman legend tells us that Jesus Christ's exterior beauty was unrivalled, but in his angry moments his ugliness was hideous, bestial.

Socrates with the body of a faun and a face that reflected all the vices, all the crimes, lived like a saint and died a hero.

Saint Vincent de Paul, who gave and gave all his life, dressed like a typically sly—even wicked—thief.

Whence those masks? Inherited from an earthly or unearthly pre-existence?

Socrates has perhaps given the solution in the famous answer to his detractors who complained about his criminal mask: "Judge then the worth of my virtue after it has had to contend with so many faults."

Free translation: the earth is a penal colony where we have to submit to the punishment for crimes committed in an earlier existence, the vague remembrance of which we keep in our consciousness to drive us toward self-improvement. As a result, we are all criminals and the pessimist is not wrong when he continually thinks and speaks evil of his neighbor.

That morning in the Allée Lenoir a trivial thing offended my eye. The straight lines of the cypresses were broken by a treetop snapped off in such a way that it hung over the path. Shaking in the wind, it signalled me to stop and I slowed down, halted. A blackbird hidden in the branches flew out, burst into chatter, perched on a cross on the transverse path. He looked at me; I looked at him. He pecked at the cross to attract my attention, and I read the epitaph: "Who follows me shall not walk in the shadows."

He flew off deep into the tombs, and I followed without a second thought. He landed on the roof of a small chapel with this inscription above the door: "Your sorrow shall be made joy."

My guide lifted his wings and led me farther into the sepulchral maze, whistling all the time in an unusual manner—calls I would very much have liked to understand.

Finally, my pilot vanished at the foot of an elder-tree, and I found myself facing a mausoleum I had never noticed before. An artist's dream, a poet's vision, or rather a half-forgotten memory refreshed by the tears of affliction. It was a child of six, high relief on gold base, being led by an angel above the clouds toward heaven.

Not one reflection of the typically criminal man in this child's face, with its perfect serenity, its wide eyes made to radiate beauty, goodness, rather than to look at this unclean world; the tip of its little nose lightly pushed-in from being habitually pressed to a mother's bosom; placed like a delicate ornament, the shell-like outlines of the nostrils above the heart-shaped mouth not meant for scenting a prey or for taking in good or bad smells, not yet an organ: Beauty for beauty's sake.

This is the child before he loses his first teeth, those pearls with no function other than to light up a smile.

Now, don't tell me he is the descendant of a monkey! Yet we must admit that a common, shaggy, wrinkled old man, with canine teeth, arched back, and collapsing knees does descend toward the simians, unless the exterior is only a mask. Progress in reverse? Or what? Did the golden age of Saturn exist, and have we degenerated from those blessed ones whom we can never forget, and whose loss the child deplores when he cries on entering a world where he is out of his element?

Are we aware of what we are doing when we feed babies on milk and honey, later, on more or less golden fruits? Reminding them of the golden age, where:

> *Flumina jam lactis, jam flumina nectaris ibant,*
> *Flavoque de viridi stillabant ilice mella.*[1]

Why do we tell children those stories of the land of Cockaigne, of elves, sprites, giants, without making them understand that they are lies? Why those toys that represent monsters and angels, antediluvian beasts, distorted plants that do not exist?

Science would reply—if it were sincere: To let the child in his imagination undergo his phylogenesis, in other words: To

[1] Now streams of milk were flowing, now streams of nectar . . . (Golden Age)—Ovid, *Metamorphoses*, Book I.—EDITOR.

experience the earlier stages of his existence, just as the foe-
tus in the womb passes through the whole line of its evolution
as an animal.

The blackbird, back from its excursion, calls me with its
sharp cry. It has settled on an iron railing, bringing in its
beak an object the shape and color of which I cannot make
out. As soon as I go nearer the bird flies off leaving its booty
on the handrail. It's the chrysalis of a butterfly, with that
unique configuration that resembles no other shape in the
animal kingdom. A scarecrow, a monster, a goblin's cowl, neither animal, vegetable, nor mineral. A shroud, a tomb, a
mummy, not *become,* because it has no ancestors here below,
but made, created by someone.

The great artist-creator has amused himself as the master
of artistry by shaping with no practical end, art for art's
sake, possibly a symbol. This mummy, I know, encloses only
a formless animal mucilage, with no structure whatever and
the smell of a fresh corpse.

And this glory is endowed with life, with the instinct for
preservation, since it squirms on the cold iron and will be
able to attach itself by threads if it feels too insecure.

A living corpse, which will surely come back to life!

And the others down there being transformed in their
chrysalises, undergoing the same necrobiosis,[2] they will never
come back to life, according to the knowledge of the academic scholars, apostates of their own master. Voltaire's statement concerning final things has been forgotten. As a Vol-
tairean, I shall take pleasure in raising this rock of offense by
quoting that skeptic who admitted everything while denying
nothing.

"Resurrection is a quite natural thing; it is no more aston-
ishing to be born twice than once."

[2] *Necrobiosis:* decay of bodily tissues.—TR.

# Inferno

Translated by Derek Coltman and Evert Sprinchorn

*Il n'y a personne de bonne foi et dont la raison ne soit pas
obscurcie ou prévenue, qui ne convienne que la vie corporelle de l'homme est une privation et une souffrance contin-
uelles. Ainsi, d'après les idées que nous avons prises de la
Justice, ce ne sera pas sans raison que nous regarderons la
durée de cette vie corporelle comme un temps de châtiment
et d'expiation; mais nous ne pouvons la regarder comme telle
sans penser aussitôt qu'il doit y avoir eu pour l'homme un
état antérieur et préférable à celui où il se trouve à présent,
et nous pouvons dire, qu'autant son état actuel est borné,
pénible et semé de dégoûts, autant l'autre doit avoir été
illimité et rempli de délices.* *

LOUIS CLAUDE DE SAINT-MARTIN

*Courbe la tête, fier Sicambre!
Adore ce que tu as brûlé,
Brûle ce que tu as adoré!*

ST. REMY,
baptizing Clovis the Frank.†

And I will set my face against that man, and will
make him a sign and a proverb, and I will cut him
off from the midst of my people; and ye shall know
that I am the Lord.

EZEKIEL 14:8†

Of whom is Hymenaeus and Alexander; whom I
have delivered unto Satan, that they may learn not
to blaspheme.

I TIMOTHY 1:20†

* Motto to the first French edition of *Inferno*, 1898.
† These mottoes are prefixed to the Swedish edition.

# I

## The Hand of The Invisible

WITH A SAVAGE JOY I walked away from the Gare du Nord, having parted there from my sweet little wife as she set off to rejoin our child who had fallen sick in a distant country. The sacrifice of my heart's love—finished! Our last words to each other—"When shall I see you again?"—"Soon."—still echoed in my ears like one of those lies whose true nature one won't admit even to oneself, although something told me that we had parted forever.

And those farewells exchanged in November of 1894 were indeed the last, since up till this moment, in May 1897, I have not seen my beloved wife again.

Reaching the Café de la Régence, I sat down at the table I used to occupy with my wife—my beautiful jailer who spied out my soul by day and by night, divined my hidden thoughts, followed the development of my plans and kept a jealous eye on my struggles to explore unknown realms. . . .

A free man once again, I felt a sudden release of the soul's energy and was sent soaring above the pettinesses of the great city, that arena of intellectual combats where I had just won a victory, petty in itself, but for me immense—a victory that constituted the fulfillment of a youthful dream cherished by all my literary contemporaries and compatriots but realized by myself alone: to have a play performed on the Paris stage. But now, the theater inspired in me that distaste we feel towards what we have achieved; and science attracted me now. Faced with the choice between love and learning, I had decided to attain the summit of knowledge; and the sacrifice of my affections made me forget the innocent victim I had immolated along with them on the altar of my ambition, or of my mission.

\*    \*    \*

Back once more in my wretched student's room in the Latin Quarter, I dug deep into my trunk and drew out from their hiding place six fine porcelain crucibles that I had bought by stealing from myself—that is, by raising a cash advance on my resources. A pair of tongs and a packet of pure sulfur completed the equipment of my laboratory.

I then proceeded to build a fire as hot as a blacksmith's forge, to lock the door, and to draw the curtains. Three months after Caserio's execution it was still not wise to be seen handling chemical apparatus in Paris.[1]

[1] The activities of the anarchists in France reached a climax in the 1890s. After the trial and sentencing of some anarchists at Clichy in 1891, following a May Day demonstration, a man named Ravachol bombed the homes of the presiding judge and the prosecuting attorney. Tried and executed in 1892 for this bombing and several murders, the notorious Ravachol became a martyr to the anarchists and his death set off a series of revenge bombings, culminating in November 1892 in the bombing of a police station, which killed six officers. Then in December 1893, a young man named Vaillant, who was trying to support a family on wages that would scarcely have kept one person alive, threw a bomb in the French Chamber of Deputies, killing no one but injuring several representatives. The government immediately passed laws seeking to suppress the printing and distribution of anarchist literature. Vaillant was tried and though he had not killed anyone and denied he had wanted to kill anyone ("I could have used a more powerful explosive"), he was sentenced to the guillotine. This, in spite of the fact that evidence brought forward during the trial made it clear that Vaillant had been urged to throw the bomb by *agents provocateurs* of the Paris police. Executed on February 5, 1894, after President Sadi Carnot refused to remit the sentence, Vaillant went to his death crying, "Death to bourgeois society! Long live Anarchy!"

Four more bombings in public places followed, reducing Paris to a state of near hysteria. The perpetrator of these outrages was executed in May 1894. Then on June 24, in Lyon, President Carnot himself was assassinated by a young man who approached the President's carriage during a parade with the apparent intention of offering him a bouquet of flowers. The bouquet was false but the knife it contained was very real. The twenty-one-year-old assassin, Santo-Jeronimo Caserio was summarily tried and executed on August 15.

The murder of Carnot brought about the arrest of three hundred people who were charged with advocating anarchy, and thirty of these were actually prosecuted. Strindberg was well known among his friends in the 1880s as a parlor anarchist, and in one of his

Night fell, the sulfur burned with hellish flames, and towards morning I observed the presence of carbon in what had hitherto been supposed a pure element, sulfur. And with this observation I supposed myself to have solved a great problem, destroyed the prevailing chemical theory, and won the only immortality allowed to mortal man.

But by then, the skin of my hands, roasted by the intense heat of the fire, was peeling off, falling in flakes, and the pain caused by the simple act of undressing was a constant reminder of the price I had paid for my triumph. Alone in my bed, still smelling of woman, I felt myself blessed and happy. Conscious of the purity of my soul, of male virginity, I looked back on my married life as something unclean, and I regretted not having anyone to whom I could give thanks for my liberation from those sordid bonds, now broken without too much fuss and bother.

For I had become an atheist in recent years, years during which the unknown powers had let the world go its own way, without giving any signs of life.

If only there were someone to whom I could give thanks and be grateful. There was no one; I was forced to be ungrateful and this ingratitude oppressed me.

*      *      *

Jealous of my discovery, I made no attempt to divulge it to the world at large. And my timidity kept me from approaching either the authorities or the universities. Nevertheless I continued my experiments, while my chapped hands became infected, the cracks widened and became caked with coke dust, the blood oozed out, and the pain became unbearable. Everything I touched hurt me. Driven wild by these tortures, which I insisted on attributing to the unknown powers that had been persecuting me and thwarting my efforts for so many years, I avoided my fellow men, eschewed all company, rejected all invitations, and thrust away my friends. A zone of silence and solitude was set up around me. It was the calm of the desert, awesome and horrible, in which, out of bravado, I deliberately provoked the unknown

---

letters he even drew a caricature of himself blowing up the king on his throne in the Royal Palace in Stockholm.–EDITOR.

to combat, to wrestle with it body against body, soul against soul. I had proved the existence of carbon in sulfur; I would continue until I had revealed the presence of hydrogen and oxygen, for they too must surely be there. But my apparatus was no longer adequate; I had insufficient money; my hands were black and bleeding, black as was my poverty, bleeding like my heart. During this period I did in fact keep up a correspondence with my wife, sending her accounts of my scientific successes to which she replied with bulletins on the subject of our child, larding them with snatches of advice on the futility of my experiments and the folly of frittering away good money.

In a sudden fit of justifiable pride, in a rage of deliberate agony, I sought to destroy myself by sending her a nefarious, an unpardonable letter, in which I repudiated wife and child alike for ever, letting it be understood that a new love had taken possession of my soul.

The blow struck home. My wife reacted by asking for a divorce.

Alone, guilty of virtual suicide and murder, I found respite from the thought of my crime in grief and distress. No one came to visit me, and I could not go to see anyone. I had offended everyone I knew.

I felt released, liberated, floating on the waves of some vast ocean. I had cut the anchor chain, but my ship had no sails.

Meanwhile, my lack of money, which was forced on my attention by an unpaid bill, was interrupting my scientific work and metaphysical speculations and driving me back to land.

In such straits did the approach of Christmas find me. I roundly refused an invitation to spend it with a Scandinavian family[2] I knew because certain painful irregularities in their household rendered the atmosphere there distasteful to me. However, that evening, as soon as I found myself alone, I repented my decision and went to them. We sat down to our meal, and the festivities commenced with exuberant and noisy manifestations of joy from all the young artists who felt

[2] The Molard family. See the Introduction. Strindberg was living at this time on Rue de l'Abbé de l'Épée.–EDITOR.

no necessity for restraint in that atmosphere. An air of intimacy that I found repugnant, their gestures, manners, and, in a word, a bohemian tone far removed from what one associates with a family party overwhelmed me with an ineffable malaise, and in the midst of that saturnalia an inner sadness brought the thought of my wife's tranquil home into my mind. The parlor where I sat suddenly evoked another vision for me: the Christmas tree, the mistletoe, my little girl and her abandoned mother. . . . I was seized with remorse; I rose, excused myself on the grounds of feeling unwell, and left.

I passed through the horrible Rue de la Gaîté, where the factitious gaiety of the crowd grated upon me, then along the dismal and silent Rue Delambre, of all streets in the neighborhood the one most capable of inspiring despair, and finally, having emerged onto the Boulevard Montparnasse, I collapsed into a chair on the terrace of the Brasserie des Lilas.

A good glass of absinthe brought me two minutes of consolation. Then I was attacked by a band of cocottes with an escort of young students. They began to flick me in the face with twigs and switches, and, as though pursued by furies, I abandoned my absinthe to its fate, making haste to find another in the Café François Premier on the Boulevard Saint-Michel.

Out of the frying pan into the fire! Another troop of revelers began hooting at me: "Hey look at the hermit!" Scourged by the Eumenides, I fled from the place, my ears lashed by the screech of their songs and the rasp of their paper whistles.[3]

The thought that these happenings might be a punishment inflicted on me for some crime did not enter my mind. In my own eyes I appeared quite blameless, the object of unjust persecution. They—the Unknown Ones—were hindering me from continuing my great work, and it was necessary for me to break down the obstacles in my path before winning the victor's crown.

[3] The original French has "mirleton," which was a toy noisemaker with a vibrating parchment to reinforce the voice. It was usually adorned with strips of paper and humorous verse.—EDITOR.

I had done wrong, yet I was in the right all the same, and would be given my rights.

That Christmas night I slept ill. An icy current of air lashed my face several times, and the sound of a Jew's harp woke me again and again.

\* \* \*

A growing infirmity slowly gained ground within me. My black and bleeding hands[4] hindered me from dressing myself and taking care of my appearance. My anxiety over the unpaid hotel bill allowed me not a moment's peace, and I paced my room like a wild animal in a cage.

I stopped taking my meals, and the pension owner advised me to go to a hospital, which was no solution since hospitals are very expensive and one has to pay in advance.

Then a swelling of the veins of one arm set in, symptomatic of blood-poisoning. This was the last straw; the news of my illness spread among my compatriots, with the result that one evening the charitable woman whose Christmas festivities I had deserted in so unworthy a manner, the woman I found so antipathetic, whom I almost despised, came to see me, inquired about my illness, learned of my plight, and advised me through her tears that a stay in the hospital was the only recourse left to me.

Judge how forlorn I felt in spirit, how contrite, when my eloquent silence gave her to understand that I was entirely without means. At that point she extended a helping hand, realizing the straits I had been driven into.

Though poor herself and burdened with worries about her own day to day existence, she declared that she would go and beg on my behalf from the rest of the Scandinavian colony, and that she intended to visit the pastor of our parish.

She was a woman who lived in sin, and she had shown pity towards a man who had just abandoned his lawful wife.

A beggar once again, asking for charity with a woman as my intermediary, I began to sense the existence of an invisible hand directing the irresistible logic of events. I bowed

[4] On the nature of the illness afflicting Strindberg's hands, see the Introduction.—EDITOR.

before the storm, resolving to pull myself upright again at the first opportunity.

*　　*　　*

I was taken to the Saint-Louis Hospital in a carriage. On the way I stopped to buy two white shirts in the Rue de Rennes.

"Shrouds. My hour of agony is upon me!"

I was obsessed with the imminence of death, without being able to say why.

Once admitted, forbidden to leave the place without permission, my hands swaddled in dressings that rendered me incapable of occupying my time, without diversions of any sort, I thought of myself as a prisoner.

I was in a bare, unadorned room, furnished with the necessities but devoid of all trace of beauty, and situated near the common room in which the other patients smoked and played cards from morning till night.

The bell rang for lunch, and sitting down at the table I found myself in a macabre company. The faces were those of dead and dying men. One had its nose missing, another an eye, yet another had a lip hanging loose, another a rotting cheek. Two of the patients, however, did not have the appearance of sick men but sat there looking morose and despondent. They were master thieves from good families who, through their powerful connections, had been released from prison on the pretext that they were ill.

A sickening smell of iodoform deprived me of all appetite and, since my hands were bound up, I was forced to rely on my companions to cut my bread and pour my drink for me. And around this banquet table of criminals and condemned men there moved the good Mother, the matron in her austere black and white garb, handing to each his poison draught. I clinked glasses with a death's head, and we drank each other's healths, I in arsenic, he in strychnine. How dismal, yet one had to be grateful, which made me furious. Being grateful for something so wretched and so unpleasant!

I was dressed and undressed, I was taken care of like a child, while the nun who nursed me grew quite fond of me, treating me like a baby and calling me "my child," while I addressed her as "mother."

How good it was to speak that word mother. I had not called anyone mother for thirty years! That old woman, a nun of the Augustinian order, wearing the costume of the dead because she had never lived in this world, gentle as renunciation itself, taught us to smile at our sufferings as though they were so many joys, for she knew well the benefits to be won from pain. Not one word of reproach, of remonstrance, of admonishment. She knew the regulations of these lay hospitals and found ways of allowing the patients little infractions that she would never have permitted herself. She allowed me to smoke in my room, for instance, and even offered to roll my cigarettes, an offer which I declined. She obtained permission for me to leave the hospital outside the usual hours, and having discovered that I was engaged in chemical experiments she saw to it that I was introduced to the hospital's pharmacist, a learned man who loaned me books and also, when I had explained my theory on the composition of the elements to him, invited me to use his laboratory for my work. This nun played a considerable role in my life, and I began to reconcile myself with my lot, thanking the happy misfortune that had led me beneath that blessed roof.

The first book I carried off with me from the pharmacist's library fell open before me of its own accord, and my gaze swooped down like a hawk upon one line from the chapter on phosphorus.

Very briefly, the author recounted that the chemist Lockyer had proved by spectral analysis that phosphorus is not an element, and that the report of his experiments had been presented to the Académie des Sciences de Paris, which had not rejected his findings.[5]

[5] Joseph Norman Lockyer (1836–1920), the renowned astronomer and spectroscopist who discovered the element helium in the sun before it was isolated on earth, presented to the French Academy of Science about 1879 a paper, "Experiments Tending to Show the Non-elementary Character of Phosphorus." The abstract of this paper reads in part: "Phosphorus heated in a tube with copper gives a gas exhibiting the spectrum of hydrogen; heated alone, phosphorus gives no gas. Phosphorus at the negative pole of a battery in a tube apparatus . . . gives a large quantity of gas

Comforted by this unexpected support, I made a sortie from the hospital, taking my crucibles and their residues of incompletely burned sulfur with me. I then handed them over to an analytical laboratory, where I was promised a certified report on their contents for the following morning.

It was my birthday. When I returned to the hospital I found a letter from my wife. She had shed tears over my misfortunes, wanted to come back to me, to take care of me, to love me.

The happiness of being loved despite everything created a need inside me to offer up thanks. . . . But to whom?

To the unknown being who had been in hiding for so many years?

My heart melted, I confessed the infamous lie I had told about my unfaithfulness to her, asked forgiveness, and found myself involved once more in an exchange of love letters with my own wife, while still postponing our meeting until some more opportune moment.

\*　　\*　　\*

The following morning, I hurried out to see my chemist on the Boulevard Magenta.

I brought the certificate of analysis in its sealed envelope back to the hospital. As I walked past the statue of Saint-Louis in the inner courtyard, the Saint's three works rose into my memory: the Quinze-Vingt asylum for the blind, the Sorbonne, and the Sainte-Chapelle. Which I construed thus: from Suffering through Knowledge to Penitence.

Having shut myself up in my room, I opened the envelope that was to decide my future. This is what I read:

> The powder submitted for our analysis presented the following characteristics:
> Grey-black in color. Leaves marks on paper.
> Density: very great, higher than the average density of graphite. It appears to be a form of hard graphite. . . .
> Chemical analysis:
> This powder burns easily, producing carbon dioxide and carbonic acid. It must therefore contain carbon.

---

which shows the spectrum of hydrogen, and is not phosphoretted hydrogen."—EDITOR.

Pure sulfur contains carbon!

I was saved—that is, I could prove henceforth to my friends and relations that I was not mad. And I had found justification for the theories expressed in my work *Antibarbarus*, which had been published a year previously and treated by the newspapers as the work of a charlatan or a madman, and which was the cause of my being driven out by my family like a rogue, a charlatan, a Cagliostro.

My adversaries were crushed—all of them! I began to swell with rightful pride, I wanted to leave the hospital, to cry my triumph in the streets, to howl it out in front of the Institute, to demolish the Sorbonne. . . . But my hands were still bound and bandaged, and when I emerged into the courtyard its high walls counselled me: Have patience.

When I communicated the result of the analysis to the hospital pharmacist, he suggested that he should get together a commission in whose presence I could prove my thesis by direct demonstrations.

I was unable to wait, however, and conscious of my timidity before an audience, I composed an article on the subject and sent it to the newspaper *Le Temps*. Two days later it was published.

The word was out. I received replies from all sides, none of them denying my claims. I found followers, the pages of a chemistry review were opened to me, and I engaged in a correspondence that provided further sustenance for my continuing search.[6]

\*      \*      \*

One Sunday, the last of my stay in the purgatory of Saint-Louis, I was sitting at the window observing the various activities outside in the courtyard. The two master thieves were walking with their wives and children, kissing them from

[6] A report on Strindberg's experiments seeking to prove that sulfur was not an element but contained carbon appeared in *Le Petit Temps*, January 30, 1895. Several professional chemists wrote commentaries on Strindberg's researches in *La Science Française* and in *Le Figaro*. And Strindberg replied to them in *La Science Française* of March 15, 1895, with an article entitled *L'Avenir du soufre*.—EDITOR.

time to time and apparently basking in the glow of the fire that had been fanned by their misfortunes.

My solitude was oppressing me, and I cursed my fate, finding it unjust, and forgetting that my crime was far more infamous than theirs.

The mailman came with a letter from my wife. She was cold as ice. The success of my experiments had hurt her and she pretended to base her skeptical attitude towards them on the opinion of a professional chemist. She then added her own opinions on the danger of illusions that can lead to mental breakdowns. And besides, what could I gain by all this? Could I feed a family with my chemical experiments? . . .

Once again the choice: love or science! Without hesitation I crushed her with a final letter of farewell, and felt the self-satisfaction of a murderer after a perfect crime.

That evening I went for a walk through the dismal district surrounding the hospital, passing the Saint-Martin canal, black as a grave, a wondrously propitious place for drowning. I stopped at the corner of the Rue Alibert. Alibert? Who was he? The graphite the chemist found in my sulfur, wasn't that called Alibert graphite? So what? It was bizarre, but the impression of something inexplicable was lodged in my mind. Then the Rue Dieu. God. Why God? Had he not been abolished by the Republic when it secularized the Panthéon? Rue Beaurepaire. A Fine Retreat? Yes, for malefactors. . . . Rue de Bondy.[7] Was the devil directing my steps? . . .

I stopped reading the street signs, I lost my way and turned back without being able to find my way again. I recoiled from a huge shed smelling of raw meat and spoiled vegetables, mainly sauerkraut . . . Suspicious-looking individuals brushed against me, hurling foul words after me . . . I was afraid, of what I couldn't say. I turned to the right, then to the left, and stumbled into a sordid street, a blind alley, a place of garbage, vice, and crime. Prostitutes barred my way, apaches jeered at me . . . My Christmas night experience all over again. *Vae soli!* Who was preparing these ambushes for me as soon as I tore myself away from the

[7] *Une forêt de Bondy* signified a place frequented by malefactors.—EDITOR.

world and men? Someone had seen to it that I fell into this trap! Where was he? I had to find him and fight him!

As I began to run, rain started to fall, rain mingled with slushy snow. . . . At the end of a little street and outlined in bister against the sky was an enormous gate, the work of titans, a gate without a palace, gaping onto a sea of light. . . . I asked a policeman where I was.

"At the Porte Saint-Martin, Monsieur."

Two steps and I was back on the grand boulevards and walking back towards the center. The clock on the theater said a quarter past six. Exactly that hour of day when my friends were waiting for me as usual at the Café Napolitain for a drink before dinner. I hurried on along the boulevard, forgetting the hospital, my troubles, my poverty. Then, as I passed in front of the Café du Cardinal, I bumped against a table at which a man was sitting. I only knew him by name; but he recognized me, and in a flash his eyes had said to me: "You here? I thought you were in the hospital. And asking for charity! How cheap!"

I sensed that the man was one of my anonymous benefactors, that he had contributed to the collection that had been taken up for me, that in his eyes I was a beggar who had no right to go into a café.

Beggar! It was the right word for me. It rang in my ears. My cheeks burned with shame, with humiliation, and with rage.

Think of it! Six weeks before I used to sit at one of those tables myself. The manager of the theater where my play was being performed used to accept my invitations to sit with me. He called me maestro. Journalists used to come and beg me for interviews. The photographer used to request the honor of selling pictures of me . . . And now: a beggar—branded and cast out from society!

Smarting, exhausted, at my last gasp, I dragged myself along the boulevard like a shameful prowler in the night, skulking back into my lair, seeking refuge among its other plague-stricken inhabitants. There, locked in my room, I felt at home.

Reflecting on my fate, I recognized the invisible hand that was chastising me, that was pushing me towards a goal I could not yet guess at. It was covering me with glory by refusing me all the honors of this world. It was humiliating me while lifting me up, casting me down in order to exalt me.

Once more I felt providence had destined me for a mission, that my education was only now beginning.

\* \* \*

In February I left the hospital. My sores were still not cured but I was; I was cured of the temptations of this world. As I left, I wanted very much to kiss the hand of the good nun who had taught me, without sermons, the way to the cross; yet a feeling of veneration for something that must not be profaned held me back.

May she accept the kiss in spirit, a gesture of gratitude offered by a lost stranger wandering in a country far from home.

# II

## Saint Louis Introduces Me to the Late Monsieur Orfila

Once settled into a modest furnished room, I continued my chemical experiments all that winter, staying at home all day then going out to eat my dinner at a crémerie[1] where some artists of various nationalities had formed a circle. After dinner, I used to visit the family I had once quitted so abruptly during a momentary attack of moral rigor. A whole circle of anarchistic artists used to gather there, and I felt myself condemned to endure what I had tried to avoid: loose living, moral indifference, and deliberate impiety. There was a great deal of talent there and an infinite amount of wit; but only

[1] The crémerie of Madame Charlotte Futterer, on the Rue de la Grande Chaumière. It was frequented by Paul Gauguin and by the Polish artist Wladislaw Skewinski, and provides the central setting for Strindberg's play *Crimes and Crimes.*—EDITOR.

one man possessed genius, an untamed spirit who had won a respected name for himself.[2]

All the same, the family loved me, and since I owed them my gratitude, I turned deaf ears and blind eyes to everything concerning their private affairs, which had nothing to do with me.

If the pride that had made me avoid these people had not been justified, then the punishment would have been logical; but in these particular circumstances, where the motive for my withdrawal had been the desire to purify my individual being and to cultivate my personality in solitary meditation, I could not understand the methods employed by providence, since I have a pliable character that always adapts itself to its environment out of pure friendliness and the fear of being ungrateful. Cast out from society by my misfortunes and my shameful poverty, I was happy to find a shelter for the long winter evenings, even though the scabrous tone of the conversation there caused me to suffer deeply.

\*      \*      \*

Having discovered the existence of an invisible hand guiding my steps along the uneven, rocky path, I no longer felt myself so entirely alone, and began to pay strict attention to my every word and action—without always succeeding in my aims, it should be added. But as soon as I committed a sin someone would always find me out immediately, and the punishment would make itself felt with a precision and a refinement of justice that left no doubt as to its being the work of some corrective power. The unknown became a personal acquaintance. I talked to him, thanked him, asked him for advice. Sometimes I envisaged him as a personal retainer, somewhat analogous to Socrates' daimon, and the knowledge that I was being supported by unknown powers supplied me with a fund of energy and self-confidence that pushed me on to efforts I had never thought myself capable of till then.

A social bankrupt, I was now reborn in another world where no one could follow me. Formerly insignificant occurrences now drew my attention; my dreams at night assumed

[2] Paul Gauguin.—EDITOR.

the form of omens. I considered myself as having died and gone on to live my life in another sphere.

❊        ❊        ❊

Having established the presence of carbon in sulfur, there remained the task of discovering the hydrogen and oxygen that reasoning by analogy told me should be present too.

Two months passed in calculation and speculations, but I lacked the necessary apparatus for experiments. A friend advised me to go to the Sorbonne where there was a research laboratory available even to foreigners. Shy and afraid of crowds, I could not bring myself to do so, with the result that my work came to a halt and a period of idleness ensued. Then, one fine spring morning, after awakening to find myself in a good humor, I walked down the Rue de la Grande Chaumière and then into the Rue de Fleurus, which gives onto the Luxembourg Gardens. The pretty little street was very quiet, the great avenue of chestnuts was green and shining, as wide and straight as a race course. At the far end, like a goal post, rose the Colonne de David, and in the far distance, high above everything, was the dome of the Panthéon, topped by its golden cross and almost lost in the clouds.

I halted, ravished by this symbolic sight. But as I lowered my eyes I observed on my right a dyer's sign hanging in the Rue de Fleurus. Ah! A vision of undeniable reality. Painted on the wooden square over the shop were my initials A. S., floating on a silver white cloud and hooped over with a rainbow.

"*Omen accipio,*" I said to myself as I recalled the words of Genesis: "I do set my bow in the cloud, and it shall be a token of a covenant between me and the earth."

I was no longer walking on the earth, I was walking on air with winged feet. I continued on into the garden, which was deserted. At that early hour of the morning the park was mine, the rose garden was mine, and I recognized all my flowers in the flowerbeds, the chrysanthemums, the verbenas, the begonias.

Walking along the race course, I reached the goal post at its end, left the garden by the iron gate opposite the Rue

Soufflot and turned down the Boulevard Saint-Michel. Stopping in front of the display shelves outside the Blanchard bookstore, quite without thinking I took up an old volume on chemistry by Orfila, opened it at random and read: "Sulfur has been classified among the elements. The ingenious experiments of H. Davy and the younger Berthollet tend to prove that it contains hydrogen, oxygen, and a certain base which it has proved impossible to isolate so far."[3]

Judge of my ecstasy, my religious ecstasy I would say, when faced with this revelation amounting almost to a miracle. Davy and Berthollet had proved the presence of oxygen and hydrogen, I had done likewise for the carbon. I was therefore the man who would discover the formula for sulfur.

Two days later I enrolled in the Faculté des Sciences at the Sorbonne (founded by Saint Louis!) and was authorized to work in the research laboratory.

❊    ❊    ❊

On that morning on which I finally went to the Sorbonne, I felt I was participating in a kind of solemn celebration. Though I had no illusions about being able to convince the professors, who had greeted me with the cold civility always reserved for foreigners, for intruders, a sweet and gentle joy lent me the courage of the martyr approaching a host of enemies. For me, at my age, youth was the natural enemy.

As I walked into the square in front of the little Eglise de la Sorbonne, I noticed that the door was open, and I walked

[3] Sir Humphry Davy (1778–1829), English scientist, inventor of the miner's safety-lamp and discoverer of sodium, magnesium, calcium, and other chemical elements.

Claude Berthollet (1748–1822), French chemist, companion of Napoleon on his Egyptian campaign, and largely responsible for establishing the present system of chemical nomenclature.

Mateo José Bonaventura Orfila (1787–1853), French physician of Spanish parentage, founder of the science of toxicology, author of a four-volume work on medical jurisprudence, which was the standard work in its field in the nineteenth century, and author of a well-known textbook on the chemical elements. It was typical of Strindberg that he should find inspiration in this sixty-year-old textbook and ignore more recent studies. The student hotel near the Sorbonne in which Strindberg resided for a time was named after Orfila. At present it is used largely by American students.—EDITOR.

in, without knowing exactly why. The Virgin Mother and Child greeted me with gentle smiles; the figure of Christ Crucified left me unmoved and appeared as incomprehensible as ever. Saint Louis, my new acquaintance, friend of those suffering from the plague or from poverty, was represented as receiving a group of young theologians. Saint Louis, was it he, my patron, my guardian angel, who had thrust me into the hospital so that I should know the fire of anguish before regaining that glory that leads to dishonor and the world's contempt? . . . Was it he who had sent me to the Blanchard bookstore? Was it he who had drawn me to this church?

From my former atheism I had now relapsed into the deepest superstition.

As I gazed at the wall plaques bearing witness to the happy issues of so many examinations, I made a solemn vow never to accept any worldly marks of merit in the event of my success.

The hour had struck, and I had to run the gauntlet down the rows of the pitiless young who, told in advance of the chimerical task I had set myself, spurned and reviled me.

*   *   *

About two weeks passed, by which time I had amassed indisputable proof that sulfur is a ternary combination of carbon, oxygen, and hydrogen.[4]

I thanked the director of the laboratory, who put on a show of being completely uninterested in my affairs, and left that new purgatory filled with an ineffable inner joy.

*   *   *

On those mornings when I did not visit the Luxembourg Gardens I used to walk in the cemetery of Montparnasse. A few days after leaving the Sorbonne, as I was passing near the circular path at the center of the cemetery, I discovered a tombstone of classic simplicity and beauty. A white marble medallion presented to the eye the noble features of an aged seer who was no other, according to the inscription on the

[4] For details see: *Tryckt och otryckt*, Stockholm 1897—*Sylva Sylvarum*, Paris 1896—*L'Hyperchimie*, Paris 1897. (Strindberg's note.)

base than Orfila, the chemist and toxicologist. It was my friend and protector, who later on was to guide me many a time through the labyrinths of chemical experiment and inquiry.

A week later, walking down the Rue d'Assas, I came to a halt in front of a house with a cloister-like appearance. A big sign announced the nature of this building: Hôtel Orfila.

Orfila yet again!

In the following chapters I shall recount all that happened in that old house, into which the invisible hand thrust me that I might be chastised, instructed, and—why not?— illuminated![5]

[5] "Illuminated" would have a special connotation to those famil-iar with the occult. Though various religious societies have desig-nated themselves the Illuminati, the most important historically was an anticlerical sect founded in 1776 by Adam Weishaupt in Bavaria. The aim of the group was to promote greater virtue and morality than that attained in ordinary society. Naturally, the gov-ernment suppressed the sect, in 1785. However, it spread to France, largely through the efforts of Louis-Claude de Saint-Martin (see note to page 226), and influenced a great number of writers and philosophers in the nineteenth century, notably Charles Fourier, Charles Nodier, Mesmer, and Balzac. Spiritism, magnetism, and alchemy were all regarded as means by which to make contact with the divine, for man was seen as placed by God in a world of symbols. When he had learned to interpret them, he would be il-luminated, that is, he would become part of God's radiance, part of the universal soul. Not resurrection but enlightenment and metempsychosis were the goals to be achieved. Eccentricity, even to the point of insanity, was considered characteristic of the man who had been illuminated, for he had shed much of the material world. The basic ideas of Illuminism can be traced back through Swedenborg to the Cabala and to oriental mysticism, and forward through Baudelaire, Rimbaud, and the Symbolists.—EDITOR.

# III

## The Temptations of the Demon

My divorce proceedings continued very slowly, interrupted from time to time by a love letter, a cry of regret, a promise of a reconciliation. And then an abrupt farewell, forever.

I loved her, she loved me, and we hated one another with a ferocious love-hate that was only intensified by the distance separating us.

Meanwhile, and in order to break this ill-fated bond, I sought an opportunity to replace this affection by another, and immediately my improper wishes were fulfilled.

As I was eating dinner one day at the crémerie, an English lady who had devoted her life to sculpture came in.[1] She spoke to me first, and I immediately found her attractive. She was beautiful, charming, distinguished, well dressed, and had the customary open and winning manner of an artist. In short, an edition *de luxe* of my wife, of whom she seemed to be a nobler and larger reflection. In order to please me, the doyen of the crémerie, the master artist,[2] invited this lady to the Thursday evening parties that were held in his studio. I went there and kept myself a little aloof; it goes against the grain with me to exhibit my feelings in front of a mocking audience.

At about eleven o'clock, the lady rose and signaled to me. I too rose, rather awkwardly, said my goodbyes, and having suggested to the young lady that I should see her home, I

[1] A Madame Lecain, in reality. She was one of the models for Henriette, the *femme fatale* in Strindberg's play *Crimes and Crimes* (1899). Some time later, in 1901, Strindberg wrote in his diary that Madame Lecain so impressed him with "her warmth and motherliness that I often wished I could bury myself under her beautiful warm wool coat as in a mother's bosom [a thought Strindberg took from *Crimes and Crimes,* act II, scene 2]. But she was a devil and Gauguin said she was a man-eater."—EDITOR.

[2] Paul Gauguin.—EDITOR.

led her to the door, amid hoots of laughter from the impudent young artists.

Both having made ourselves ridiculous, and each on the other's account, we left without saying a word, ashamed of ourselves as though we had been stripped naked in front of that jeering crowd.

And then it chanced that we were forced to walk down the Rue de la Gaîté, where the pimps and prostitutes pelted our cheeks with their outrageous insults, taking us to be two of their kind who had wandered there from some other neighborhood.

It's not easy to be charming when one is choking with fury. Locked in the pillory, bent beneath the whip, I was unable to carry myself upright. As we turned onto the Boulevard Raspail, we were attacked by a fine, harrying shower of rain that lashed us like so many slender rods. Since we had no umbrella, what could have been more reasonable than to seek shelter in a well-heated and well-lighted cafe? With a lordly gesture I waved my companion towards the most expensive of the nearby restaurants. We began to cross the boulevard with light steps . . . —and—I remembered I hadn't a cent to my name. I felt as though I had been hit on the head with a hammer.

I forget how I extricated myself from that situation, but I shall never forget the sensations that assailed me during the night after I had left the lady outside her front door.

The punishment, however immediate and severe, and though administered by an experienced hand that I could not fail to recognize, appeared to me nevertheless to be insufficient. A beggar, with obligations still unfulfilled towards my own family, I had attempted to enter into a liaison which would have endangered the reputation of a respectable woman. It was manifestly a crime, a sin, and I inflicted on myself the appropriate penitence. I denied myself my evening at the crémerie, I fasted and avoided everything that might encourage this fatal passion.

But the tempter was on the watch, and at one of the evening parties in the studio I met my beautiful lady again. She was wearing an oriental costume that set off her beauty and drove me out of my mind.

And yet, facing her, I could find nothing to say. I behaved idiotically, and realizing suddenly that this woman deserved no more than the simple and frank declaration: "I desire you," I fled, scorched to the bone by the flames of an unholy wish.

The next day I went back to the crémerie. She was there, charming as ever, caressing me with her purring voice, tantalizing me with catlike eyes. We entered into conversation and everything was going as well as could be wished when, at the critical moment, young Minna dashed noisily in. She was an artist's daughter, a model, the mistress of one of our circle, a goodhearted girl, welcome everywhere. I knew her too, and one evening we had become very good friends, though without passing the bounds of convention. Anyway, she rushed in, threw herself into my arms—she was a little drunk —kissed my cheeks, and began to talk very familiarly.

The English lady rose, paid, and left. It was completely over this time. She never came back!—thanks to Minna, who, I might add, had already warned me against the lady for reasons I shall not go into.

No more love! The powers had given their orders and I accepted them with resignation, certain, too, that there was a higher motive behind this decision, as there was behind everything else.

*     *     *

Encouraged by my successful experiments with sulfur, I went on to investigate iodine, and no sooner had I ventured an article in *Le Temps* on one of the methods of synthesizing iodine than a gentleman I had never met came to visit me at my hotel. He introduced himself as representing all the iodine manufacturers in Europe and informed me that he had just read my article, adding that as soon as my claims had been confirmed, we could together produce a crash on the Stock Exchange, thereby earning ourselves a profit of several millions each, by the simple expedient of taking out a patent.

I replied that my research represented not an industrial invention but a scientific discovery as yet unripe, and one whose commercial aspects did not interest me sufficiently to draw me into financial speculation.

He left. The manageress of the hotel, who had at one time been on terms of intimacy with my unknown visitor, learned the great news from him as he left, and for the next two days I was looked upon as a millionaire-to-be.

The businessman came back, this time more excited than ever. Having looked into the matter, he was now convinced that the discovery could really be turned to profit and suggested I go with him at once to Berlin so that he could set his schemes in motion.

I thanked him and advised him to have the necessary analyses made before involving himself further.

He offered me a hundred thousand francs by that evening if I would only go with him. . . .

I showed him to the door, sensing something crooked behind the offer.

Downstairs, stopping in to visit the manageress, he spoke of me as though I were mad.

During the next few days I was left in a state of calm that enabled me to reflect on the matter. On the one hand lay the threat of poverty, my unpaid debts and my uncertain future. On the other: independence, freedom to continue my studies, a life of ease. Don't all discoveries have their price?

I had begun to repent my former attitude, though lacking the courage to resume negotiations myself, when a telegram arrived from my visitor informing me that an assistant chemist at the school of medicine, who was also a deputy, already well known then and now notorious, had begun to take an interest in the iodine problem.

I then began a series of methodical experiments, all of which produced constant results amounting to proof that iodine can be derived from benzine.

As a result of these events, and after I had discussed the matter with the chemist, a day was fixed for an interview, to be followed by a series of decisive experiments.

On the morning which was to decide the matter once and for all, I hired a carriage and took all the retorts and necessary reagents with me to the businessman's home in the Marais district, where it had been arranged that we should all meet. My visitor was there, but the chemist, having realized that the day was a holiday, had excused himself and adjourned our session until the following day.

It was the feast of Pentecost, and I had not realized it until that moment. The grimy office looking out onto a black, mud-filled street made my heart ache. Childhood memories began to awake in me: Pentecost, the time of the descent of the Holy Ghost, when the little church, decorated with green branches, with tulips and lilac and lily-of-the-valley, opened its doors for the first communion . . . the young girls dressed like white angels . . . the notes of the organ . . . the bells. . . .

A feeling of shame suddenly gripped me, and I returned to my room very moved, determined at all costs to break away from any temptation to use science for my own personal profit. I set about clearing the room of the apparatus and chemicals that were cluttering it. I scrubbed, I dusted, I threw things away. I sent out for some flowers, mostly narcissuses. After taking a bath and changing my shirt I felt that I had been cleansed of my impurities. Then I went out and walked in the Montparnasse cemetery, where a new serenity of soul induced in me gentle thoughts and a sense of contrition the like of which I had seldom experienced.

*O crux ave spes unica.*[3] With such words did the gravestones augur my destiny. Farewell to love! Farewell to money! Farewell to honors! The way of the cross, the only way that leads to Wisdom.

## IV

### *Paradise Regained*

I count the summer and the fall of 1895, despite everything, among the happy periods of a life that has been filled with

---

[3] These are the words on the wooden cross that marks Strindberg's grave in Stockholm.–EDITOR.

troubles. Everything I set my hand to prospered. Unknown friends brought me food as the ravens did to Elijah. Money flew into my hands.[1] I was able to buy books and things to help me in my studies in natural history, among other things a microscope which revealed to me the mysteries of life.

Dead to the world, now that I had renounced the empty pleasures of Paris, I did not venture outside my own neighborhood, visiting the dead every morning in the cemetery of Montparnasse, then walking down to the Luxembourg Gardens to pass the time of day with my flowers. Sometimes a compatriot passing through the city would stop by to invite me over to the other side of the river for lunch and a visit to the theater. I always refused. The Right Bank was a forbidden thing to me, constituting as it did the world proper, the world of the living, and the world of vanity.

The reason for this was, though I could not formulate it clearly, that a sort of religion had been born within me—a state of soul rather than a view based on theories; a disordered chaos of sensations more or less condensed into ideas.

Having brought a Roman Catholic Missal, I read through it calmly and meditatively. The Old Testament both consoled and chastened me in some confused way, whereas the New Testament left me cold. All of which did not prevent a volume of Buddhist scriptures exercising an even stronger influence over me than all other sacred books because it exalted positive suffering above mere abstinence. The Buddha displayed the courage to renounce his wife and his childhood home while in full possession of his vital forces and while still enjoying great conjugal happiness, whereas Christ avoided from the beginning all commerce with the joys permitted in this world.

I did not, however, enter into further speculation about the feelings that were rising within me. I held myself aloof, letting things take their course, and granting myself the same freedom that I felt I must allow to others.

*        *        *

[1] Strindberg was sent money by well-wishers. See the Introduction.—EDITOR.

The great event of the Paris season was M. Brunetière's call to arms announcing the bankruptcy of science.[2] Though I had been initiated into the natural sciences in childhood, and had been something of a Darwinian as a young man, I had since then come to recognize the deficiencies of a scientific method that recognizes the machine-like structure of the universe without admitting the existence of a machinist. The weakness of this system had since made itself manifest in a general deterioration of all science, which had by this time laid down a line of demarcation beyond which it was forbidden to progress. *We* had resolved all the problems. The universe held no more mysteries. This presumptuous falsehood had already begun to irritate me in 1880 or thereabouts, and during the following fifteen years I had undertaken a revision of the natural sciences. In 1884, for example, I had called into question the accepted composition of the atmosphere, as well as the identity of the nitrogen present in air with the nitrogen produced by the decomposition of a nitrogen salt. In 1891 I had visited the physics laboratories at the University of Lund for the purpose of making comparisons between the spectra of these two types of nitrogen, which I knew to be dissimilar. Need I describe the reception I was accorded by the learned mechanists there?

But during this year, 1895, it so happened that the discovery of argon[3] confirmed the suppositions I had previously made and gave me fresh energy to pursue the researches interrupted by a rash and hasty marriage.

It was not science that had gone bankrupt but only an outdated, distorted branch of science, and M. Brunetière, although mainly in the right, was still wrong.

Meanwhile, at a time when everyone was recognizing the homogeneity of matter, all proclaiming themselves to be monists without being so in fact, I went a step further, drawing the final conclusions from this doctrine and eliminating the frontiers separating matter from what was called mind.

[2] Ferdinand Brunetière's essay "Après une visite au Vatican" appeared in the January 1, 1895, issue of *Revue des Deux Mondes*–EDITOR.

[3] Ramsay and Rayleigh succeeded in isolating argon in 1894.–EDITOR.

It was in the light of this theory, in 1894 in my book *Anti-barbarus,* that I had treated the psychology of sulfur, interpreting it as a process of ontogenesis, in other words, describing the embryonic development of sulfur.

I refer those who are interested to my study *Sylva Sylvarum,* published in the beginning of 1896. Proudly aware of my clairvoyant powers, I there penetrated to the very heart of the secret of creation, especially in the animal and vegetable kingdoms. I also refer them to my essay "In the Cemetery" ["Études funèbres"] (included in *Printed and Unprinted* [*Tryckt och otryckt*], published in Sweden in 1897), which reveals how I, alone and suffering, was led back to a vague conception of God and immortality.[4]

# V

## *The Fall and Paradise Lost*

Once introduced into this new world where no one could follow me, I conceived a disgust for the company of others and felt an irresistible desire to detach myself from the circle in which I moved. I therefore informed my friends that I was going to settle at Meudon in order to write a book that demanded solitude and silence. At the same time, a

[4] In place of this paragraph the French edition has the following:

Instead of reworking the material gathered in the summer and fall of 1895, I reprint here selected passages from *Sylva Sylvarum* (first part), several hundred copies of which were published in the beginning of 1896, and are still unsold, forgotten.

There then follow in the French edition three chapters of excerpts from Strindberg's mystico-scientific writings:

Chapter V:    "Sylva Sylvarum"
Chapter VI:   "La Tête-de-mort (*Acherontia atropos*): Essai de mysticisme rationnel"
Chapter VII:  "Études funebrès".
              This essay is reprinted above.–EDITOR.

series of trivial disagreements brought about a rupture with the group of artists in the crémerie, with the result that one fine day I suddenly found myself left completely on my own. The first consequence of this was an unprecedented expansion of my inner senses: a psychic energy that insisted on making itself felt. I thought of myself as the repository of limitless powers, and pride insinuated into my head the mad idea of attempting to work miracles.

At a previous period, during the great crisis of my life, I had observed that I was able to exercise an influence on absent friends from a distance. Folk tales have always been much concerned with questions of telepathy and witchcraft. Now, I should not like to incriminate myself unduly, nor attempt to absolve myself from the consequences of a wicked act, but I believe now that my evil wishes could not have been so very evil in fact since the effect of them was that they recoiled on me. An unhealthy curiosity, a sudden eruption of idiotic love caused by my horrible solitude, inspired me with an immoderate desire to renew relations with my wife and child, since I loved them both. But what was I to do now that the divorce proceedings were already under way? Some extraordinary event, a common misfortune, a stroke of lightning, a fire, a flood—in short, some catastrophe that would reunite two hearts, as in novels the hands of enemies reach out for each other at the bedside of a sick person they both love. Yes! That was it. Someone falling ill. Children are always ill to some extent—the mother's sensibility exaggerates the danger—a cable to Paris and the thing would be accomplished.

Though I was ignorant of even the rudiments of black magic, a deadly instinct whispered in my ear what it was I had to do to the portrait of my darling little girl, my darling little girl who was later to become the sole consolation in my cursed life.

Further on I shall give an account of the effects of an operation in which the evil intention made itself felt through the medium of a symbolic action.

However, the results did not manifest themselves immediately, and I continued my work, feeling an inexplicable uneasiness accompanied by a presentiment of fresh misfortunes to come.

* * *

One evening, alone with my microscope, an incident occurred that I did not understand at the time, though it did not fail to leave a strong impression on me.

Having left a walnut to germinate four days before, I now detached from it the heart-shaped embryo, no bigger than a pear pip, embedded between the two cotyledons whose shape reminds one of the human brain. It may be imagined what emotion I felt when on the plate of the microscope I perceived two tiny white hands, white as alabaster, raised and clasped as though in prayer. Was it a vision? A hallucination? By no means! A searing reality that filled me with horror. Motionless, stretched up towards me as though in invocation, I could plainly count their five fingers, the thumb shorter than the others, and manifestly the hands of a woman or a child!

A friend came in to find me gazing at this stupefying sight, and I asked him to verify the phenomenon. He did not have to be clairvoyant in order to make out with his observing eye the two hands clasped in prayer.

What was it? The two first, rudimentary leaves of a walnut tree, *juglans regia*, the Jupiter gland. Nothing but that! And yet it was undeniable all the same that there were ten fingers forming a pair of human hands, joined together in a gesture of supplication: *de profundis clamavi ad te!*

Still too skeptical, my mind still dulled by an empirical education, I dismissed the matter.

* * *

The Fall had taken place! The feeling that the powers had withdrawn their grace weighed heavy on me, the hand of the invisible was raised, and now the blows fell thick upon my head.

First, my anonymous friend, who had subsidized me until that point, was wounded by the presumptuous tone of a letter and withdrew his support, so that I was left high and dry without means.

And similarly, when I received the proofs of *Sylva Syl-*

*varum* I discovered that the pages had been put together exactly like a pack of very well shuffled cards. Not only were the middle pages wrongly numbered, but the various sections had been thrown together pell-mell, ironically symbolizing the "great disorder" that reigns in nature.[1] After infinite delays and postponements the pamphlet was at last printed, but then the printer presented me with a bill amounting to double the amount originally agreed upon. Regretfully I was forced to take my microscope to the pawnshop, together with my black suit and the few valuables I still owned. But, anyway, I was in print at last, and for the first time in my life I was sure of having said something new, great, and beautiful.

My overweening attitude when I finally went to mail the pamphlets is therefore understandable. With a gesture of disdain towards the heavens, I threw the rolled-up brochures into the box and insolently challenged the hostile powers with the thought: "Hey there, sphinx! I have solved your riddle, and I defy you!"

Back at the hotel I was greeted by my bill and an accompanying letter.

Irritated by this blow, which was unexpected since I had been staying there for the whole of the past year, I began to notice many small nuisances that had escaped my attention up till then. In the adjoining rooms there were three pianos all being played at once.

I told myself that it was a plot cooked up by the Scandinavian ladies whose company I had rejected.

Three pianos! And I was unable to move to another hotel for want of money.

I went to sleep that night cursing heaven, raging against the lady piano-players and against fate. Next morning I was awakened by an unusual noise. Someone was hammering a nail in the wall of the adjoining room, right above my bed.

---

[1] In *Sylva Sylvarum* Strindberg had written:

"Here is my universe, as I have created it, and as it has revealed itself to me.

"Pilgrim, wayfarer, if you choose to follow me, you will breathe more freely, for in my universe disorder reigns, and in disorder lies freedom."—EDITOR.

Then there was a hammering from the room on the other side.

A plot, a conspiracy as stupid as the lady painters themselves. I deliberately ignored it as beneath my notice.

But when, after lunch, I went as usual to take a siesta on my bed, such a tremendous hammering began above the alcove where I lay that pieces of plaster began to fall from the ceiling onto my head.

I went down to see the manageress and complained about the behavior of her female lodgers. She claimed, in the sweetest manner possible, that she had heard nothing, but promised that she would throw out anyone who dared to disturb me, since business was rather poor just then and she was very anxious that I should continue to stay in her hotel.

Though I put no faith in the words of a woman, I concluded that it was in her own interest to see that I was well treated.

The noises continued, however, and I began to realize that the ladies must be trying to make me believe they were caused by poltergeists. Foolish creatures!

It was also just at this time that my comrades in the crémerie changed their behavior towards me. I began to observe a mute hostility in them, manifested by sidelong glances and sly mutterings.

Tired of the struggle, I said goodbye to both hotel and crémerie—stripped of everything, leaving my books and knickknacks behind, naked as a little John the Baptist. And on February 21, 1896, I made my entry into the house of the late M. Orfila.

# VI

## *Purgatory*

The Hôtel Orfila,[1] with its cloister-like appearance, was a
boardinghouse for students of the Cercle Catholique. It was
under the supervision of a gentle and lovable abbé. Silence,
order, and moral rigor reigned within its walls. And I was
relieved to find, after my recent annoyances, that women
were not admitted.

The house was an old one. The rooms were low, the corridors dark, with wooden staircases intertwined among them
to form a labyrinth. The building exuded an atmosphere of
mysticism that had attracted me for some time. My room
looked out onto a blind alley, so that, from the middle of the
room, the view consisted only of a moss-covered wall pierced
by two oeil-de-boeuf windows; but when once I was at my
table in front of the window I looked out on a ravishing and
unexpected prospect.

Beneath an enclosing wall all hung with ivy, there was a
convent yard for young ladies, plane trees, paulownias, and
mock acacias. A delicious, gothic-style chapel. Farther away,
high walls pierced with innumerable little barred windows,
reminding me of a monastery. Farther off still, in the valley,
a forest of chimneys bristling above old half-hidden houses.
And in the remote background, the church tower of Notre-
Dame-des-Champs, with its cross and, at the very top, a
weathercock.

In my room, an etched portrait of Saint Vincent-de-Paul,
and, hanging in the alcove above my bed, an etching of St.
Peter, keeper of the heavenly gates! What biting irony there
was in that picture for me, the author who had held up this
very apostle to ridicule a few years before in a fantasy play
I had written.[2]

[1] At 60 Rue d'Assas.–EDITOR.

[2] *The Keys to the Kingdom of Heaven* (*Himmelrikets nycklar*),
written 1892.–EDITOR.

Feeling extremely satisfied with my room, I slept well the first night.

Next day I discovered that the water closet was situated in the alley beneath my window, so close that the whole mechanism was clearly audible, even the click-clack of the flush ball opening and shutting the valve. Then I discovered that the two oeil-de-boeuf windows opposite also belonged to water closets. Finally, I was left in no doubt that the innumerable little windows stretching out into the distance were also those of as many water closets situated at the back of a series of houses.

At first I seethed with rage, but since there was no possibility of moving, I calmed myself while cursing fate.

At about one in the afternoon, the serving-boy brought in my lunch, and since I refused to disturb the contents of my work table he set the tray down on the night table containing my chamber pot.

I commented on this and the serving-boy apologized, pointing out that there was no other table available. He appeared to be a decent sort and not at all malicious, so I forgave him, whereupon the chamber pot was removed.

If I had been familiar with Swedenborg at this time I should have understood that the powers had condemned me for the time being to the excrementitious hell.[3] For a short while I fulminated against the black run of ill fortune that had been persecuting me for so many years. Then I calmed down and achieved a state of gloomy resignation, bending to the will of fate. I edified myself by reading the Book of Job, convinced that the Everlasting had delivered me over to Satan in order to test me. This thought consoled me, and I began to rejoice in my suffering as a proof that the Almighty had confidence in me.

At this time there began a series of manifestations that I am unable to explain without assuming some form of intervention by unknown powers, and from this moment on I began to make a series of notes that accumulated little by little to form a diary, of which I shall publish some extracts in this book.

[3] Swedenborg, *Arcana cœlestia*, I.—Strindberg's note.

\*    \*    \*

Icy silence now greeted my chemical investigations. In order to achieve recognition and to strike a decisive blow, I decided to grapple with the problem of making gold. My point of departure was the following question: Why does iron sulfate cause metallic gold to be precipitated out from a solution of any gold salt? The answer appeared to me to be: because iron and sulfur are both constituents of gold. In fact, all the combinations of sulfur and iron found in nature contain a greater or lesser amount of gold.

I therefore began to work with solutions of iron sulfate.

One morning I awoke with a vague desire to go for an excursion into the country, which was contrary to my usual tastes and habits. Having arrived by chance at the Gare Montparnasse, I took a train for Meudon. I alighted in the very center of a village I had never visited before, walked up the main street, and turned right into an alley enclosed by high walls on either side. Twenty paces in front of me, rising from the earth in which it was half-embedded, was a Roman knight in grayish iron armor. The figure was very delicately modeled, though in miniature, but I was not deceived into thinking it anything but the unpolished stone it in fact was. From close up the deceit was evident, and I halted my steps, deliberately preserving the illusion which was giving me so much pleasure. The knight was looking towards one of the alley walls, and following the direction of his eyes I noticed a charcoal inscription on the whitewash. Seeing the letters F and S intertwined made me think of my wife's initials. She still loved me!—The next instant I was illumined by a vision of the chemical signs for iron (Fe) and sulfur (S), one superimposed upon the other, and displaying the secret of gold before my eyes.

Then, turning my eyes to the ground, I found two small circles of lead joined by a piece of twine. The one seal bore the letters V.P., the other a royal crown.

Without attempting to interpret this incident in detail, I returned to Paris convinced that I had witnessed something like a miracle.

\*    \*    \*

The coal I burned in my fireplace was of a type called "monks' heads" because of the roundness and smoothness of the pieces. One day, when the fire had gone out before the coals had been completely consumed, I picked out of the grate a conglomerate mass of coal that resembled in every way a fantastic sculptured figure. A cock's head with a superb crest and a form more like a human body than anything else. With writhing limbs. It could have been one of those demons we see depicted in medieval sabbaths.

Next day I picked out a magnificent group of two drunken gnomes or goblins hugging each other and wearing flowing robes—a masterpiece of primitive sculpture.

The third day it was a madonna and child, modeled in the Byzantine style, with an incomparably beautiful line.

After making charcoal drawings of them, I laid all three out on my table.

A painter friend came to visit me. Looking at the three statuettes with ever-growing curiosity, he finally asked me, "Who made those?"

Made?—To test him, I gave the name of a certain Norwegian sculptor.

"Did he really! I can believe it," the painter replied without demur. "I was going to guess it was Kittelsen,[4] the famous illustrator of the Scandinavian folk tales."

I didn't believe in the existence of demons, but desirous of seeing the impression my statuettes made on the sparrows that were accustomed to come and eat bread crumbs outside my window, I set them out on the roof.

The sparrows were frightened by them and would not eat the bread. This meant that there was a resemblance there perceptible even to animals, and that there is a reality underlying the play of inert matter and flames.

The sun, as it heated my figurines, broke into pieces the demon with the coxcomb. I recalled the folklore saying that goblins die if they stay abroad after sunrise.

❉　　❉　　❉

[4] Theodore Kittelsen was renowned for the trolls he had created in his illustrations for Asbjørnsen and Moe's collection of Norwegian folk tales.—EDITOR.

And things were happening in the Hôtel Orfila that I found very disturbing.

The day after my arrival I found a letter propped on the board where the room-keys hung. It was addressed to a certain Monsieur X . . . , a student who had the same family name as my wife. It was postmarked Dornach, the name of an Austrian village where my wife and child were living at that time. But since I was certain that there was no post office at Dornach, the affair remained an unsolved riddle.

This letter, placed on the board in such a conspicuous manner, as though with the deliberate intention of provoking me, was only the first of several such letters.

The second was addressed to Doctor Bitter and postmarked Vienna; a third bore the Polish pseudonym Schmulachowsky.[5]

The devil had taken a hand in the business now. For behind these grotesque and parodic names lurked another name, and I realized whom it was meant to remind me of: one of my mortal enemies who lived in Berlin.

Another time it was a Swedish name, recalling an enemy in my home country. Finally there appeared a letter postmarked Vienna with the address of Doctor Eder's chemical analysis laboratory printed in block letters. This meant that my attempts to synthesize gold were being spied upon.

Beyond a shadow of a doubt, a plot was being hatched around me. But it was the devil himself who had dealt the cards to these sharpers. Sending my suspicions to wander through every corner of the world was too ingenious a trick for a mere mortal.

When I asked the serving-boy for information about this M. X . . . , he replied foolishly that he was a native of Alsace. That was all he knew. One fine morning as I came in from my walk, I found a postcard in the pigeonhole next to my key. For a moment I was seized by the temptation to resolve this enigma by glancing briefly at the card, but my guardian angel struck my hand with paralysis just at the precise moment when a young man stepped out from his hiding place behind the door.

[5] Maryan von Smoluchowski, a Polish medical man, resided at the Hôtel Orfila in 1895 and 1896.–EDITOR.

I stared him in the face. I noticed he resembled my wife. Silently we bowed to one another and went our separate ways.

To this very day I have failed to unravel this intrigue, or even identify the people involved in it, since my wife has no brothers or even cousins.

This state of uncertainty, this perpetual threat of vengeance provided me with sufficient tortures for a period of six months. I submitted to them, as I had submitted to all the others, as a punishment imposed on me for sins I had committed, whether I knew of them or not.

        ✿     ✿     ✿

At New Year's there had been a new addition to the circle of artists I frequented at the crémerie. He was a painter,[6] an American, who had arrived just in time to bring fresh blood into our languishing group. With his lively mind, cosmopolitan outlook, and bold manner, he made a pleasant companion, even though he aroused in me a vague feeling of mistrust. Despite his self-confidence and assured manner, I sensed that his situation was in fact not too well assured.

The crash came much sooner than one might have expected. One evening the unfortunate man came into my room and begged my permission to stay for a moment. He had the air of a ruined man, and indeed was one.

Having been driven out of his studio by the landlord, abandoned by his mistress because he was riddled with debts and besieged by creditors, then insulted in the street by the *souteneurs* of women models he had been unable to pay, he had been finally and utterly crushed by the cruelty of his landlord in seizing as payment the canvas he had intended for the Champ de Mars exhibition, and on the success of which he had been staking a great deal, for the subject seemed to him original and full of vigor. It pictured an emancipated woman, pregnant, nailed to a cross, and being mocked by the crowd.

Now he had run up a bill at the crémerie, and found himself in the gutter with an empty stomach.

After making these admissions he finished his statement

[6] Paul Herrmann. See Introduction.–EDITOR.

by confessing that he had already tried taking a double dose of morphine, but that death had not yet been prepared to receive him.

After deliberating the matter seriously, we agreed that he must leave the neighborhood and that we would continue to dine together in a rôtisserie unknown to the others, so that his lack of friends should not make him too disheartened to paint another canvas for the Salon des Indépendants.

*      *      *

Because I took them all upon myself, the misfortunes and torments of this man, who became my only friend, only served to increase my own suffering. This was a piece of bravado on my part that began an experiment of great value. He revealed his whole past to me. He was of German origin but had spent the last seven years in America because of a misfortune that had overtaken his family and also as a consequence of a youthful escapade—a blasphemous pamphlet that had brought the wrath of the law upon him.

I discovered he had a rare intelligence and a melancholic disposition coupled with an unbridled sensuality. But behind this human persona, deepened by a cosmopolitan education, I glimpsed a secret that intrigued me, and that I hoped one day to have revealed to me.

I waited for two months, during which time I fused my own existence together with this foreigner's, and suffered all the miseries of an artist who has not arrived, forgetting that my own career was already an accomplished fact, that I was someone, that my name was listed in *Tout-Paris*,[7] and that I was registered as a member of the Society of Dramatic Authors in Paris—none of which was of any interest to me as a chemist. I found, in any case, that as long as I said nothing of my proven successes my companion felt great affection for me; but when I was obliged to make some reference to them, he was hurt and played the woebegone starveling, despised by the world. In commiseration, I took care to treat myself as nothing but an aging failure. In this way I dragged

[7] *Tout-Paris. Annuaire de la société Parisienne.* In the volume for 1896 Strindberg is listed as living at Rue de la Grande-Chaumière, 12. In the 1897 volume Strindberg's address is Rue d'Assas, 60, that is, the Hôtel Orfila.—EDITOR.

myself down, step by step, while he, with his future open before him, rose as steadily at my expense. I made myself into the corpse buried beside the roots of a tree that is stretching its branches to the sky, drawing its nourishment from the life decomposing below it.

While studying certain Buddhist scriptures at this time, I wondered at my own abnegation in sacrificing myself in this way for another. Good deeds will have their reward, and here is what I gained by mine.

One day the *Revue des Revues* provided me with a portrait of the American prophet and healer Francis Schlatter, who cured five thousand sick people in 1895 and then disappeared forever from this world.[8]

[8] Francis Schlatter was a German shoemaker who began attracting great attention as a faith healer in the West about October 1895. He traveled from town to town, but it was in Denver that his career reached its climax. Hundreds, if not thousands of people, many of whom worked for the Union Pacific Railroad, testified that Schlatter had cured them of physical ills by merely touching them. When interviewed, he stated that a quick treatment was as efficacious as a long one. He said, "All that is really necessary is for me to touch them but the people would not be satisfied. In cases where the persons are too weak to stand in line, let their friends send a handkerchief. The handkerchief is just as good as a treatment."

Schlatter never took money for administering to the sick, and when a businessman offered him $5000 simply to appear in St. Louis, the "prophet" refused.

He was described as about thirty-nine years old, with a powerful physique, broad shoulders, deep chest, and with no excess flesh on his sturdy frame. He wore a leather wamus, like that of a butcher, brown corduroy pantaloons, a gray flannel shirt, and brogan shoes.

In November the government authorities decided to look into the situation, apparently because of the growing crowds that gathered around Schlatter. The United States Commissioner in Denver called Schlatter as a witness "against the 'blessed' handkerchief fakirs," according to a report in the New York *Times*. He was scheduled to appear in court on November 15, but during the night of the fourteenth and fifteenth he mysteriously disappeared from the house of a Mr. Fox, with whom he was living at the time. The *Times* stated that Schlatter had grown very restless the previous day under "the increasing excitement" of the crowd.

Having had his hearing restored by the healer, Mr. Fox believed the German cobbler was a second Christ and provided him with free room and board. Schlatter left a note to him which read:

Now, the features of this healer bore a striking and marvelous resemblance to those of my friend. In order to obtain proof of what I suspected, I took the magazine with me to the Café de Versailles, where a Swedish sculptor was waiting for me. He remarked on the resemblance and pointed out a singular coincidence that had escaped me, to wit, that both men were of German origin and both had worked in America. What is more, the disappearance of Schlatter coincided with our friend's appearance in Paris. Having initiated myself slightly by this time into the technical terms of occultism, I expressed the opinion that this Francis Schlatter must be the "double of our artist friend," leading, without knowing it, an independent existence.

No sooner had I pronounced the word "double" than my sculptor friend opened his eyes wide and drew my attention to the fact that our friend always used two sets of lodgings, one on the Right Bank, the other on the Left Bank. Besides which, I discovered that my mysterious friend was leading a double life in the sense that after having spent the evening with me, plunged deep into philosophic and religious meditation, he was always to be seen during the night at the Bal Bullier.[9]

---

"Mr. Fox: My mission is finished. The Father takes me away. F. Schlatter."

"The blind, the lame, and the halt," along with "the curious and the doubting," began gathering outside Fox's house at three o'clock in the morning of the fifteenth, and by daybreak there was a crowd of three thousand. The *Times* reported that the vendors of coffee and the photographers did a brisk business. On that day 2104 letters addressed to Schlatter were received, and during the previous four weeks 42,000 letters had been sent to him.

The defaulted witness was believed to be wandering in the hills, but though there were many rumors as to his whereabouts, he was not actually found again until the end of December. As soon as he disappeared from Denver, the government lost interest and preferred no charges against him. But three men, including one who had benefited from Schlatter's healing hand, traced the "Messiah" to an obscure Mexican settlement, west of Caboza and eighty miles from Albuquerque. Schlatter refused to return with them, saying the Father had told him to go to Central America. He thereupon mounted his white horse and rode off to the southwest.—EDITOR.

[9] The Bal Bullier, situated in the Place de l'Observatoire, was a

Now, there was a fairly reliable way of proving that these two men were identical twins, since the article in the *Revue des Revues* included a facsimile of Francis Schlatter's last letter.

"Come and have dinner with us this evening," I suggested to the sculptor, "and I'll make him write down Schlatter's letter from my dictation. If the two handwritings are alike, and especially the signatures, that should be proof enough."

At dinner that evening, everything was confirmed. The handwriting was the same, so was the signature and the flourish after it. Everything was there.

Though slightly surprised, the painter agreed to an interrogation, and when it was over asked: "But what do you want this for?"

"Do you know Francis Schlatter?"

"I've never heard the name before."

"Don't you remember the American faith-healer last year?"

"Oh yes, that charlatan!"

At this, I showed him the portrait and the facsimile of the letter.

He laughed skeptically and appeared quite calm and uninterested.

\*　　\*　　\*

Some days later, my mysterious friend and I were sitting at a table on the terrace of the Café de Versailles with two glasses of absinthe when a man dressed like a common laborer, and with a very ugly manner, began to cause a disturbance among the customers. Turning to my companion, he yelled at the top of his voice:

"So I've caught you, have I, you cheating swine! What do you mean, ordering a thirty-franc cross from me, then running off when I bring it to you! Bloody hell, do you think crosses just make themselves! . . ."

He kept up this outburst for what seemed like an eternity, and the waiters, in an attempt to make him move on, threatened to call for the police, while the wretched, penniless painter sat like a condemned man without moving, without

dance hall like the Moulin Rouge; but the Bullier was frequented mainly by students.—EDITOR.

uttering a sound, absolutely annihilated in front of an audience of artists, all of whom knew him more or less.

When the incident was over, amazed and confused as
though I had witnessed a scene from a witches' sabbath, I
asked him, "The cross? What thirty-franc cross? I don't understand this business. . . ."

"It was a copy of Joan of Arc's cross, for my model. You
know the thing I had made for my picture of the woman being crucified."

"But he was like the devil himself, that workingman!"

After a pause, I went on, "It's very strange, all the same,
but we shouldn't make fun of the cross, or of Joan of Arc."

"You mean you believe in them?"

"I don't know. I don't know anything any more. But those
thirty pieces of silver!"

"That's enough!" he cried, wincing. "Let it alone!"

*     *     *

On Good Friday, when I walked into the rôtisserie where
we ate together, I found my companion in misery asleep with
his head on the table.

Feeling suddenly playful, I woke him by exclaiming, "You
here!"

"What do you mean?"

"I thought you stayed on the cross till at least six o'clock
on Good Friday."

"Six o'clock! Well, as a matter of fact, I have been asleep
the whole day, right up until six, and I don't have any idea
why."

"I have."

"By which you mean that the astral body can wander
around on its own, don't you? In America . . . and all the
rest."

From that evening on a certain coldness became increasingly apparent between us after a period of intimacy that
had lasted for four horrible months. During the time my comrade had been able to re-educate himself completely and
had found the time to change his method of painting, so
that he now scoffed at his crucified woman as a piece of old
junk. He had come to accept suffering as a bitter medicine,

the only reliable cure, and the calm of resignation had followed. His patience and endurance were positively heroic. I admired him when he made the journey from Montrouge to les Halles and back again all in the same day, on foot, the heels falling off his boots, and without achieving a thing for his pains. That same evening, after visiting the offices of seventeen different illustrated magazines he finally placed three drawings, but without receiving any cash payment, and then went off to the Bal Bullier after making a meal of a two-sous roll.

In the end we dissolved our mutual aid association by tacit agreement. We both heard an inner voice telling us that our destinies were to fulfill themselves separately, and when we finally exchanged farewells I knew that they were to be the last.

I never saw this man again, and I have never learned what befell him afterwards.[10]

*    *    *

In the spring, while still oppressed by my own adversities as well as those of my companion, I received from the children of my first marriage a letter telling me that they had all been taken seriously ill and removed to a hospital. Comparing the date of this event with that of my experiment in witchcraft, I was filled with horror at myself. Frivolously I had called hidden forces into play, and the evil wish had gone out into the world only to return, guided by an invisible hand, and bury itself in my own heart.

I shall not attempt to excuse myself. I simply beg the reader to remember this fact in case he should ever decide to practice magic, and particularly that branch of it properly referred to as bewitchment, which consists in casting spells on others and which Rochas[11] has shown is not only possible but that it has actually happened.

[10] See pages 75–77 in the Introduction and also pages 286 and 287 below.–EDITOR.

[11] *L'Extériorisation de la sensibilité.*–Strindberg's note. This work was published in 1895. According to the *Encyclopedia of Occultism,* Rochas d'Aiglun was "an exponent of the fluidic theory of magnetism." Since black magic contributes so much to the design of *Inferno,* it may not be amiss to remind the reader that the sub-

One Sunday before Easter, I awoke and went for a walk in the Luxembourg Gardens, continuing across them to the other side and crossing the street. Having directed my steps beneath the Odéon arcade, I came to a halt and stood mo-

---

ject was very fashionable in the latter part of the nineteenth century among certain avant-garde writers. Strindberg's stories of bewitchment and sorcery may seem exaggerated but they are tame compared to what a French adept of the 1890s would have heard —or witnessed. In particular, *envoûtement,* or the use of black magic to cast a spell or to kill someone at a considerable distance, was much talked about in Paris circles; and if one is to believe some of the members of those circles, it was not only talked about but occasionally practiced. The most notorious case involved, as might be supposed, the Rosicrucians and a few eccentric Catholics, the latter represented by Huysmans and his disciple Jules Bois. Huysmans, famous for his decadent novels *A rebours* and *Là-bas,* had become a convert to Catholicism in 1892. The Cabalistic Order of the Rosy Cross, which was to leave such a deep mark on Yeats and his poetry, had been founded in 1888, mainly by Stanislas de Guaita, a disciple of the unfrocked priest Éliphas Lévi (Abbé Alphonse Constant), who had been a follower of the Martinists, a friend of Baudelaire, and author of such indispensable occult works as *Dogme et rituel de la haute magie* (1861). It was from Lévi that Madame Blavatsky, leader of the theosophists, got most of her ideas. The governing council of the Rosicrucians included Sâr Peladan and Dr. Papus (Gérard Encausse), in addition to Guaita himself. Huysmans had designated the Rosicrucians as the leaders of Satanism in Paris. His friend, the Abbé Boullan, warned him that the Satanists would attempt to punish him by means of black magic, especially at night, and indeed Huysmans was cuffed and buffeted by "fluid fists" as he lay in bed. Now, Boullan, who was actually an unfrocked priest, claimed to be the true head of a certain branch of Masonry at Lyon and to possess not only the manuscript of the "Glorious Sacrifice of Melchizedek" but a whole barrel of unconsecrated hosts for the rite. According to Huysmans, Guaita tried to steal some of these hosts and to read the secret liturgy. (All this forms part of the background to *Là-bas.*) Failing this, Guaita sought to destroy Boullan. It was now Huysmans' turn to warn the abbé that distance meant nothing to the Satanists and that they were about to send mesmeric fluids from Paris to Lyon to assail Boullan. Shortly thereafter came the news from the abbé that he had felt the fluids penetrate his heart. He told Huysmans that he was able to save himself on more than one occasion by hurrying to his private altar to munch on one of the hosts and to read the sacrifice. One day, however, the abbé was found dead. Huysmans accused the Rosicrucians of having murdered the abbé tionless in front of the blue backs of an edition of Balzac. Selecting a volume at random, I picked up *Séraphita*.[12] Why that very book?

Perhaps it was a subconscious memory left in my mind

---

through black magic. There was no recourse but a duel of honor. This was fought on January 10, 1893, between Jules Bois and the Marquis Stanislas de Guaita, a remarkable duel in which two shots were fired, but one bullet never left its barrel. Later that same year a second duel was fought, this time between Jules Bois and Dr. Papus, which likewise did not resolve the matter. Huysmans learned later that the Abbé Boullan had made up the story about being attacked by mysterious fluids in order to destroy the reputation of the Rosicrucians.

Strindberg was not in Paris at the time of these events and seems to have heard about them first in a conversation with Georg Brandes at the end of 1896. However, Strindberg's interest in black magic and bewitchment goes back at least to 1893 and his Berlin period, when he was probably introduced to the subject by Przybyszewski who stood in close rapport with the new movements in Paris. For Przybyszewski Satanism was almost an obsession that had its origin in a frightening childhood experience. A young serving-girl in the Pryzbyszewski home had a reputation as a witch. One day, having been severely chastised by Przybyszewski's father, the girl resolved to take her revenge through the child Stanislas. She cut small gashes in his face, spat on some still-green berries, and squeezed the juice into the wounds. She then made the child swear to say that the condition of his face was caused by hitting his head on the table. If he told the truth, she would throw him alive into the fire. Stanislas came down with a severe fever, but the old family nurse suspected that the serving-girl had bewitched the child. She prepared a compress of leaves and herbs and applied it to his face while murmuring certain words. The following day the child was feeling much better. But the serving-girl had to be rushed to the hospital with a raging fever, and died shortly thereafter. Przybyszewski called this a classic example of "choc en retour."

Przybyszewski's deep involvement with black magic is apparent from his pamphlet *Die Synagogue des Satan* (Berlin, 1897), which provides a history and philosophy of occultism and Satanism, and from his novel *Satanskinder*, the story of a revolutionist and Satanist too bold to be published by anyone except Albert Langen (Paris, Leipzig, and Munich, 1897). It was dedicated to Edvard Munch "in cordial friendship."–EDITOR.

[12] Gauguin was much interested in Balzac's *Séraphita*, and it is quite likely that Strindberg, who was a great admirer of Balzac, would have discussed the work with the painter and remembered what Gauguin said about it. Furthermore, *Séraphita* was being talked about in art and literary circles at this time, and a dramatiza-

after reading a copy of *L'Initiation*[13] in which a critic, reviewing *Sylva Sylvarum,* had referred to me as a compatriot of Swedenborg.

When I got back home I opened it, this book that was by now almost entirely strange to me after the many years that has passed since my first reading of it.

---

tion of the novel was scheduled for production toward the end of 1894 at the Théâtre de la Rive Gauche. Though Strindberg had read Balzac intensively in 1890, *Séraphita* appears to have made no impression on him until he heard about it from Gauguin and his fellow occultists in 1894 or 1895. By then he was ripe for it. Balzac's mystic novel, written 1833 to 1835, consists of the thinnest of plots filled out with long discussions of Swedenborg's religious views. The earth is a nursery for heaven, and the angelic spirits are those men on earth who are prepared for heaven. The protagonist of Balzac's novel is the androgynous and clairvoyant Séraphita-Séraphitus, a teen-ager with the soul of a woman and the body of a boy. Angelic spirits progress through three stages of love—love of self, love of the world, love of heaven. Sickness brings one closer to the infinite, and to die is to enter the true life. A pale spirit like Séraphita is poised on the very brink of the infinite. On earth we move from a life of suffering, in which our torments make us thirst for love, to a life of loving, in which devotion to our fellow creatures teaches us devotion to the Creator; and thence to a life of silence, in which we seek for traces of the Word, the creative world of the spirit; and finally to a life of high aspiration and a life of prayer. As in conventional religions, earth and spirit, God and matter, provide in Swedenborg the necessary dualism. Between the visible things of the earth and the imponderable things of the spirit world exist correspondences, which Swedenborg sought to systematize or at least clarify, and which Baudelaire established as a poetic principle. Science is the language of the temporal world as love is that of the spirit world. The greatest scientists eventually "perceive the necessity for considering all bodies, not merely from the point of view of their mathematical properties, but also from that of their whole relations and occult affinities." Newton discerned "that all things were at the same time cause and effect reciprocally; that the visible worlds were co-ordinated to each other and captive to invisible spheres." Thus the principle of cause and effect yields to that of simultaneity. In this universe where everything is connected to everything else, every road leads to God, that is, every road that rises as steeply through resignation, abstinence, and martyrdom, as the paths over the Norwegian cliffs in Balzac's novel.–EDITOR.

[13] *L'Initiation:* a journal of the occult published in Paris 1888 to 1912. Its editor was Dr. Papus (Gérard Encausse).–EDITOR.

Indeed, it proved absolutely new to me, and now that my mind was prepared for it I was able to absorb the contents of this extraordinary book. I had never read any of Swedenborg's works (for in his own country—which is also mine—he is accounted a charlatan, a madman with a lubricious imagination), and I was seized with ecstatic admiration as I listened to the voice of this angelic giant of a previous century being interpreted to me by the most profound of all French geniuses.

Then, as I read on with a religious concentration, I came to page 16, where the date of Swedenborg's death is given as being March 29. I stopped, thought a moment, then opened my calendar. It was in fact March 29 that very day, and Palm Sunday as well.

In this way Swedenborg revealed himself as a spiritual mentor in my life—in which he has played a tremendous role —and thus, on the anniversary of his death, he presented me with palms—whether of victory or martyrdom who could say?

*Séraphita* became my gospel and led me to renew relations with the beyond, to such an extent that life was now distasteful to me, and I was driven on by an irresistible nostalgia for heaven. There was no further doubt: I was prepared for a higher existence. I despised the earth, this loathsome world we live in; I abhorred man and all his works. I saw that I was the just man without iniquity whom the Everlasting had put to the test, and whom the purgatory of this world was to make worthy of a speedy deliverance.

This pride, first aroused by my intimacy with the powers, continued to grow unceasingly, and it was given added strength by the fact that my scientific research was also prospering. Prospering so well, in fact, that according to my own calculations and the findings of the metallurgists I had actually succeeded in making gold. I thought I would be able to prove incontrovertibly that I had done so, and I sent a sample to a chemist friend in Rouen.

He furnished me with proof that I was mistaken in my contentions, and a week went by without my being able to reply to him. Then, as I was leafing through the treatise on chemistry written by my patron Orfila, I came upon the secret of my whole procedure.

Thus did this old chemistry book, published in 1830, now forgotten and despised, become the oracle that came to my aid at critical moments. Orfila and Swedenborg, my friends, were protecting me, encouraging me, and punishing me. I did not see them but I sensed their presence. They did not show themselves to me either by means of visions or hallucinations, but little day by day events that I began to notice made me aware of their intervention in the ups and downs of my existence.

For the spirits have now become as positivist as the times we live in and are not content to conjure up visions.

As an example, I mention the following incident, which it would be impossible to explain away as mere coincidence.

Having succeeded in producing specks of gold on paper, I was attempting to make it in quantity, using a dry process[14] and a blowtorch instead of solutions. After two hundred attempts I had not achieved the slightest result and I finally put away the blowtorch in despair.

My morning walk took me along the Avenue de l'Observatoire, where I often used to admire the Four Corners of the Earth, for the secret reason that the most appealing of Carpeaux's figures bears a resemblance to my wife. She stands posed opposite Pisces, beneath the armillary sphere, and some sparrows had made their nest behind her back.

At the foot of the monument I came upon two pieces of cardboard cut into ovals. One had the number 207 printed on it, the other the number 28. This signified lead (atomic weight 207) and silicon (atomic weight 28). I picked up this prize and stored the two pieces of cardboard away among my chemistry notes. Returning home, I began a series of experiments on lead, leaving the silicon until a later date. Knowing as I did from my metallurgical studies that lead refined in a crucible lined with bone ash always gives up a certain amount of silver and that this silver is regularly found to contain a little gold, I said to myself that the calcium phosphate which is the principal ingredient of bone ash must constitute

---

[14] By the dry process Strindberg is apparently referring to calcination, the reduction of a solid to powder by the application of heat. It was one of the standard processes employed by alchemists.–EDITOR.

the essential factor in the production of gold extracted from
lead.

And the lead, when melted on a bed of calcium phosphate,
did in fact always take on a golden yellow coloration on its
under side. But the will of the powers interrupted me before
I could bring the experiment to its conclusion.

A year later, at a time when I was in Lund, in Sweden, a
sculptor employed in the porcelain works there made me a
gift of some glaze that was composed of lead and silicon,
thanks to which I was able for the first time to produce in a
heated crucible a mineralized gold of perfect beauty.

In thanking the sculptor I showed him the two pieces of
cardboard with the numbers 207 and 28.

Where is there room for chance or coincidence in an event
so deeply marked with unshakable logic?

\*    \*    \*

I repeat, I was never haunted by visions, but real objects
did often appear to me as being endowed with human shapes,
often producing effects of startling grandeur.

My pillow, for example, pushed out of shape during my
afternoon nap, presented me with marble heads sculptured in
the style of Michelangelo. One evening, returning to my room
with the American faith-healer's double, I perceived in the
half-shadow of the bed alcove a gigantic Zeus reclining on my
bed.[15] Faced with this unexpected sight, my comrade stood
motionless in the grip of an almost religious terror. Artist that
he was, he responded to the beauty of the lines, one after
another: "The great vanished art of the past born again! I
tell you there's a whole school of drawing here!"

---

[15] As Gunnar Brandell has pointed out, the Zeus figure undoubtedly has some psychological significance. During the years 1874
to 1882 Strindberg was employed in the Royal Library in Stockholm, and his chief was G. E. Klemming, a spiritualist and a
Swedenborgian, whom Strindberg regarded with true awe, a mixture of terror and veneration. In a story "Schleichwege," written
in German in 1887, a story that concerns itself with the exposure
of a spiritualistic medium, Klemming is called "the Zeus head."
Elsewhere Strindberg describes him as "omniscient and just, gentle
and awesome, like the Almighty." Klemming was clearly a father substitute to Strindberg. (See Brandell, *Strindbergs Infernokris*, Stockholm, 1950, pp. 10–11.)–EDITOR.

The longer we stood gazing, the more real, alive, and awesome became the apparition.

"It's obvious the spirits have become realists too, just as we mortals have."

This particular incident was certainly not a product of chance, since on certain days the pillow also took on the shapes of hideous monsters, Gothic gargoyles and dragons. One night, coming home from some orgy or other, I was greeted by the devil, the real medieval-style devil with his goat's head and all the rest. I was never seized by feelings of fear—it was all far too natural—but there was etched in my soul the impression of something abnormal, of something almost supernatural.

When I called in my sculptor friend as a witness, he displayed not the slightest surprise, but invited me up to his studio, where I was immediately struck by the beautiful lines of a charcoal drawing hanging on one wall.

"Where did you find that? It's a madonna isn't it?"

"Yes, a Versailles madonna, sketched from the floating weeds in the Lac des Suisses in the park there."

Here was a new art revealed, an art taken from Nature herself! Nature's clairvoyance! Why spit our contempt on Naturalism when it is inaugurating a new form of art, rich with youth and hope? The Gods are returning, and the battle cry sounding from writers and artists alike "To Pan! To Pan!" has reverberated so vigorously that nature has now awakened again after her sleep of several centuries! Nothing is ever done in this world without the consent of the powers. If Naturalism was then, let it be now, and may the harmony of matter and spirit be born again.

My sculptor friend had sixth sight. He told me how he had seen Orpheus and Christ sculptured together in a rock in Brittany, adding that he was intending to go back there and use the figures as models for a group he was planning for the Salon.

One evening while walking down the Rue de Rennes, my clairvoyant friend stopped in front of a bookstore window in which some colored lithographs were on show. They composed a series of scenes in all of which there were human figures depicted with pansies instead of faces. Though an observant botanist, I myself had never remarked the resemblance of the flower to the human face. My companion was unable to shake off what was in fact a double astonishment.

"Just think of it, yesterday evening when I went back to my room, the pansies outside my window kept staring at me in a very irritating way, and suddenly I saw that they were so many human faces. I took this to be an illusion produced by my own nervous state. And today I find the same thing actually reproduced in an old print. It must be a reality then, not an illusion, if an unknown artist has made the same observation before me."

We were making progress as seers, for I in my turn saw Napoleon and his marshals on the dome of the Invalides.

If you take the Boulevard des Invalides as you walk down from Montparnasse, below the Rue Oudinot the dome is visible in all its sunset splendor, so that the corbels and other elements jutting out of the drum supporting the dome take on the aspect of human figures, which change their shapes according to the distance from which they are viewed. Napoleon is there, and Bernadotte and Bethier; and my friend has sketched them "from nature."

"How do you explain this phenomenon?"

"Explain? Has anyone ever explained anything, except by paraphrasing one bunch of words with another bunch of words?"

"Then you don't think that the architect was working under subconscious orders from his own mind?"

"Listen, my dear fellow. Jules Mansard built the dome in 1706. It was impossible for him to have foreseen the silhouette of Napoleon, because he wasn't born until 1769 . . . Is that enough for you?"

\*     \*     \*

Sometimes at night I had dreams predicting the future, forearming me against dangers ahead, and revealing secrets to me. It was in this way that a friend, dead a long while before, appeared to me in my sleep carrying an unusually large silver coin. I asked him where this extraordinary coin had come from. He replied, "From America," and vanished with his treasure.

Next day a letter with an American postmark sent by a friend I had not seen for twenty years arrived to tell me that a commission to write a piece for the Chicago Exhibition had been following me all over Europe without catching up to me. The payment for it would have been 12,000 francs, an enormous sum in my desperate situation at that time, and which I had now lost. Those 12,000 francs would have assured me of a settled future, and I alone knew that the loss of this money was a punishment. Once in a fit of anger brought on by the treachery of a literary rival, I had acted wickedly, and here was my retribution.

*     *     *

In another dream, of much wider import, Jonas Lie appeared, carrying a gilt bronze pendulum clock decorated in a most unusual style.[16]

Some days later, as I was walking on the Boulevard Saint-Michel, a clockmaker's display window drew my attention: "Jonas Lie's clock!" I cried.

And it was indeed the same. The movement, topped with a sphere representing the heavens, against which two women leaned their backs, was supported by four columns. Set in the sphere was a dial indicating the days of the months. It had stopped at August 13.

I shall tell in a later chapter what this fatal date, August 13, held in store for me. These little incidents and many more like them occurred during my stay in the Hôtel Orfila between February 6 and July 19, 1896.

Parallel to these events, there unfolded at irregular intervals another series of incidents that resulted finally in my ex-

---

[16] Jonas Lie (1833–1908) was along with Ibsen, Bjørnson, and Kielland, one of the "big four" among Norwegian writers at this time. Lie and Strindberg became acquainted with each other in France in the mid-1880s during Strindberg's anarchist and nihilist period. Lie said of the Swedish writer, "Far from being an assailant with the aggressor's exaggerated courage and need to act, Strindberg is one of those all-too-gentle souls, skinless and sensitive, a man terrified by the world he sees around him . . . one of those who are first to run out into the street shouting Fire!" Lie is another father-figure in Strindberg's world, and the pendulum clock another sex symbol.—EDITOR.

pulsion from the Orfila and the inauguration of a new period in my life.

Spring had arrived. The vale of tears that fell away beneath my window grew green and burst into flower. Green grass appeared to cover the earth and hide the garbage, and Gehenna was transformed into the Valley of Sharon, not only filled with lilies and lilac but flowering with acacias and paulownias.

I was so sad I felt like dying, but the joyous laughter of the young girls playing down below, invisible beneath the trees, touched my heart and called me back to life. Life was flowing past, and old age was drawing near. Wife, children, home, everything laid waste. Autumn within, spring outside.

The Book of Job and the Lamentations of Jeremiah brought me consolation, for I was sure there was at least an analogy between Job's fate and my own. Had I not been struck down with an incurable ulcer? Had I not been crushed by poverty, deserted by my friends?

"I went mourning without the sun: I stood up, and I cried in the congregation. I am a brother to dragons and a companion to owls. My skin is black upon me, and my bones are burned with heat. My harp also is turned to mourning, and my organ into the voice of them that weep."

Thus spake Job. And Jeremiah had expressed the deep gulf of my unhappiness in one short phrase: "I forgat prosperity."

It was in this state of mind that, bent over my work by the sultry weight of the afternoon, I sat listening to the sounds of a piano beneath my window, the souce of the sound hidden by the thick leaves of the valley. I pricked up my ears, as the charger does at the sound of the trumpet. I straightened up and felt comfort enter my soul; I breathed again. Yes, it was Schumann's *Aufschwung*. And more than that, the person I could hear playing it was really him! It was my friend the Russian, my disciple who used to call me "father" because he had learned everything from me, my *famulus* who gave me the title of master as he kissed my hands, because his life began or perished with my own.[17] It was he, and he

---

[17] "My friend the Russian, my disciple who used to call me 'father'"—this is Stanislaw Pryzbyszewski, who figures in *Inferno* under the name Popoffsky. See Introduction.—EDITOR.

had come to Paris from Berlin so that he could kill me as he
had killed me in Berlin.—And for what reason? . . . Because
fate had decreed that his present wife should also have been
my mistress before he ever knew her. Was it my fault if things
had worked out that way? No, that is quite certain, and yet
he swore a deadly hate against me all the same, slandered
me, prevented me from placing my plays in the theaters
there, intrigued against me so that I should be deprived of
the means to live. It was then that in a fit of rage I had struck
at him in a brutal and cowardly manner, so cowardly that I
suffered as much from having done it as if I had committed
murder.

Now he had come to kill me, and that thought brought relief, for death alone could deliver me from my remorse.

It was he, then, who had disturbed my mind with those
falsely addressed letters, downstairs on the room-key board.
Let him strike then! I would not defend myself. He was in
the right and my life was nothing to me.

He was still playing *Aufschwung*, no one else could play
it as he did. Unseen behind the wall of foliage, he was sending the magic harmonies over the flowering, green treetops.
I thought I could actually see them fluttering there, like so
many butterflies in the sun.

And why was he playing? To let me know he had arrived,
to fill me with fear so that he could pursue me as I fled!

Perhaps I should be able to find out the truth at the
crémerie, where the other Russians had been announcing the
arrival of their compatriot for some long time already. I
went there that evening at the dinner hour, and as soon as
I entered the door I was raked by hostile glances. Having
been told of my brawls with the Russian, all the regular
diners there had formed a league against me. In order to
disarm them I opened fire myself.

"Popoffsky is in Paris?" I said, phrasing it as a question.

"No, not yet!" one of them answered.

"Yes he is," protested another. "Someone saw him at the
*Mercure de France* offices."

Contradictions then followed on either side, and in the end
I remained very uncertain about the truth of the matter,
though keeping up a pretence of believing everything that I

was told. The too evident hostility in the place made me vow to avoid it in future, though regretfully, because I had come to feel myself truly in sympathy with some of the habitués of the place. Cut off once more, expelled from society by my cursed enemy, I began to detest him, and my hate gnawed at me and made me savage. I gave up the idea of dying. I did not wish to die by the hand of a man who was my inferior. It would be too great a humiliation for me and too high an honor for him. I decided to struggle, to defend myself, and in order to set my mind at rest on the matter I betook myself to the Rue de la Santé, behind the Val-de-Grâce, in order to visit a Danish painter there,[18] one of Popoffsky's intimate friends. This painter, once a friend of mine, had arrived in Paris six weeks before, and when I met him in the street he had greeted me as though I were a stranger, almost as an enemy. The next day, on the other hand, he had come to visit me and invited me to go back with him to his studio, though all the while behaving far too charmingly not to leave me with the impression that his friendly manner was false. When I asked him for news of Popoffsky he took refuge behind a series of subterfuges, though confirming the Russian's imminent arrival in Paris.

"Coming to murder me!" I added in conclusion.

"Certainly, certainly. So beware!"

That morning when I opened the *porte cochère* of my Danish friend's house on my way up to visit him, a Great Dane—what a coincidence!—of gigantic proportions and monstrous appearance was lying stretched out across the flagged courtyard, barring my passage. Instinctively, and without a moment's doubt or hesitation, I stepped back, walked out into the street again and retraced my steps, giving thanks to the powers for the warning they had given me, so convinced was I of having escaped some hidden danger. A few days later, going back to the house to renew my visit, I found a child sitting on the step before the open door holding a playing card in one hand. Frankly yielding to superstition, I glanced briefly at the card. It was the ten of spades!

[18] "My Danish friend." Edvard Munch. See the Introduction—EDITOR.

The cards had been stacked against me in that house.

And I turned back once more.

That evening, however, after the scene in the crémerie, I was quite determined to brave the Cerberus and every spade in the pack; but fate had decided otherwise, and I chanced to run across my man in the Brasserie des Lilas. He was charmed to see me and we sat down together at a table on the sidewalk.

As we reminisced about the times we had shared in Berlin, he fell back into his old role of good companion, grew ecstatic at his own stories, forgot our former differences, and admitted facts that he had once publicly denied.—Then, as though suddenly remembering some promise, some resolution he had made, he became mute, cold, hostile, and annoyed at having allowed me to pump him.

When I asked him directly whether or not Popoffsky was in Paris, he replied with a "no" so curt that it was obvious to me that he was lying, and we said good night.

At this point I ought to remark that this Danish painter had been Mme. Popoffsky's lover before me, and that he still harbored a grudge against his ex-mistress for having deserted him for me. Now he was playing the role of family friend, aided by Popoffsky's own lack of experience in such matters, though the latter was certainly not ignorant of his wife's former relations with "Pretty Boy Henry."

\*　　\*　　\*

Though Schumann's *Aufschwung* continued to soar above the dense foliage of the treetops, the pianist remained invisible, and I could not discover where he was. For a whole month the music continued, every evening, from four till five.

One morning, after walking down the Rue de Fleurus to comfort myself with a glimpse of my rainbow over the dyer's shop, I had just turned off into the Luxembourg Gardens, which were in full flower and as beautiful as a fairy tale, when I came upon two dry twigs, broken off by the wind and now lying on the ground. They were in the form of the two Greek letters, P—y. I saw that they were an abbreviation of "Popoffsky." It was true then: he was my persecutor, and the powers had decided to forewarn me of the danger. I could not help feeling uneasy, despite this indication of the good offices of the invisible. I invoked the protection of providence; I read the Psalms of David directed against his enemies; I hated my enemy with the religious hatred of the Old Testament. Yet at the same time I no longer had the heart to employ the resources of the black magic I had recently been studying.

"Be pleased, O Lord, to deliver me: O Lord, make haste to help me. Let them be ashamed and confounded together that seek after my soul to destroy it; let them be driven backward and put to shame that wish me evil. Let them be desolate for a reward of their shame that say unto me, Aha, Aha."

This prayer seemed fair and honest to me then, and in my eyes the mercy of the New Testament was merely cowardice.

To what hidden power did my impious invocation take its flight? I cannot say. But the rest of this adventure will show at least that the prayer was answered.

*　　*　　*

### EXTRACTS FROM MY JOURNAL—1896

*May 13.*    A letter from my wife. Learning from the newspapers that a Monsieur S.[19] was about to set off for the North Pole in a balloon, she cried out in distress, confessed her undying love for me, and begged me to give up the idea of a project that seemed tantamount to suicide.

I wrote to clear up the error she had made, informing her that the person in question was a first cousin of mine who was about to risk his life for the sake of science.

[19] Monsieur S.—Nils Strindberg (1872–1897)—was a son of August Strindberg's cousin. Nils was a member of the three-man Andrée expedition that attempted to reach the North Pole in a balloon. Bad weather cut short their plans in 1896.

In May and June of 1897, when Strindberg was writing these pages of *Inferno*, Andrée, Nils Strindberg, and Fraenkel were making their much publicized preparations for their second, ill-fated attempt. Their balloon lifted off from Spitzbergen on July 11 and traveled for sixty-five hours before it came down on an ice pack. The three men reached White Island where they perished. The remains of the expedition, including Andrée's diary, were not found until 1930.—Editor.

*May 14.* Last night I had a dream. A severed head had been stuck on the torso of a man who looked like an alcoholic actor. The head began to speak. I was terrified, and pushing a Russian in front of me to protect me from the attack of the maddened creature, I knocked over my screen.

Later in the night a mosquito bit me, and I killed it. In the morning the palm of my right hand was spattered with blood.

Walking in the Boulevard Port-Royal, I saw a pool of blood on the sidewalk. Some sparrows had made their nest in the flue from the stove in my room. They were twittering sweetly, as though they were living in my room with me.

*May 17 and days following.* My six o'clock absinthe on the terrace of the Brasserie des Lilas, behind Marshal Ney,[20] had become my single remaining vice, my last delight in life. At that hour, after the day's work, exhausted in body and soul, I used to collect myself once more in the heart of help me. Let them be ashamed and confounded together that that green liquid, with a cigarette, the latest issue of *le Temps,* and a copy of *Journal des Débats.*

How good life is when a gentle, drunken daze dims the miseries of existence. Probably the powers envied me this hour of assumed bliss between six and seven in the dusk, for from this particular evening onwards my felicity was disturbed by a series of upsetting incidents that I was finally forced to recognize as more than a mere matter of chance.

For on May 17 the place I had occupied regularly for almost two years was already taken; and so were all the others. I was forced to move on to another café, a circumstance that I found indescribably depressing.

*May 18.* My old place at the Lilas was free. I felt contented, almost happy, sitting under my chestnut tree behind Marshal Ney. My absinthe was before me, just the right amount of water added, my cigarette lit, my copy of *le Temps* deflowered.

At that very moment a drunkard came by, disgustingly

[20] The statue on Marshal Ney, by Rude, stands at the Carrefour de l'Observatoire, near the Luxembourg Gardens, and marks the spot where Ney was executed in 1815 for having fought with Napoleon after the latter's return from Elba.–EDITOR.

hideous to look at, and stared at me in a sly, mocking way. His face was the color of wine lees, his nose Prussian blue, his eyes full of spite. I took a sip of my absinthe, happy to think I did not look like this toper. . . . But, without my ever knowing how it happened, I suddenly found that my glass was overturned, empty. Not having enough money to order another, I paid, rose to my feet, and left the café, convinced that it was the Devil [Le Malin] who had cast a spell on me.

*May 19.* Did not dare go to the café.

*May 20.* Prowling near the Lilas, I saw that my old corner was free. The Devil had to be wrestled with, and I entered the lists. I had mixed my absinthe, I was puffing on my cigarette, *le Temps* was full of important news—and at that very moment!—please believe my good faith in this, reader—a fire broke out in the chimney of the café building, just above my head. General panic. I stayed seated, but a will stronger than my own let fall a cloud of soot, and guided its fall so well that two black flakes came to rest in my glass. I left feeling dashed, but still skeptical, still incredulous.

*June 1.* After a prolonged period of abstinence, I was once again seized with the desire to find consolation under my chestnut tree. My table was occupied, so I took another, a quiet one set apart from the rest. The Evil One had to be wrestled with . . . At that very moment (again!) a family of small tradespeople sat down at the table next to me. The members of this family were innumerable, and fresh reinforcements arrived every moment—women who banged against my chair, children doing their business out in the open, before my very eyes, young men who took my matches without so much as a by-your-leave. Though surrounded by this noisy, insolent crowd, I was determined not to give up my seat. Whereupon a scene took place that must without any doubt have been planned by subtle and invisible hands, since it was too cleverly brought off for me to think it the result of a plot hatched by people whom I had never met before.

A young man, with a gesture I did not understand, put down a five-centime piece on my table. Being a foreigner and alone among all those people, I did not dare to protest. But, blinded with rage, I tried to sort out in my mind what had happened.

"He has given me a sou as though I were a beggar."

A beggar! That was the dagger I plunged into my own breast. A beggar! Yes, that is what you are! You earn nothing, and . . .

The waiter came over and offered me a more congenial table. I moved, leaving the coin on the table as I left. The waiter brought it over to me—what an affront!—and politely informed me that the young man had picked it up from under the table and supposed it to be mine.

I was filled with shame! And in order to calm the storm within me, I ordered a second glass of absinthe.

The absinthe arrived, everything seemed to have turned out for the best, when I suddenly felt myself being suffocated by the noisome stench of ammonium sulfate.

What was the meaning of this new attack! In point of fact it had a most natural explanation, one without any trace of the miraculous or ill intent. . . . The drain leading down to the sewers was situated exactly below the spot at the edge of the sidewalk where my chair was placed. Only then did I begin to grasp the fact that the good spirits were trying to deliver me from the grip of a vice that leads to the madhouse! Praise be to Providence for having rescued me!

\*         \*         \*

*May 25.*   Despite a house rule that forbids women to live in the Hôtel Orfila, a family has moved into the room next to mine. They have a baby that cries day and night, and this is a genuine pleasure to me, for it reminds me of the good old days, the blooming fruitful years between thirty and forty.

*May 26.*   The couple next door quarrel with each other! The baby howls. How familiar it all is! And how sweet to me . . . now.

This evening I saw the English lady again. She was charming, and gave me a sweet motherly smile. She had painted a snake-dancer, and the figure looks like a walnut or a brain. The picture is hung, almost out of sight, behind the counter in Mme. Charlotte's crémerie.

*May 29.*   A letter from the children of my first marriage.

They have received a telegram from Stockholm summoning them to participate in the farewell celebrations prior to my departure for the North Pole in a balloon. They can't make head or tail of the business, and neither can I. What a fateful error!

The newspapers are full of the disaster in St. Louis (N.B., St. Louis!), America, where a thousand people have been killed by a tornado.[21]

*June 2.* In the Avenue de l'Observatoire I found two pebbles in the exact shape of hearts. In the evening, while in the garden belonging to a Russian painter,[22] I found a third to make up the set, the same size as the others and exactly alike in every way. I no longer hear Schumann's *Aufschwung,* and am at peace once more.

*June 4.* I paid a visit on the Danish painter in the Rue de la Santé. The huge dog had disappeared, the entrance was clear, and we went to eat dinner at a sidewalk café on the Boulevard Port-Royal. My friend felt cold and said he wasn't feeling good. Since he had forgotten his overcoat, I put mine over his shoulders. This calmed him down soon enough. He submitted to me, allowed me to tame him. He no longer dared to rebel against me; he admitted that Popoffsky is an evildoer and that all my disasters may be traced back to him. Suddenly he became nervous and began to tremble like a medium under the influence of a hypnotist. He moved about restlessly; shook off the coat. He stopped eating, threw down his fork, rose to his feet, and then, having given me back my coat, said goodbye.

[21] On May 28, 1896, St. Louis and East St. Louis were "visited by the worst tornado of their history." According to the New York *Times* for June 2, the total loss of lives in St. Louis and vicinity was 552, and the property loss was estimated at $1,000,000. It was considered the greatest natural disaster in America since the Johnstown flood.–EDITOR.

[22] This is probably the Polish painter Wladyslaw Slewinski (1854–1918). He was a close friend of Gauguin, having first met him in Paris around 1888, and he spent several years with him in Pont-Aven. Slewinski was part of the group of artists who ate at Madame Charlotte's crémerie. His portrait of Strindberg, which was painted around 1894 or 1895, is reproduced in *August Strindberg: Mannaår och ålderdom,* edited by Stellan Ahlström and Torsten Eklund, Stockholm, 1961, p. 96.–EDITOR.

What did this mean? Was my coat the shirt of Nessus? Was it my nervous fluid stored up in the garment that had subjugated him with a polar force opposite to his? This must be what Ezekiel meant, in Chapter 13, verse 18:

"Thus saith the Lord God; Woe to the women that sew pillows to all armholes, and make kerchiefs upon the head of every stature *to hunt souls!* . . . I will tear them from your arms, and will let the souls go, even the souls that ye hunt to make them fly."

Have I become a sorcerer without knowing it?

*June 9.* I visited my Danish friend to take a look at his paintings. When I arrived he was lively and well, but at the end of half an hour he was seized by a sudden attack of nerves that later rose to such a pitch he was forced to undress and go to bed.

What was wrong with him? His own bad conscience?

*June 14.* Sunday.   Found a fourth heart-shaped pebble, this time in the Luxembourg Gardens, but exactly similar to the first three. Stuck into the stone was a yellow spangle the color of gold. I could not solve the riddle, but I sensed that here was an omen. As I was comparing the four pebbles in front of my open window the bells of Saint-Sulpice began to ring out, then the deep chimes of Notre-Dame, and beneath these familiar peals there sounded also a heavy, solemn reverberation that seemed to emerge from the bowels of the earth.

When the serving-boy brought up my mail, I asked him what this sound meant.

"It's the Grande Savoyarde[23] ringing in the Church of the Sacred Heart up on Montmartre."

"You mean it's the feast of the Sacred Heart?"

And I gazed down at my four hearts made of hard stone, rather moved by this flagrant coincidence.

I heard a cuckoo singing over towards the church of Notre-Dame-des-Champs. And yet that is impossible; unless my ears

[23] The Grande Savoyarde is the largest bell in the Sacré-Coeur basilica and, 10 feet high and weighing nearly 19 tons without the tongue, one of the largest bells in the world. Donated by the province of Savoy, it was cast in 1895, and I doubt that it had been installed in Sacré-Coeur at the time Strindberg wrote this. About 1900 it was on exhibit in a temporary shed to the right of the façade of the basilica.—EDITOR.

have become so hypersensitive that they can catch sounds made as far away as the forest of Meudon.

*June 15.* Went into the center of Paris to cash a check. The Quai Voltaire shook beneath my feet, which astonished me. Yet I know quite well that the Pont du Carrousel vibrates under the weight of the carriages passing over it. But this morning the oscillations had spread as far as the Cour des Tuileries and along the Avenue de l'Opéra. Naturally, a big city is bound to vibrate, but to sense the vibrations one must have nerves tuned to an extremely high pitch.

The other side of the river is a foreign country to us denizens of Montparnasse. Almost a year had gone by since my last foray, which even then had extended no farther than the Crédit Lyonnais or the Café de la Régence. Walking along the Boulevard des Italiens, I was suddenly gripped by homesickness and hurried back to the other bank, where the mere sight of the Rue des Saint-Pères brought me relief and comfort.

Near the church of Saint-Germain-des-Prés, I passed a hearse, then two colossal madonnas being carried on a truck. One of them, kneeling, hands clasped, gaze upturned to heaven, made a deep impression on me.

*June 16.* Stopped on the Boulevard Saint-Michel to buy a marble paperweight. It was decorated with a glass globe which contained a figure of the Lourdes Madonna set in a reproduction of the famous grotto. In front of her is a lady on her knees wearing a veil. I have placed it near the window in the sun, and it casts miraculous shadows on the wall. On the back of the grotto, by a stroke of chance not intended by the sculptor, the plaster has taken the form of a head of Christ.

*June 18.* My Danish friend came into my room, distraught and trembling in every limb. Popoffsky has been arrested in Berlin on a charge of murdering a woman and two children, his mistress and the two children he had had before his marriage. After the first shock, followed by a sincere feeling of pity for a friend who, after all, had shown me so much ardent affection, a profound calm took possession of my mind, agitated for so many months past by the threats hanging over me.

Unable to conceal my justifiable self-concern, I gave free rein to my emotions.

"How horrible. But I'm relieved when I think of the danger I've just escaped!"

But what was his motive for the crime? Possibly his wife, jealous of his former mistress and his children and angered by the additional expense they caused. . . .

"Perhaps even . . ."

"What?"

"Perhaps his killer's instincts, frustrated in Paris for so long, had to have another outlet, no matter where."

Inwardly I asked myself: is it possible that my fervent prayers parried the murderer's dagger, causing it to pierce his own heart?

I probed no further into the matter, but like a generous conqueror made the following suggestion.

"We can at least rescue our friend's literary reputation. I'll write an article about his talent as a writer, you can draw a flattering portrait of him, and we will offer them both to the *Revue Blanche.*"

Back in the Dane's studio—no longer guarded by the dog! —we looked at a portrait of Popoffsky painted two years earlier.[24] The painting was of his head alone, cut off at the neck by a cloud, and beneath it there was a group of bones such as one sees depicted on tombs. The severed head made us shiver, and my dream of May 13 came back to haunt my mind.

"What gave you the idea for this decollation?"

"Difficult to say, but there was an air of fatality always hovering over that fine mind. Traces of a forced and artificial genius, that he had, and he aspired to the topmost heights of fame, but he was never willing to pay the price. Life admits of only two choices: the laurels or voluptas.

"So you've finally found that out, have you?"

*       *       *

*June 23.*   I picked up a pin of imitation gold set with an imitation pearl. I also fished out a golden heart from the bath in which I synthesize my gold.

[24] This oil portrait of Przybyszewski, which was painted in Berlin in 1893 or 1894, is reproduced in Ingrid Langaard, *Edvard Munch, Modningsår,* Oslo, 1960, p. 239.–EDITOR.

In the evening, walking along the Rue de Luxembourg, at the end of the first avenue of trees on the right and up above them, I saw the outline of a doe against the sky. As I stood admiring the beauty of its modeling and coloring, it made a sign to me with its head, a nod towards the southeast (the Danube!).[25]

These last few days, ever since I heard of the Russian's catastrophe, I have felt restless, uneasy, disturbed. I have the impression that someone somewhere is concentrating all his thoughts on me, and I confessed to my Danish painter friend that the hatred of the imprisoned Popoffsky is making me suffer as if from the current flowing from an electric generator.

There are moments when I sense that my stay in Paris will soon come to an end, and that a new turn of fortune is awaiting me.

The weathercock on the cross of Notre-Dame-des-Champs seems to me to beat its wings as if it were trying to fly away to the north.

Divining that my departure is imminent, I am making haste to conclude my studies at the Jardin des Plantes.

The zinc bowl in which I synthesize gold from various salt solutions reveals a landscape formed on its curved interior by the residues of evaporating iron salts. I have interpreted this as an omen, but all my attempts to guess where this extraordinary landscape might be situated have so far been in vain. There are hills covered with coniferous trees, especially firs; then, between these rounded hills, plains covered with fruit trees, fields of wheat, the whole indicating the presence of a river nearby. One of the hills, with precipitous cliffs of stratified rock, has a ruined castle on its summit.

I have failed to recognize it yet, but I shall before long.

*June 25.* Was invited to visit the head of scientific occultism, the editor of *L'Initiation*.[26] As the doctor and I arrived

[25] The family of Frida Uhl, Strindberg's second wife, lived in Austria.—EDITOR.

[26] *L'Initiation* was a journal of occultism published in Paris and edited by Dr. Gérard Encausse, who went under the name Doctor Papus. He sought to give occult ideas a firmer basis by linking them to the Nancy school of psychology. He concerned himself especially with the power of suggestion—hence Strindberg's interest, for Strindberg in the 1880s had read the Nancy psychologists,

at Marolles-en-Brie, we were greeted by three pieces of bad news. A weasel had killed all the ducks—a maid had fallen ill—the third escapes me.

That evening, back in Paris again, I was reading a newspaper when I came across an account of the now famous haunted house at Valence-en-Brie.

Brie? Being very suspicious, I was afraid that the other people living in the hotel might draw their own conclusion about my trip to Brie and accuse me of having staged this practical joke, or rather this bit of witchcraft, with the aid of my alchemical knowledge.

Have bought a rosary. Why? It's beautiful, and the Evil One is afraid of the cross. Anyway, I no longer try to explain the motives for my actions. I live by improvising as I go along; life is more fun that way!

The Popoffsky affair has suddenly taken a new turn. His friend, the Dane, has begun to doubt that Popoffsky could have committed the crime and argues that the police investigation has produced no real evidence. Our article has therefore been postponed, and the old coldness has returned between us. At the same time the monstrous dog appeared once more: a reminder that I must keep my wits about me.

*     *     *

In the afternoon as I sat writing at my table in front of the window, a storm broke. The first drops of rain blew in on my manuscript and splashed on it in such a way that the letters making up the word "alp"[27] ran together and made a blot like a giant's face. I have held on to this drawing: it resembles the Japanese thunder god as depicted in Camille Flammarion's *Atmosphère*.

*June 28.*   I dreamt of my wife. Her front teeth were missing, and she handed me a guitar that looked like the boats one sees on the Danube.

---

studied the various theories of hypnotism and thought suggestion, and come to view life as a battle of minds. Several short pieces by Strindberg were printed in *L'Initiation* during the spring and summer of 1896.–EDITOR.

[27] In German, alp is a kind of goblin. In Byron's *Siege of Corinth*, Alp is the renegade who renounces the Christian faith to lead the Turkish hosts.–EDITOR.

In the same dream I was threatened with a prison sentence.

In the morning I picked up a piece of paper in the Rue d'Assas that contained all the colors of the rainbow.

In the afternoon I had occasion to amalgamate some mercury, tin, sulfur, and ammonium chlorate on a piece of cardboard. When I removed the mixture, the cardboard had a face imprinted on it exactly like my wife's in the previous night's dream.

*July 1.* I am waiting for an eruption, an earthquake, a thunderbolt, without knowing exactly where it will strike. I am as nervous as a horse scenting wolves. I can smell danger in the air. I am packing my bags to be ready for flight, and yet I am unable to move.

The Russian has been let out of prison because they have no proof against him. His friend the Dane has become my enemy. The artists at the crémerie have begun to make trouble for me. The last dinner I ate there was served in the courtyard because of the heat. They had set up the table between the garbage cans and the water closets. They had also hung the painting of my former friend, the American, above the garbage cans as a spiteful gesture, because he had left without paying what he owed. Near the table the Russians had placed a statuette depicting a warrior armed with a scythe, their national symbol. They were trying to frighten me! A little urchin belonging to the place went to the water closet behind my back with the obvious intention of annoying me. The walls of the courtyard, which is like a deep well, were too high for the sun to reach over them. The prostitutes, of whom there seemed to be several on every floor, opened their windows and let fall a hail of abuse and filthy language. The maids kept bringing baskets full of garbage to throw into the garbage cans.—This was hell. And my two neighbors, both self-confessed pederasts, kept up a distasteful conversation with the deliberate intention of provoking a quarrel with me.

Why was I there? Because my loneliness forced me to seek out human company, to go where I could hear the sound of human voices.

Then, just as I reached the peak of my spiritual torment, I caught sight of a few pansies blooming in the narrow flower bed there. They shook their heads at me as though to warn me of some danger, and one of them, with the face of a child and great, deep, shining eyes, was signaling to me, "Go away."

I rose from the table and paid my bill. As I left, the urchin saluted my going with sly insults that filled me with disgust, but did not provoke me to anger.

I felt only pity for myself and shame for all the others.

Then I absolved them of all guilt. I thought of them as demons who were simply fulfilling their duties.

And yet it was only too evident that providence had withdrawn its grace from me, and, once back in the hotel, I began to examine my balance sheet. Up till this point—and this had been my strength—I could not possibly have broken down and admitted that others might be in the right. But now, crushed by the hand of the invisible, I tried to put myself in the wrong, and examining my conduct over the last few weeks more closely, I was gripped by fear. My conscience mercilessly stripped me naked.

I had sinned through pride, through *hubris,* the sole vice that the Gods will not forgive. Encouraged by the friendship of Doctor Papus, who had given his approval to my scientific research, I had imagined myself to have found the answer to the riddle of the Sphinx. I was the rival of Orpheus and it was my role to bring back to life an inanimate nature that had been killed by the scientists.

Conscious of the protection of the powers, I had flattered myself I could not be conquered by my enemies, to such an extent that I was now flouting even the simplest rules of modesty.

This seems an opportune moment to insert the story of a mysterious friend of mine[28] who had appeared in my life and

---

[28] The mysterious friend was Torsten Hedlund (1855–1935), Swedish publisher and avid theosophist. Sensing theosophist ideas in Strindberg's novel *By the Open Sea* (*I havsbandet*), printed 1890, Hedlund asked for Strindberg's opinion of Madame Blavatsky. Strindberg replied (July 29, 1891) that he had been familiar with the doctrines of theosophy since 1884, that he had expressed his views of the movement in the long short story *Schleichwege* (printed in a German periodical in 1887), and that he believed the theosophists consisted of a few "power-mad souls who wanted to lump together in one big pile Darwinists, spiritualists, atheists, and

come to play a decisive role in it as mentor, adviser, consoler, administer of punishments, and, besides all these things, as a support and provider of the means to live during my intermittent periods of poverty. He had written me a first letter as early as 1890, prompted by a recently published book of mine. Having found several points of contact between my own ideas and those of the theosophists, he had asked me for my opinion of the occult doctrine and of Mme. Blavatsky, the priestess of Isis. The presumptuous tone of the letter had displeased me and I made this clear in my reply. Four years later my *Antibarbarus*[29] was published, and at this, the most critical moment of my life, I received a second letter from this stranger, written in an elevated, almost prophetic style, in which he predicted an anguished and glorious future for me. He also explained to me the motives for this resumption of

---

socialists, and thus build a universal school on the analogy of the Volapük movement." He dismissed Madame Blavatsky as "probably" a "great self-deceiver who, with all the suggestive power her sex exercises on the other sex, had succeeded in creating the illusion that she was an exceptionally profound mind." He went on to say that he did not believe in hypnosis but did believe in the power of suggestion, and that he "often had reason to suspect the possibility of transference of thought in a wakeful but ecstatic state." "This in brief," he concluded, "is my position in regard to these new movements which I find can only be explained on purely 'materialistic' grounds."

It was Strindberg, not Hedlund as he implies, who reopened the correspondence on July 23, 1894, when he wrote Hedlund from Ardagger in Lower Austria to inquire about Jollivet-Castelot, whose work *La vie et l'âme de la matière* contained ideas similar to those in Strindberg's *Antibarbarus,* printed a few months before. In the ensuing correspondence Hedlund wrote of Charcot's experiments with hypnotism and acquainted Strindberg with the experiments of Albert de Rochas, which suggested that hypnotic phenomena were the result of currents analogous to electric currents. The Strindberg-Hedlund correspondence from 1894 through 1896 is regarded as the most significant autobiographical material for that period.

Except for a few brief exchanges, the correspondence was broken off in November 1896.–EDITOR.

[29] *Antibarbarus,* translated into German by Bengt Lidforss, was published in Berlin in 1894. This pamphlet begins with a defense of Haeckel's monism, after which Strindberg goes on to align himself with the modern alchemists.–EDITOR.

our correspondence, the most important of them being a presentiment that I was undergoing a spiritual crisis at that time, and that I was perhaps in the greatest need of a consoling word. Finally, he offered me financial support, which I declined, preferring to remain poor but independent.

In the autumn of 1895 it was I who reopened our correspondence, asking him for help in publishing my writings on natural history. From this time on, we wrote to one another regularly, maintaining a very friendly relationship, even an intimate one, with the exception of a short rupture caused by the lordly language he employed when explaining obvious facts to me, or when arrogantly lecturing me about my lack of modesty.

Nevertheless, after our reconciliation I communicated all my observations to him, giving up all my secrets without a thought as to the ultimate wisdom of such a course. I confessed myself to this man I had never seen and allowed him to remonstrate with me in the severest terms, because I looked upon him more as an ideal figure than a real person. For me he was a messenger employed by Providence, a paraclete.

Now it happened that there were two capital points upon which our opinions differed, and these led us into very lively discussions, though without ever degenerating into bitter quarreling. As a theosophist, he preached the dogma of Karma, which is to say that the abstract sum of human destinies balance each other out and so result in a sort of Nemesis. He therefore believed in a mechanistic universe and was an epigonus of the so-called materialist school. I for my part saw the powers as one or more concrete, living, individualized beings directing the course of the world and the careers of men consciously and hypostatically, as the theologians say.

The second point on which we differed was that of self-abnegation and self-mortification, which appeared to me then, and still appear to me now, as madness.

Everything I know—and it is so little!—derives from my self, the central point of my being. The cult of self—no, the cultivation of one's self must therefore be viewed without question as the supreme and final aim of our existence.[30] My definitive and perpetual reply to his objections took this formula: the mortification of the Self is suicide.

Besides, before whom was I expected to bow down? Before the theosophists? Never! In the face of the Everlasting, the Powers, and Providence, I yield to my baser instincts, always and in all ways as much as I can. To struggle for the preservation of my Self against all the influences brought to bear upon me by the ambitions of any sect or party, I consider that as my duty, a duty dictated by the conscience bestowed on me by the grace of my divine protectors.

And yet, out of consideration for the good qualities of this man whom I had never seen but whom I loved and admired, I tolerated his arrogance even when he treated me as an inferior being. I always took the trouble to reply to his letters and never made the slightest attempt to conceal the repugnance I felt for theosophy.

Finally—in the middle of the Popoffsky affair—his language grew so insolent and his manner so intolerably overbearing

[30] The phrase "culte de moi" had gained currency through Maurice Barrès' trilogy of novels *Le culte de Moi* (1888–1891), which stressed the need for the development of the individual and of the self. In advocating a life of the senses, Barrès' cult of self appealed to the decadents. The love of self would perfect the senses which in turn would furnish man the means whereby he might embrace the universe. Also, in the late 'eighties Max Stirner's *Der Einzige und sein Eigenthum* (The Ego and His Own), which was first published in 1845, was rediscovered and widely read. And along with this went the surge of interest in Nietzsche in the 1890s and the spread of anarchism, with which Strindberg was sympathetic. Stirner, like the anarchists, abjured all political and moral ties on the individual.

Strindberg's use of the phrase here presents a problem for the translator. In his original French manuscript and in the Swedish translation the meaning is as rendered above. However, the published French text provides quite a different meaning: "The cultivation, no the cult of self must . . ."

In a letter of July 22, 1894, Strindberg wrote, "The only thing that exists is the self (le culte de moi), and I know nothing of the world and 'the others' except through myself"—a solipsistic view that was entertained by many Symbolists at this time. And in a letter to his wife Frida Uhl, Strindberg declared, "The struggle within me and between us is part of the eternal struggle for the preservation of the personality, one's ego."—EDITOR.

that I feared he considered me mad. He called me Simon
Magus, a black magician, and recommended that I turn to
Mme. Blavatsky. I retorted by letting him know that I had no
need of Madame B, and that *I had nothing to learn from anybody*. And what was he threatening me with? He said that he
would see to it that I was guided back onto the right path
with the aid of powers stronger than those I recognized. At
this, I asked him if he would mind leaving my destiny alone,
since it was already taken very good care of by the providence
that had always guided me till then. And as an illustration of
my thoughts on this subject I told him the following story—
one small incident in a life rich in providential events—while
at the same time acquainting him with my fear that by revealing my secret I might be drawing the vengeance of
Nemesis herself upon me.

\*    \*    \*

It was during the most scandalous part of my literary
career, at the time, ten years before, when I rose in revolt
against the feminist movement which everyone in the Scandinavian countries, with the sole exception of myself, was
at that time supporting.[31] I let myself become carried away
by the excitement of the battle, and went beyond the limits
of respectable behavior, to such an extent indeed that my
fellow countrymen thought I must be insane.

I was living in Bavaria, with my first wife and my children,
when a letter arrived from a friend of my youth inviting me
to spend a year in his home with my children. He made no
mention of my wife.

The character of this letter aroused a certain amount of
suspicion because of its pompous style and the large number
of erasures and corrections, which indicated that the author
had felt some hesitation as to the choice of reasons he should
put forward. Sensing a trap, I declined the offer with some
vague expressions of gratitude.

Two years later, when my divorce from my first wife was
just a matter of time, I invited myself, without any of my

[31] For the consequences of Strindberg's revolt against the feminist
movement, see the Introduction to Strindberg, *The Son of a Servant*
(Doubleday Anchor Books), pp. ix–x.—EDITOR.

family, to stay with this friend in his house on an island at the edge of the Baltic, where he was employed as customs inspector.

I was welcomed cordially enough, yet the air reeked of lies, his words were double-edged, and talking to him was like being questioned by a detective. After a night of reflection, I felt I had gotten to the bottom of the matter. This man, whose ego I had wounded in one of my novels, still bore me a grudge, despite his otherwise genuinely sympathetic feelings towards me. A despot second to none, he now wanted to hold the reins of my destiny, tame my spirit, subjugate me, and by so doing demonstrate that he was my superior.

Displaying almost no scruples in his choice of methods, he tortured me for a week, poisoning me with slanders and tales invented deliberately for this purpose. But he conducted his campaign so clumsily that I remained convinced that the trap he had previously set for me had certainly been arranged with the purpose of having me locked up as a madman.

I allowed things to take their course, putting up no show of resistance, but trusting to my lucky stars to deliver me in good time.

My apparent submission resulted in my torturer's conceiving an affection for me, and since he lived cut off on an island in the middle of the sea, loathed by his neighbors and subordinates, he yielded to the need to confide in me. With a simplicity of mind inconceivable in a man fifty years old, he told me that his sister had gone mad the winter before, and that, in the course of a hysterical attack, she had burned all her savings.

The following day brought fresh confessions. I learned that his brother had also been committed to a lunatic asylum in the country.

I then asked myself, "Is this the reason—is it because he seeks vengeance against his own fate that he wants to have me put away also?"

Nevertheless I joined with him in lamenting his misfortunes and completely won his affection, so that I was able to leave his house and take lodgings on a neighboring island, where I was reunited with my family. A month later, a letter arrived summoning me to the home of my "friend" who was completely crushed by grief because his brother had gone mad and smashed in his own head. I went to him and consoled him, my torturer and executioner. The last straw was provided by his weeping wife, who confessed to me in confidence that she had been expecting for a long time to see her husband suffer the same fate as the rest of his family.

A year went by, and then the newspapers brought the news that my friend's eldest brother had killed himself in circumstances that left no doubt as to his being mentally deranged.

Three thunderbolts, all striking the head of this man who had tried to play with forces too strong for him![32]

"What a strange coincidence!" people may say. But really something much more than that! What a fateful coincidence! For every time I have told this story I have been punished for it.

\* \* \*

July has brought the heat of high summer in its train. Life has become intolerable. Everything smells bad, and the hundred water closets worse than the rest. I am expecting some

[32] Strindberg tells virtually the same story in more detail in an essay "Nemesis Divina" in *Vivisections*, Second Series, written in 1894.

The subject of the story is Ossian Ekbohrn, a rather eccentric man, amateur ornithologist, and a government inspector on the island of Sandhamn in the Stockholm archipelago. Strindberg had first met him in 1868. In 1889 upon his return from Denmark, Strindberg, his wife and children settled in a cottage on the island of Runmarö in the archipelago. But his marriage was breaking up, and after a quarrel Strindberg left his wife and moved over to Sandhamn. Ekbohrn thus became a close observer of Strindberg's domestic troubles. In "Nemesis Divina" it is made clear that Strindberg's dislike for his old friend stems from the summer of 1891, when Strindberg was once again living in the archipelago and deeply entangled in the divorce proceedings. Ekbohrn took the part of Strindberg's wife Siri. This was bad enough from Strindberg's point of view; but even worse was the fact that Ekbohrn had invited Siri and her close friend Marie David, whom Strindberg considered a lesbian, to stay with him. It is quite apparent from extant letters that it was not Ekbohrn who bore a grudge against Strindberg because his vanity had been wounded, as Strindberg says, but rather Strindberg who bore a grudge against Ekbohrn because of the latter's partiality toward Siri in 1891.–EDITOR.

catastrophe, without being able to say what form it will take.

I have picked up a piece of paper in the street with the word *marten* on it. In another street, a similar piece of paper had the word *vulture* on it. Both words were written in the same handwriting. Popoffsky has a perfect resemblance to a marten, and his wife to a vulture. Have they perhaps come to Paris to kill me? He is an unrepentant murderer, and quite capable of anything, since he has murdered a woman and two children.

I am reading a delightful pamphlet called *The Joy of Dying*,[33] which fills me with a desire to leave this world. In order to reconnoiter the frontier between life and death, I lie down on my bed, uncork my vial of potassium cyanide, and allow it to exhale its deadly perfume. He begins to draw near, the man with the scythe. He comes closer, gently, sensuously. But at the last moment someone or something always comes in unexpectedly; sometimes the serving-boy with some excuse or other, sometimes a wasp flying in through the window.

The powers refuse to grant me the one and only joy, and I submit to their will.

\* \* \*

At the beginning of July the students all went away on vacation, leaving the hotel empty.

For this reason, the arrival of a stranger who took the room adjacent to my work table excited my curiosity. He never spoke. He seemed completely taken up with writing; I could hear him on the other side of the wall that separated us. All the same, it was bizarre the way he drew back his chair every time I pushed mine forward, and copied every movement I made, as though trying to irritate me by imitating my every movement.

This went on for three days. On the fourth, I noticed that when I went to bed, he also went to bed on the other side of the wall against which my table stood. But once I was in bed I could hear him getting into his bed in the room on the *opposite* side, and the bed he climbed into was only the

[33] A. E. Badaire, *La Joie de mourir,* Paris: Chamuel, 1894.– EDITOR.

thickness of the wall from mine. I listened to him as he lay stretched out there, parallel with me. He would leaf through a book, then turn out his lamp, breathe deeply, turn over, and go to sleep.

And there was complete silence in the room next to my table. He must be in both rooms simultaneously. Unpleasant to be besieged on both sides at once.

\*    \*    \*

Alone, completely alone, I ate dinner off a tray in my room, and I ate so little that even the serving-boy looked sympathetically at me. I did not hear the sound of my own voice for a whole week, and it had begun to fade into a treble from want of use. I hadn't a cent left: I had neither tobacco nor postage stamps.

Then, with a supreme and final effort, I concentrated all my will on one goal. I *would* make gold—by the dry process, heating the constituents in a crucible. I found the money somehow, and assembled the heaters, the crucibles, the fuel, the bellows, the tongs.

The heat was extreme, and I sweated in front of the flaming coals, stripped to the waist like a blacksmith. But the sparrows had built their nest in the chimney, and the smoke from the coal fire was forced out into the room. I flew into a rage after the first attempt because of the headache it gave me and of the futility of my experiments. Everything had gone wrong. After remelting the material in the crucible three times over the fire, I stopped to examine it. The borax had run into the shape of a death's head with two glowing eyes that pierced my soul with a glance of supernatural irony.

Still not a trace of metal! And I gave up the idea of any further experiments.

Sitting in my armchair, I opened the Bible at random and read:

"And none considereth in his heart, neither is there knowledge nor understanding to say, I have burned part of it in the fire; yea, also I have baked bread upon the coals thereof; I have roasted flesh, and eaten it: and shall I make the residue thereof an abomination? Shall I fall down to the stock of a tree? He feedeth on ashes: a deceived heart hath turned him aside, that he cannot deliver his soul, nor say: Is there not a lie in my right hand? . . . Thus saith the Lord, thy redeemer, and he that formed thee from the womb, I am the Lord that maketh all things; that stretcheth forth the heavens alone; that spreadeth abroad the earth by myself; *that frustrated the tokens of the liars, and maketh diviners mad; that turneth wise men backward, and maketh their knowledge foolish.*"

For the first time, I began to have doubts about my scientific researches. Suppose they were mere folly! I had sacrificed all the happiness of my life, as well as that of my wife and my children, for an illusion!

Woe to me in my madness! The abyss yawned between my family and this fleeting instant! A year and a half, so many days and so many nights, so much grief for no good cause!

No, it must not be! It cannot be!

Lost in a dark forest? No, the bringer of light must have led me on the right path, towards the Fortunate Islands, and it was the Devil tempting me now! Or punishing me!

I sank back into the armchair. An unaccustomed heaviness weighed upon my soul. It seemed to me that there was a magnetic fluid flowing towards me through the partition, and my limbs were overwhelmed with lethargy. Collecting all my strength, I rose to leave the room. Then, as I walked along the corridor, I heard voices whispering in the room next to my table.

Why were they whispering? Obviously, to keep their presence hidden from me.

I walked down the Rue d'Assas and into the Luxembourg Gardens. Dragging my feet—I felt paralyzed from the base of my spine downwards—I collapsed on a bench behind Adam and his family.

I had been poisoned! That was the first idea that came into my head. And Popoffsky, who had killed his wife and children with poisonous gas, had arrived in Paris. It was he who had sent a stream of gas through the wall, as in Pettenkofer's famous experiment.[34]

[34] Max von Pettenkofer (1818–1901), German chemist, was one of the founders of scientific hygiene. Among his many published

What could I do? Go to the police station? No! Without the necessary evidence, I would be locked up as a madman.

*Vae soli!* Woe to the man who is alone, to the sparrow on the rooftop! The wretchedness of my existence was never greater than at that moment, and I wept like a lost child, afraid of the dark.

That evening I no longer dared even to stay near my table, such was my fear of a fresh attack. I got into bed but did not dare go to sleep. It was dark; the lamp was lighted. On the wall, opposite my window, I could see the shadows of a human figure. I could not tell whether it was a man or a woman, but right now, thinking about it, I feel it must have been a woman.

When I got up to investigate, the curtain was lowered, quickly, noisily. Then I heard the stranger going into the room next to my bed. Then silence.

For three hours I remained awake, unable to fall asleep, which I normally did very quickly.

Then I felt an alarming sensation glide all through my body. I was the victim of an electric current flowing between the two rooms on either side of mine. The tension steadily increased, and although I fought against it I finally left my bed, obsessed by a single idea:

"They're killing me! I don't want to be killed!"

I went out to look for the serving-boy in his cubbyhole at the end of the corridor. But alas, he wasn't there! Obviously, got out of the way, bribed, a secret accomplice.

I went down the staircase, stalked down the corridor, woke up the manager of the hotel.

With a presence of mind that I would not have believed myself capable of, I pretended that I had been made ill by fumes from the chemicals I had been using, and asked him to give me another room for the night.

By a chance, which must be ascribed to the wrath of providence, the only available room was situated below that of my enemy.

Once alone, I opened the window and breathed in the

---

works is *Beziehungen der Luft zu Kleidung, Wohnung und Boden* (Movement of Air through Clothing, Rooms, and Floors), 4th edition, 1877.--EDITOR.

fresh air of a star-filled night. Above the roofs of the Rue
d'Assas and the Rue Madame, the Great Bear and the North
Star were shining bright.

"To the north, then! *Omen accipio!*"

And as I drew the curtains around the bed, I heard my
enemy in the room above climb out of his bed and drop
some heavy object into a trunk, the lid of which he then
closed and locked.

Which meant he must be hiding something—the electric
machine, perhaps?

* * *

Next day, a Sunday, I packed my bags and pretended that
I was taking a trip to the seaside.

I shouted, "Gare Saint-Lazare," to the coachman. But once
we had reached the Odéon, I told him to take me to the
Rue de la Clef, near the Jardin des Plantes.

I shall stay here, incognito, long enough to finish my research before leaving for Sweden.

# VII

## *Inferno*

At last a pause in the tortures. Settled in an armchair on the
verandah of the pavilion, I sat for hours gazing at the flowers
in the garden and reflecting on the past. The peace of mind
that ensued from my flight proved to me that I had not been
suffering from an illness, but that my enemies had been
persecuting me. During the day, I worked; at night I slept
peacefully.

Delivered from the unclean atmosphere I had left behind,
I felt myself growing young again as I contemplated the
hollyhocks, the flowers of my youth.

And that marvel in the heart of Paris, the Jardin des
Plantes, unknown to Parisians, had become my private park.
I wandered without peril in the midst of savage beasts, the

entire creation gathered into that small space, a Noah's Ark, a Paradise regained. It was too much happiness. Starting from the minerals, I passed through the kingdoms of the plants and animals and came to man, behind whom I made out the presence of the Creator. The Creator, that great artist who extends his own being as he creates, making sketches and rejecting them, reworking abortive ideas, perfecting and multiplying primitive forms. All, without doubt, is the work of his hand. Often he has taken great steps forward by inventing entirely new species; then along comes science and declares that there are gaps, missing links, and imagines that the intermediate species have disappeared.

*　　*　　*

After a while, feeling safe at last from my persecutors, I sent my new address to the Hôtel Orfila, in order to reestablish communication with the outside world through the post office. Not a letter had reached me since my flight.

But scarcely had I rid myself of my incognito than the calm was broken. Disturbing incidents began to occur again, and I was oppressed by the same feelings of uneasiness as before. First of all, I noticed that an unoccupied and unfurnished room on the first floor, next door to mine, was beginning to be piled high with objects whose purpose remained inexplicable to me. An old man with gray, spiteful eyes, like a bear's, kept bringing in empty crates, pieces of sheet iron, and other objects, objects which I could not quite define.

At the same time, the noises from the Rue de la Grande-Chaumière began again over my hand. Someone was hauling in cables, banging with hammers, exactly as though some infernal machine like those employed by the Nihilists was being assembled.

Then, the manageress of the hotel, who had been charming when I first moved in, changed her behavior towards me. She began spying on me and greeting me in a way I found deliberately irritating.

What is more, the occupant of the second-floor room above mine had changed. The silent old gentleman whose heavy tread I had come to know was no longer there. Retired, and living on a private income, he had been living in the house for years, and was doing so still. He had simply changed rooms. Why?

The maid who cleaned my room and served my meals had become very solemn in her manner and kept glancing at me with pity when she thought I wasn't looking.

And in the room above there was a wheel turning all day long, round and round and round.

I was condemned to death! Of that I was convinced. By whom? By the Russians, the pietists, the Catholics, the Jesuits, the theosophists! On what grounds? Sorcery or black magic?

Or else by the police! As an anarchist? A charge often employed to deport personal enemies.

Now, as I write this, I still do not know what happened that July night when death hurled itself upon me, but it taught me a lesson that I shall never forget as long as I live.

Even if it were admitted, and openly recognized by those who know the secret of this affair, that it was indeed the result of a plot hatched by human hands, I bear them no grudge for it, since I am convinced now that another and stronger hand was guiding theirs, unknown to them, and in spite of them.

*     *     *

On the other hand, supposing that there was no plot, then I must necessarily have created these chastising spirits in my own imagination in order to punish myself. We shall see later on how very improbable such a supposition must be.

*     *     *

On the morning of the last day, I rose from my bed in a state of resignation that I am disposed to term religious. There was nothing binding me any longer to this life. I put my papers in order, wrote all the necessary letters, and burned all that had to be destroyed.

Then I went out into the Jardin des Plantes in order to say my farewell to Creation.

The blocks of magnetic iron-ore from Sweden in front of the mineral museum greeted me on the part of my homeland. Robin's acacia, the cedars of Lebanon, monuments from all the great and still living periods of science, I greeted them too.

I brought some bread and cherries as a treat for my old friend Martin the bear who knew me personally, because I was the only person who brought him cherries in the morning when he woke up and at night when he went to sleep.

Farewell vultures, dwellers of the sky locked in a mud-filled cage. Farewell bison, thou behemoth, thou demon in chains. Farewell sea lions, well-matched couple consoled by conjugal love for the loss of your ocean and its wide horizons. Farewell stones, plants, flowers, trees, butterflies, birds, snakes, all of you, created by the hand of a good God! And you great men, Bernadin de Saint-Pierre, Linnaeus, Geoffroy Saint-Hilaire, Haüy, you whose names are writ in letter of gold on the temple front—farewell! Or rather: au revoir!

As I left that earthly paradise the sublime words of Séraphita came into my mind: "Farewell, poor earth! Farewell!"

Back in the hotel garden, I caught the scent of someone who had arrived while I was away. I could not see him; I could only sense that he was there.

My uneasiness was increased by the evident changes that had been made in the room next to my own. First, a bed-cover had been hung over a length of cord, obviously in order to conceal something behind it. Then, on the mantel shelf, there were piles of metal plates all separated from one another by cross pieces of wood. On the top of each pile there was a photograph album or book of some sort, placed there in all likelihood for the purpose of giving an innocent appearance to these infernal machines, which I suspect could most accurately be called storage batteries.

In addition, I noticed two workmen up on the roof of a house on the Rue Censier, just opposite the smaller house where I was staying. What they were doing up there I could not exactly make out, but they were holding objects in their hands—which again I was unable to distinguish precisely—and looking along them towards the french windows into my room.

Why did I not make up my mind to flee? I was too proud. And, besides, one must face the inevitable.

So I prepared myself for the night. I took a bath and made

sure I scrubbed my feet clean and white—a thing I am very particular about because my mother taught me as a child that dirty feet are a sign of shame.

I shaved and put cologne on my nightshirt, a garment bought for my wedding night three years before, in Vienna. . . . The condemned man's toilette.

I took up my Bible and read the psalms in which David calls down the vengeance of the Almighty upon his enemies.

As for the psalms of penitence, no, I hadn't the right to repent, for it was not I who had guided my destiny. I had never done evil for evil's sake, but only in self-defense. To repent is to criticize Providence for inflicting upon us those sins that enable us to be purified by the disgust that our evil actions inspire in us.

My account with life was settled. The score even. If I had sinned, then in all conscience I had already been punished for it enough. No doubt of that! Afraid of Hell? But I had already gone through a thousand hells here below without flinching, and the journey had simply created a burning desire inside me to leave the vanities and the mocking joys of a world I had always detested. Born with a nostalgia for heaven, I had even as a young man wept for the sullied nature of this existence, and felt myself a stranger far from home when among my own relations and the society they lived in.

Ever since my childhood I had been searching for God, and I had found the Devil. As a boy, I had worn the cross of Jesus Christ, and I had abjured a God who is content to dominate over a world of serfs, of slaves who abase themselves and bend their knees to their executioners.

\*       \*       \*

As I lowered the curtains over the glazed door to my room, I noticed a group of ladies and gentlemen in the private drawing room drinking champagne. They were obviously foreigners who had arrived that evening. But it was evident that they were not there simply for the purpose of making merry, since they were all looking serious, discussing something or other, making plans and talking in low voices, behaving in general like conspirators. To cap my torments, they all kept turning in their chairs and pointing with their fingers towards my room.

At ten o'clock I turned off my lamp and I went off to sleep, calm, resigned, as though I lay on my deathbed.

I awoke. A clock chimed two, a door closed, and . . . and I rose from my bed as though sucked up by a vacuum that was trying to tear the heart from my body. As I stood there, a shower of electricity fell upon my neck and pressed me down onto the floor.

I got to my feet again, snatched up my clothes and hurled myself out into the garden, my heart racked by the most horrible palpitations.

Once dressed, I realized very clearly that I ought to go and find a police inspector so that he could search the house.

But, as fate would have it, the front door was locked, so was the concierge's lodge, and I had to grope my way forward, open a door on the right and go into the kitchen, where a nightlight burned. I knocked it over, and stood there in the profound darkness of the night.

My fear brought me back to my senses, and guided by the thought that if I had made a mistake I was lost, I found my way back to my room.

I dragged an armchair out into the garden, and sitting there beneath the starry vault I thought back over what had happened.

An illness? Impossible, since I felt perfectly well before I got rid of my incognito. An attempt on my person? Obviously, since I had seen with my own eyes the preparations being made for it. But in any case, out in the garden, out of my enemies' reach, I had by now recovered and felt my heart functioning perfectly again. And while these thoughts were turning over in my mind, I heard someone cough in the room next to mine. Immediately another little cough sounded in reply from the room above. They seemed to be signals, exactly like the ones I had heard during my last night in the Hôtel Orfila. I approached the glazed door of the ground floor room, hoping to force the lock, but my efforts were in vain.

Worn out by my useless struggle against invisible opponents, I sank back into the armchair, whereupon sleep took pity on me and I dozed off beneath the stars of a beautiful

summer's night, to the sound of the hollyhocks murmuring in
a gentle July breeze.

\* \* \*

I was awakened by the sun, and giving thanks to Providence for having wrested me from death's clutches, I threw
some things into a suitcase with the intention of leaving for
Dieppe, where I had friends who would take me in. Though
I had neglected them like all the rest, they were indulgent
and generous towards all castaways and derelicts.

When I asked for the manageress, I was told that she could
not see me, the excuse being that she was indisposed. I ought
to have foreseen that, of course, certain as I was of her com-
plicity in the plot.

As I left the hotel, I flung back a curse at the heads of
the malefactors inside it, and called down the fire of heaven
upon that robbers' den—whether rightly or wrongly who can
tell?

\* \* \*

In Dieppe, my generous friends were appalled when they
saw me struggling up the little hill to the Villa des Orchidées
carrying my suitcase full of heavy manuscripts.

"Where have you come from, poor fellow?"

"From death."

"I believe it. You look like an exhumed corpse."

The good and charming lady of the house took me by the
hand and led me to a looking-glass. Face blackened with
the smoke from the railways, hollow cheeks, hair grizzled
and drenched with sweat, haggard eyes, grimy shirt—I was
a pitiable sight.

When the gracious lady, who was treating me like a sick
and abandoned child, left me alone in front of my dressing
table, I examined my face more closely. There was an expression imprinted on all its features that filled me with
horror.

It was not death, not vice, it was something else. And if I
had known Swedenborg then, the impress left upon me by
the Evil One would have made clear to me at that moment
the state of my soul and the events of the previous weeks.

For the moment I was seized with shame and horror at

myself, and I repented having been ungrateful towards this family who had provided me with a refuge once before, and not only me but many other castaways.[1]

It was in order that I might do penance that the furies had driven me there. My host was an artist; his house was beautiful; moreover it was a home in the true sense, full of connubial love, ravishing children, comfort and cleanliness, unlimited hospitality, liberal ideas, an atmosphere of beauty and goodness that seared my heart. Surrounded by all this, I could not enjoy it; I felt like a cursed soul in heaven. It was in this place that I began to discover I was indeed damned.

There, spread out before my eyes, was everything that life can offer in the way of blessings, and everything that I had lost.

\* \* \*

I was given an attic room looking out onto a hilltop on which stood a home for the aged. In the evening, I glanced out and noticed two men leaning over the wall of the grounds. They were spying on our villa and pointing up towards my window. The idea that I was being persecuted by enemies with electrical devices began to obsess me once more.

It was on the night of July 25 and 26, 1896. My friends had done their utmost to reassure me. We had gone up together and inspected all the attics near to mine, even the loft, to prove to me that there was no one hidden up there with criminal intent. However, as I opened the door of a junk room, I glimpsed an object which, though insignificant in itself, made my heart sink within me. It was a polar bear made into a rug. But its gaping jaws, its menacing fangs, its glittering eyes, set my nerves on edge. Why did the animal have to be there, just at that moment?

[1] Strindberg's host in Dieppe was Fritz Thaulow (1847–1906), a Norwegian landscape painter, whom Oscar Wilde described as "a giant with the temperament of Corot" (letter to Lord Alfred Douglas, June 23, 1897). Wilde was released from Reading Gaol on May 18, 1897, and arrived in Dieppe a day or two later. Thaulow, one of the few people who was not embarrassed to be seen with Wilde, often invited Wilde to dinner at the Villa des Orchidées during May and June. Strindberg would have been writing this section of *Inferno* at this very time, and the reference to castaways suggests that Strindberg had Wilde in mind.–EDITOR.

I lay down on my bed without undressing, having decided to wait until the fateful hour of two had struck.

I waited until midnight, occupying my mind with reading. One o'clock passed and the whole house was sleeping peacefully. At last the two o'clock chimes rang out! Nothing happened! Seized by a fit of arrogance and as a gesture of defiance to my invisible enemies, perhaps even with the intention of performing a scientific experiment, I got up, opened both windows, and lit two candles. Sitting at the table on which I had placed the candlesticks, proffering my bared breast as a target, I challenged my unknown opponents.

"Here I am, you fools!"

At that moment I began to feel a current of what felt like electricity, very weak at first. I looked at the compass I had set up as an indicator. However, the needle showed no sign of deviation, proving there was no electricity.

But the tension increased and my heart was beating fiercely; I resisted, but a fluid coursed through my body with all the speed of lightning, asphyxiating me and sucking at my heart. . . .

I hurled myself down the staircase towards the drawing room on the first floor where a makeshift bed had been made up for me in case of need. Was it radiant electricity? No, because the compass had not moved. Was it a sickness brought on by my fears of what would happen at two o'clock? No, it couldn't be that either, for I was not lacking in the courage to face these attacks. Then why did I have to light the candles that attracted the unknown fluid of which I was the victim?

Unable to find any answer, lost in a labyrinth of dead ends, I forced myself to sleep. But then a fresh discharge hurled itself through me like a tornado, tore me from the bed, and—the hunt began again. I hid myself behind the wall, I lay down in the doorways, and in front of the stoves. Everywhere, everywhere, the furies found me out. Anguish of soul gained the upper hand. Panicked by everything and by nothing at all, I fled from room to room and at last took refuge on the balcony, where I stayed huddled on the floor.

The yellow-gray morning light and the sepia clouds twisting themselves into strange and monstrous shapes augmented my despair. I found my way down to my friend's studio and there, lying on the carpet, I closed my eyes. Five minutes later I was awakened by an irritating noise. A mouse was looking at me with the evident intention of coming closer. I drove it away; it came back again with another. My God, was I in the grip of delirium tremens, I who hadn't been drunk in three years? (Next day I confirmed that there were in fact mice in the studio. It was all a coincidence, then. But arranged by whom, and for what purpose?)

I moved again and went to lie on the carpet in the hall. Sleep took pity on me and flowed through my tortured mind so that I lost all consciousness of suffering for perhaps half an hour.

I was awakened by a clearly articulated cry of "Alp!"—the word that had been written by the raindrops that fell on my paper during the storm at the Hôtel Orfila!

Who had shouted that word? No one; all the inhabitants of the house were asleep. Demons at play! A poetical metaphor that perhaps contained the whole truth.

I climbed back up the stairs to my attic room. The candles were burned out. Silence reigned.

At that moment the Angelus rang. It was the Lord's day.

I took up my Roman Catholic Missal and read: *De profundis clamavi ad te, Domine!* Consoled by this, I fell onto my bed and slept like a dead man.

\* \* \*

Sunday, July 26, 1896. A tornado had devastated the Jardin des Plantes. The newspapers reported the details of this event, which I found singularly interesting, though I could not say why. It was the day that Andrée's balloon was scheduled to set off for the North Pole, but the prognostics were bad. The tornado had brought down various balloons, all launched in different places, and several aeronauts had been killed. Elisée Reclus[2] had broken a leg. Similarly, in Berlin a certain Pieska had committed suicide under the

[2] Elisée Reclus (1830–1905), French geographer and anarchist. He fought on the ramparts with the Communards in Paris in 1871, and was the co-founder with Kropotkin of the anarchist journal *La Révolte*, which was suppressed by the authorities in 1894. In 1896 Reclus was living in exile in Brussels.—EDITOR.

most extraordinary circumstances, slitting open his belly after the Japanese fashion; a tragic and bloody affair.

Next day I left Dieppe, this time with a blessing upon the house whose legitimate happiness had been darkened by my torments.

Rejecting once more the idea that there had been an intervention on the part of the spiritual powers, I now imagined that I was suffering from a nervous disease. For this reason I had decided to go to Sweden and seek out a doctor friend of mine.

As a souvenir of Dieppe I took away with me a pebble made of a type of iron ore, three-lobed in shape like a gothic window, and stamped with a Maltese cross. It had been given to me by one of the children who had found it on the beach. He told me that stones of this sort fell from the sky and were washed ashore by the waves.

I wanted to believe his explanation, and I kept the gift as a talisman whose meaning has still not been revealed to me.

(On the coasts of Brittany, after a storm the fisherfolk gather up from the beach stones that are shaped like crosses and have the appearance of gold. They are made of a mineral called staurolite.)

*     *     *

In the very south of Sweden on the seacoast, there stands a little town, once a stronghold of pirates and smugglers, that still retains exotic traces from the four corners of the earth left there by sailors and world travelers.

One such trace was found in my doctor's house which presented the appearance of a Buddhist monastery. The four wings of the building, which had only one story, formed a square, and in the center of the inner courtyard there stood a domed edifice resembling the tomb of Tamberlaine at Samarkand. This structure and the Chinese tiles on its roof, combined to give an impression of the Far East. An apathetic tortoise dragged itself across the flagstones, and, plunging into the tall grass nearby, lost itself in a green nirvana that merged with eternity itself.

The exterior wall of the west wing, of which I was the sole occupant, was decorated with a great mass of Bengal roses.

To reach the two gardens from the inner courtyard one had to pass first through a kitchen-yard that contained a chestnut tree and a flock of black chickens, always fighting mad—a sort of dark, dank alley.

In the pleasure garden there was a summerhouse, covered with birthwort and built like a pagoda.

This monastery with its innumerable rooms housed but one single and solitary inhabitant, the director of the local hospital. A widower, independent and of an eremitic disposition, he had received a cruel education from life and his fellow men, both of which he had come to despise with that vigorous and noble contempt that leads eventually to a profound awareness of the relative meaninglessness of everything, the individual self included.[3]

The entrance of this man onto the stage of my life was so unexpected that I am tempted to class it among those coups de théâtre termed *ex machina*.

During our first interview after my arrival from Dieppe, he fixed me with an observant eye, and then said suddenly, "What's the matter with you? Depressed! Yes! But there's something else underneath. There's an unhealthy look about your eyes I've never seen there before. What have you been up to? Debauchery, secret vices, lost illusions, religion? Let's have the whole story, old fellow!"

But I told him nothing. The first thought that came into my suspicious mind was that he had been forewarned against

[3] The doctor was Anders Eliasson (1844–1900) of Ystad. He was a highly respected member of his profession and had a wide practice. He was also known to be rather unsociable and given to temperamental outbursts. His few close friends found him to be a good drinking companion and of a frank and open nature. Strindberg first met him in 1891 and later kept him informed of his alchemical experiments. In 1895, a year before the visit described above in *Inferno*, Strindberg wrote Eliasson from Paris asking the doctor if he would put him up for a month or so, and also asking for 300 kronor.

In a long letter dated November 16, 1897, but probably never mailed, Dr. Eliasson broke with Strindberg because of the way in which Strindberg had portrayed him in *Inferno*, which was published in Sweden in the fall of 1897. The tone of the letter reveals a deeply wounded man. Point by point Eliasson shows how Strindberg distorted the truth.—EDITOR.

me, that he had been given information from other sources, and that I was already interned.

I made up a story about nervousness, insomnia, nightmares, and then turned to trivial matters. Our talk petered out in chitchat.

As I unpacked in my little suite of rooms, I immediately noticed the iron bedstead, American style. The four posts at the corners, each topped with a brass ball, looked like the conductors of a machine for generating electricity. Add to this the spring mattress, made up of spiral copper springs, very similar to Rumkhorff's induction coils, and you may judge the rage I felt at this diabolical coincidence. It was impossible to ask for the bed to be changed without my being suspected of mania. Wishing to reassure myself that there was nothing concealed above my bed, I went up into the loft. To complete my ill luck there was but a single object up there—an enormous mesh of iron wire, rolled up and placed exactly above my bed. That, I said to myself, is without doubt a battery. Should there be a storm—and they're very common in these parts—the coil of iron wire would attract the lightning and I should be lying below on the conductor. But I did not dare say anything. At the same time, I was disturbed by a sound of machinery. I had been persecuted ever since my departure from the Hôtel Orfila by a humming in my ears, something like the thrumming of a water wheel.

Doubting the reality of this noise, I asked what it was.—
"It's the printing press next door."

Everything was explained so perfectly, and yet it was the very simplicity behind it that filled me with panic and drove me mad.

Came the night with its terrors. The sky was overcast, the air heavy with a gathering storm. I did not dare lie down and I passed two hours in writing letters. Overwhelmed with fatigue, I took off my clothes and slid between the sheets. A horror-filled silence reigned in the house as I turned out my lamp. I could sense someone there in the darkness, waiting for an opportunity, brushing against me, feeling for my heart, sucking at it.

Without further delay, I leaped from my bed, opened the

window, and hurled myself out into the courtyard—where the rosebushes stood, and my nightshirt gave me no protection at all as their thorns lacerated me. Torn, bleeding, my bare feet sandpapered by the gravel, scratched and stung by the thistles and nettles, slipping and sliding on unrecognizable objects, I crossed the courtyard and reached the door of the kitchen adjoining the doctor's rooms. I knocked. No reply!— Only then, and not until then, did I realize that it was raining. Wretchedness on top of wretchedness! What had I done to deserve these torments? Surely I was in hell! *Miserere! Miserere!*

I knocked again—and again!

Was it not more than a little strange that no one was ever around when I was attacked? Everyone was always somewhere else! They always had their alibis. It had to be a plot, and they were all accomplices in it!

The doctor's voice at last: "Who's there?"

"It's me. I'm sick. Open up or I'm done for!"

He opened the door.

"What's the matter with you?"

I began my story with the attack made on me when I was living on the Rue de la Clef, which I attributed to enemies in possession of electrical machines. . . .

"Stop, stop, poor fellow. You're suffering from a mental illness."

"Mental illness! What nonsense! Just test my intelligence. Read some of the stuff I write every day, stuff that gets published . . ."

"Silence! Not a word of this to anyone! The insane asylum records are full of detailed accounts of enemies with electrical machines!"

"Go to the devil! Your records don't worry me. Just to settle my mind on that score I'll leave for the Lund asylum tomorrow to have myself examined!"

"I wouldn't if I were you. If you do you're done for. Now, not another word. And go straight to bed in this room next to mine."

I insisted, I demanded that he hear me out. He refused and wouldn't listen to another word.

When I was alone, I asked myself, "Is it possible that a

friend, an honest man who has remained untainted all his life by sordid commercial considerations, should have yielded to temptation at the very end of an honorable career?" Temptation by whom? I did not know the answer, but there was no lack of possibilities.

Every man his price, as the English say. And in this case the sum must have been considerable if it was in proportion to the virtue bought.—But to what end? Simple vengeance is not worth very much. The interests involved must have been immense! Exactly! That was it! I had made gold, the doctor had half admitted as much, yet that very day he had denied having tried for himself the experiments which I had communicated to him in my letters. He had denied it, and yet that very evening I had found samples labeled in his own hand lying around on the flagstones of the courtyard. He had been lying!

What is more, he had spoken at length, again this very evening, on the dire consequences that would ensue for all humanity if the possibility of manufacturing gold were to be confirmed. Universal bankruptcy, general chaos, anarchy, the decline and fall of the civilized world.

"The man who could make gold would have to be done away!" Those had been his final words.

Then again, familiar as I was with my friend's financial situation, which was fairly modest, I was astonished to hear him say that he was about to buy the property on which he was living. In debt, on the verge of financial difficulties, yet dreaming of becoming a landowner!

Everything concurred to make me suspect and incriminate my good friend.

Persecution mania? All right, but where was the artisan who was forging the links in these infernal syllogisms? Where?—"He would have to be done away!"—That was the last thought I was able to fix on in the midst of my torments before drifting off to sleep just about daybreak.

*    *    *

We began a series of cold water treatments, and I was given a new room to sleep in, so that my nights became relatively calm, except for a few inevitable relapses.

One evening the doctor noticed the Missal on my bedside table and began to rail at me like a madman.

"Religion, religion, always religion! That's a symptom, don't you see?"

"Or a need like any other!"

"Enough! I'm not an atheist; but I do believe that the Almighty no longer cares to have man intimate and familiar with him as he once did. The days when we were forced to coax and wheedle the Everlasting are gone now. I hold to the same principles as the Mohammedan, who asks for nothing in his prayers but the resignation that will allow him to bear the burden of existence."

Big words, from which I panned a few grains of gold.

He took away my Missal and my Bible.

"Read about subjects you're more or less indifferent to, things of secondary interest, world history, mythology; and leave all this visionary stuff alone. Above all: beware of occultism. That's an abuse of knowledge. It is forbidden to spy upon the creator's secrets, and woe to those who unravel them!"

When I objected, telling him that an occultist school had already been founded in Paris, he roared, "Woe to them!"

That evening he brought me Victor Rydberg's *Germanic Mythology*, though without any ulterior motive, I can swear to that.

"Here's a book full of stories guaranteed to send you straight off to sleep. Works better than sulfonal."

If my excellent friend had known what fuse he had now lit, he would sooner have handed me any other book on earth.

The two-volume, thousand-page mythology fell open in my hands by itself, and my gaze was caught immediately by the following lines, which engraved themselves in my memory in letters of fire:

"According to the legend, Bhrigu, having been taught by his father, grew big with pride and imagined himself surpassing his master. The latter sent him to hell, in which place, to his humiliation, he was forced to witness a thousand horrible sights the like of which he had never suspected."

That was it. Punished for pride, presumption, *hybris*

(ὕβρις), by my father and master. And I was now in hell, driven there by the powers. And who was my master? Swedenborg?

I went on turning the pages of this miraculous book.

"This fable is sometimes compared with the Germanic myth of the *Field of Thorns that lash* the feet of the unrighteous. . . .[4]

Enough! No more! The thorns too! That was too much!

Beyond a shadow of a doubt, I was in hell! And in truth, reality confirmed this fancy so persuasively that I came to believe it.

The doctor appeared to be torn among a variety of different feelings towards me. Sometimes he was preoccupied, gave me sidelong glances, and treated me with humiliating rudeness. Sometimes, being unhappy himself, he took care of me and comforted me as though I were a sick child. Again, he could rejoice at being able to trample under foot a man of merit whom he had formerly esteemed; and then he would play the role of torturer and read me sermons.

"You must work, you must rid yourself of exaggerated ambitions. You must fulfill your duties towards your country and your family. Let chemistry alone; it's a chimaera, and there are so many authorized specialists in the field, so many learned and professional chemists who know what they're talking about . . ."

One day he suggested I write something for the lowest of the gutter press papers in Stockholm.

"They pay well!"

I retorted that I had no need to write articles for the worst of the Stockholm newspapers when the first newspaper in Paris, and in the world, had accepted copy from me.

Whereupon he played the skeptic and treated me as

---

[4] The quoted passages are from Viktor Rydberg, *Undersökningar i Germanisk mytologi* (2 vols.; Stockholm, 1886–1889), Vol. II, p. 164 and p. 157.

In the letter referred to in footnote 3 above, Eliasson says that he recommended Rydberg's book to Strindberg in *1895*, not *1896*. At that time Strindberg seemed uninterested in it. In *1896* it was Strindberg who asked for it. Eliasson also denied ever saying that Rydberg was a more effective soporific than sulfonal.–EDITOR.

though I were making it all up, even though he had read my articles in *Le Figaro* and had himself commissioned a translation of a leading article I wrote for *Gil Blas*.[5]

Understand, I bear him no grudge for his behavior. He was simply playing the part he had been cast for by Providence.

At the time, however, I was obliged to keep a firm hold on myself in order to repress my hatred for this extemporary devil, and I cursed the destiny that was perverting my feelings towards a generous friend from gratitude to ingratitude.

\* \* \*

A steady series of apparently trivial incidents continually renewed my suspicion of the good doctor's malevolent intentions.

One day, on the verandah overlooking the garden, he laid out a row of newly bought axes and saws and hammers that could have been of no possible use to him. There were also two shotguns and a revolver in his bedroom, and in one of the corridors another collection of axes, all too big to be of use around the house. What a satanic coincidence!—these instruments of torture exhibited to my gaze, doubly disturbing to me because they were of no possible use and looked so out of place.

My nights had by now become fairly calm, whereas the doctor had begun making alarming nocturnal excursions. For example, I was awakened in the middle of one very dark night by the sound of a gunshot. I was discreet, and behaved as though I had not heard it. In the morning he explained it away, claiming that a flock of magpies had settled in the garden and prevented him from sleeping.

[5] To *Le Figaro littéraire* Strindberg contributed "Sensations détraquées," printed in the issues of November 17, 1894, January 26, 1895, and February 9, 1895; and also "Césarine," an article on Dumas *fils'* play *La Femme de Claude*. This appeared in the issue of September 30, 1894. *Gil Blas* in the summer of 1895 carried two pieces by Strindberg: "Misogynie et gynolâtrie" (July 24) and "Le Barbare à Paris" (August 8). The latter essay was occasioned by the success the Scandinavian dramatists Ibsen, Bjørnson, and Strindberg had scored at the avant-garde theaters of Paris. This had roused some French critics to wage war on the "barbarian" invaders. Strindberg used the historical approach to point out politely that Sweden was as civilized as France.—EDITOR.

Another night it was the cleaning woman who began shrieking raucously at two in the morning. And on yet another night it was the doctor I heard, first moaning and then calling upon the "Lord Sabaoth."

Was I in a haunted house? And if so, who had sent me there?

I could not keep myself from smiling when I observed how the nightmare that had been obsessing me was now attacking my jailers. But such impious joy is soon punished. A horrible attack caught me unawares. I was awakened by a syncope, and the sound of some words that I noted down in my diary. An unknown voice was crying: "Luthardt the Druggist."

Druggist? Was I being slowly poisoned with delirium-producing alkaloids, such as henbane, hashish, digitalis, or scopolamine?

I don't know; but from that moment my suspicions redoubled.

They were afraid to kill me; they wanted simply to drive me mad with stratagems and then spirit me away into some asylum for incurable lunatics. Appearances spoke even more strongly against the doctor. I discovered that he had been developing my method of synthesizing gold and that he now knew more about it than I did. Moreover, everything he said was immediately contradicted the moment after. And faced with all these lies my imagination took the bit between its teeth and bolted away beyond the bounds of reason.

On August 8 I went for a morning walk outside the town. There was a telegraph pole making a humming sound near the road. I went over to it and listened closely, standing there as though bewitched. A horseshoe had happened to fall by chance at the foot of the pole. I picked it up, taking it to be a good omen, and carried it back with me to the house.

*August 10.* At the end of the evening I said good night to the doctor, whose behavior over the last few days had been disturbing me more than ever. He looked very strange, and it was clear that some struggle had been going on inside him. His face was leaden, his eyes dull and lifeless. He had spent the whole day singing or whistling. A letter he had received that morning had made a very strong impression on him.

During the afternoon, after having performed an operation, he had returned to the house, hands covered with blood, carrying a two-month-old fetus. He looked like a butcher and talked about the mother's abortion in the most repellent way.

"Kill the weak and protect the strong! Pity and commiseration are degenerating the human race!"

I conceived a great horror of him, and after we had exchanged our good nights at the door between our two rooms I continued to keep watch on him. First of all, he went out into the garden without my being able to hear what he was up to. Next he walked up onto the verandah next to my bedroom and remained standing there. He had some fairly heavy object in his hands and was winding up a spring that was definitely not part of a clock. All his actions were carried out in a muffled silence, furtively, secretly.

Half-undressed, holding my breath, I stood without moving and awaited the effect of these mysterious preliminaries.

Then through the wall beside my bed, the usual and all too familiar effluvium began irradiating me, groping its way across my chest, trying to find my heart. The tension increased. . . . I picked up my clothes, slipped out through the window, and didn't get dressed until I had left the street gate far, far behind me.

And there I was out in the street once more, in the gutter, leaving behind me my last refuge, my only friend. I walked on and on, aimlessly. Coming to myself once more, I went directly to a doctor in town. I had to ring the bell, I had to wait and think of a story that would not incriminate my friend.

At last the doctor appeared. I apologized for visiting him at so late an hour—but the insomnia, the dizzy spells of a sick man who has lost confidence in his physician, and so forth. The excellent friend whose hospitality I had accepted had been treating me as though my illness were merely imaginary and would not listen to me.

As though he had been expecting my visit, the doctor offered me a chair, a cigar, and a glass of wine.

It was like a spiritual deliverance for me, to be received like a properly educated man after having been treated like a wretched idiot. We talked together for about two hours, and the doctor disclosed to me the fact that he was a theosophist and that I could tell him everything without fear of compromising myself.

Finally, a little after midnight, I rose from my chair with the intention of going to find a hotel. The doctor advised me to go back to the house.

"Never! He is capable of killing me!"

"What if I were to come with you?"

"Very well, we'll face the enemy's fire together. But he'll never forgive me."

"Let us go all the same!"

And so I retraced my steps to the house. Finding the door bolted, I knocked.

After we had waited for a minute, my friend opened the door and now it was my turn to be seized by pity. He, the surgeon who was accustomed to inflict suffering without displaying a trace of compassion, this prophet of premeditated murder, now presented the most pitiable appearance. He was as pale as a corpse. He trembled, stammered, and, at the sight of the doctor standing behind me, collapsed, seized by a terror that frightened me more than all the preceding horrors.

Was it possible that this man had been meditating murder, and that he was now afraid of being discovered! No, no, of course not. The thought was too ungodly, too evil.

After the exchange of a few meaningless phrases, including some almost playful words on my side, we parted and went to bed.

\*    \*    \*

There are some incidents in life so horrible that the mind refuses to picture them clearly at the moment they occur. Nevertheless, the first impression is firmly etched in the mind and soon enough reveals itself despite all resistance.

And so it was that upon returning to my room, I suddenly recalled a scene that had taken place in the local doctor's drawing room during my visit that night.

The doctor had left me there while he went to find the wine. Left alone, I examined a paneled armoire made of walnut or carved elm—I can no longer be quite sure which. As was to be expected, the grain of the wood formed a variety of patterns. As I looked, there appeared the head of a goat, drawn in the most masterly fashion. I immediately turned my back upon it. Pan himself, as depicted by the traditions of antiquity, Pan whom the Middle Ages later transformed into Satan. There was no doubt that it was he! I shall do no more here than merely recount this incident. The doctor, the owner of the armoire, would be performing a service to the science of the occult by having the panel photographed. Doctor Marc Haven has written an article in *L'Initiation* (November 1896) on such phenomena, which are extremely common in all realms of nature, and I recommend the reader to give his closest attention to the face observable on the carapace of the crab.

\* \* \*

As a consequence of this latest episode, a manifest hostility became apparent between my friend and myself. He gave me to understand that I was a good-for-nothing and that my presence was superfluous. I replied that I was awaiting the arrival of an important letter, but that I was prepared to move into a hotel. Whereupon he behaved as though he were offended.

As a matter of fact, I could not have moved if I had wanted to. I had no money. And besides, I could sense the approach of some imminent change in my destiny.

Also, my health having been restored, I was sleeping peacefully at night and working during the day.

The downfall threatened by Providence appeared to have been postponed and luck attended my efforts on every side. Whenever I took up a book at random in the doctor's library, the explanation I was seeking was always there. It was in this way, in an old chemistry book, that I came upon the secret of my gold making, so that I was able to prove metallurgically by means of calculations and analogies, not only that I had made gold, but that men had always made gold, even when they thought they were extracting it from ores.

I sent a memorandum based on this new material to a

French review,[6] where it was printed immediately. I hurried to show the article to the doctor, who, being unable to deny the facts, became incensed at me.

At that point, I was forced to admit to myself that since my success only caused him pain, he was no longer my friend.

\* \* \*

*August 12.* I bought an album at the bookstore. It was a sort of notebook in a deluxe leather binding, tooled and gilt. The decoration on the front attracted my attention, and —a very odd thing—constituted in fact an omen, whose interpretation I will give later on. On the left was the crescent moon in its first quarter surrounded by a flowering branch and three horses' heads (*trijugum*) emerging from the moon; above, a laurel branch with three chevrons (three times three) below it; on the right, a bell with fleurons pouring out of it, a wheel in the form of a sun, etc. . . .

*August 13.* The day predicted by the clock on the Boulevard Saint-Michel. I waited for some incident or other to occur, but in vain. Nevertheless I was certain that something had taken place somewhere, and that I would be informed of its consequences before very long.

*August 14.* In the street I picked up a leaf from a business calendar that had AUGUST 13 printed on it in large capitals (the date on the clock), and above this, in lower case: "Never do in secret what you would not do in public." (Black magic!)

*August 15.* A letter from my wife. She expressed pity for all that had befallen me. She still loved me, she said, and for our child's sake she hoped that my condition would soon improve. Her relations, who had hated me before, were now moved by my sufferings, and I was invited to go and see my daughter, that angel now living in the country with her grandparents.

I felt as if I had been called back to life! My child, my daughter, held the first place in my heart—she took precedence even of her mother. To kiss that poor innocent whom I had tried to harm, to ask her pardon, to enliven her existence with

[6] Evidently "Synthèse d'or," published in *Hyperchimie*, November 1896.—EDITOR.

all the little attentions of a father eager to lavish on her all the feelings he had been hoarding up for so many years! I felt reborn again. I awoke at last from my bad dream, and I understood the benevolent will of the stern Master who had been punishing me with a severe and conscious hand. Now I understood the obscure and sublime words of Job: "Happy is the man whom God correcteth!"

Happy, because for "the others" He does not trouble himself at all.

I did not know whether I was going to meet my wife again on the banks of the Danube. It had become almost a matter of indifference to me because I sensed that our characters were incompatible. And yet I began to make preparations for my pilgrimage, well aware that this was to be a journey of penitence and that new calvaries were in store for me.

\*    \*    \*

Thirty days of torment before the doors of the torture chamber opened. I left my friend and torturer without bitterness. He had been no more than the scourge decreed for me by Providence.

"Happy is the man whom God correcteth!"

# VIII

## *Beatrice*

In Berlin I took a hackney cab from the Stettin railroad station over to the Anhalt station. The half-hour drive seemed to me like a trip through a hedge of thorns, so deeply did all the memories embodied in the city pierce my heart. I drove along the street where my friend Popoffsky used to live with his first wife, unknown, or rather misunderstood, struggling with poverty and his passions. The wife had since died and the child had died, in that house on the left. Our friendship had been transformed into a cruel hatred.

There on the right, the beer tavern where all the artists

and writers used to meet—the scene of so many intellectual and sexual orgies.

There the Cantina Italiana, where I used to meet the woman who was then my fiancée, three years ago. It was there that we had changed my first Italian royalties into Chianti.

There, the Schiffbauerdamm, with the Pension Fulda, where we had lived when we were first married. Here, my theater, my bookstore, my tailor, my pharmacy.

What fatal instinct impelled the driver to take me along that *via dolorosa*, paved with buried memories that came to life again at that late hour of the night like so many ghosts? I could not understand why he deliberately drove down that alley in which our little bar, the "Black Pig," stood, famous once as the favorite haunt of Heine and E. T. A. Hoffman. Even the owner was there, standing on the steps, and above his head hung the beast that was the tavern sign. He looked at me without seeing me. And then, just for one single instant, the luster inside sent its rays, colored by the rows of bottles in the window, straight into my eyes, making me relive a whole year of my life, the richest of all in sorrows and joys, in friendship and in love. Yet at the same time I was vividly aware that all that was finished, that it had to remain buried to make room for the new that was to come.

\*        \*        \*

After sleeping the night in Berlin, I woke up toward morning to see above the rooftops a pink glow, a rosy tint, greeting me in the eastern sky. I remembered having observed this same rose tint over Malmö on the day before my departure. And so I left Berlin, which had become my second country, where I had spent my *seconda primavera*, and my last. I left behind in the Anhalt station not only my memories but also all hope for a spring and for a love that would never come again, never.

\*        \*        \*

After spending a night at Tabor where the rosy glow still pursued me, I dropped down towards the Danube through the forest of Bohemia. There the railroad came to an end, and it was in a horse-drawn carriage that I set out across the low-lying plain that follows the course of the Danube as far as Grein, continuing my way between apple and pear trees, between fields of wheat and green meadows. In the distance on the other side of the river I made out a little church on top of a hill. I had never visited it, but I recognized it as being the culminating point of the landscape visible from the front of the little house where my daughter had been born two years before, during that unforgettable month of May. I drove through villages, passed by castles, monasteries, and all along the roadside were innumerable expiatory chapels, Calvaries, ex-votos, and shrines built in commemoration of accidents, thunderbolts, sudden deaths. And no doubt at the end of my pilgrimage, down there in the distance, the twelve stations of Golgotha were awaiting me.

The Crucified One, wearing his crown of thorns, reappeared every hundred yards or so, encouraging me, showing me the way to my cross and my sufferings.

I was mortifying my flesh, convincing myself in advance that she would not be there—a fact I already knew.

And since my wife would not be there to shield me against the family storms, I would be forced to submit to the reprisals of her older relations whom I had left in such hurtful circumstances, refusing even to bid them goodbye. And so I arrived, resigning myself to my punishment in order to achieve peace of mind. As I went through the last village and past the last crucifix, I could feel in advance the tortures of my damnation.

*　　*　　*

I had said goodbye to a baby six weeks old, and I returned to find a little girl two and a half years old. At our first meeting she gazed into the depths of my soul, her manner not severe but very serious, apparently looking to see whether I had come for her or for her mother. Reassured, she allowed herself to be kissed, and clung with her little arms around my neck.

It was Doctor Faust's return to earthly life; but sweeter and more pure. I could not have enough of carrying my little girl in my arms and feeling her little heart beating against my own. To love a child is for a man to bring out the womanly part in him, to depose the male, to feel the asexual love of the cœlicolea, as Swedenborg calls them. This was to be the beginning of my education for heaven. But first, the expiation!

The situation was this. My wife was living with her married sister[1] because her grandmother, who held all the family money, had out of the intense hatred she bore me for my ingratitude, and for other reasons, sworn to have our marriage dissolved. I was welcomed on account of the child, who could never cease to be mine, and I was to be the guest of my mother-in-law for an indefinite stay. I accepted the situation as I found it, and with pleasure. My mother-in-law,[2] who had the conciliatory spirit and true resignation of the deeply religious woman, had forgiven me everything.

\*       \*       \*

September 1st, 1896.—I am living in the room where my wife spent the two years of our separation. This was where she suffered while I was undergoing my tortures in Paris. Poor, poor woman! Was it a punishment for the crime we had committed in treating love too lightly?

\*       \*       \*

At supper that evening, an incident: Since my little girl couldn't eat properly on her own yet, I took her hand, very gently, with nothing but the most loving intention of helping her. She gave a cry, pulled away her hand, and looked at me with horror. When her grandmother asked her what was the matter, she answered: "He hurt me!"

Abashed, I was unable to utter a single word. If I now caused harm without wanting to, how much harm must I have caused when I intended to?

That night I dreamed that an eagle was tearing at my hand as a punishment for some unknown crime.

In the morning my daughter came to see me, tender, loving, anxious to hug me. She sat with me while I drank my coffee, then settled herself at my writing table where I showed her some picture books.

We were already good friends, and my mother-in-law was

---

[1] Professor Marie Weyr, whom Strindberg usually called his "aunt."—EDITOR.

[2] Frau Marie Uhl.—EDITOR.

delighted that she now had someone who could help her with the little girl's education.

That evening I had to watch my little angel being put to bed and hear her say her prayers. She was a Catholic, and when she urged me to pray as well and make the sign of the cross, I could think of no reply, Protestant that I was.

*September 2.* General alarm. My mother-in-law's mother who lived a few kilometers away, along the river, was trying to have me evicted. She wanted me to leave immediately and was threatening to disinherit her daughter if she refused to obey. My mother-in-law's sister, a good woman, also separated from her husband, invited me to stay with her in the next village until the storm subsided. With this end in view she had driven over to take me back with her. We climbed up a mountain ridge for about two kilometers. Arriving at the summit, we beheld below us a deep, circular valley, in the center of which were a vast number of hills, bristling with pine trees, and rising up from the valley floor like volcanic craters. In the middle of this hollow stood the village with its church, and above it on top of a steep mountain stood the castle, which looked like a medieval walled town. Here and there squeezed between the hills were meadows and cultivated fields, watered by a stream that plunged down into a ravine below the castle.

Struck by the sight of this strange prospect, unique of its kind, the idea immediately came into my head that I had seen it before. But where?

In the zinc bowl during my stay at the Hôtel Orfila! Patterned in the iron oxide. It was the same landscape! Positively!

We continued down into the village where "Aunt Marie," as I called her, occupied an apartment consisting of three large rooms in a vast building that also contained a bakery, a butcher's shop, and a bar. The house was provided with a lightning conductor because the loft had been set on fire during a storm the year before. When Aunt Marie, a sincerely religious woman like her sister, took me to see the room she had got ready for me, I was rooted to the spot as I crossed the threshold, overcome by the vision. The walls were all rose-colored, the same shade of rose as the dawns that had haunted me during my journey. The curtains were rose and the light filtering through the flowers around the windows was also rose-tinted. A miraculous cleanliness reigned everywhere in that place, and the antique bed, its tester supported by four columns, was a virgin's sleeping place. The whole room was furnished in a way that made it a poem, the inspiration of a soul only partly of this earth. No crucified figure; only the Virgin Mary, and a holy water stoup guarding the entrance against evil spirits.

My heart was flooded with shame. I was afraid of sullying this dream created by one so pure in heart, this temple raised to the Virgin Mother on the tomb of the old woman's only love, already buried for more than ten years. In clumsy phrases I tried to decline so generous an offer.

But the good old woman insisted.

"It will do you good to sacrifice your earthly love to the love of God, and to the affection you have for your child. Believe me when I tell you that this love without thorns will give you peace of mind and an untroubled heart. Under the protection of the Virgin you will sleep calmly."

I kissed her hand to express my gratitude for the sacrifice she was making on my behalf, and with more compunction than I thought my soul contained, I accepted it whole-heartedly, certain that I would be pardoned by the powers who now seemed to have postponed the torments that were designed for my betterment.

Nevertheless I did reserve the right, on some pretext or other, to sleep one last night at Saxen and to postpone my final removal until the following day. Accompanied by Aunt Marie, I returned to my child. But walking down the village street, I could see that the lightning conductor and the wire running down from it were fixed exactly above my bed.

A devilish coincidence! I felt that I was the victim of some personal harassment!

Similarly, I noticed that the view from my windows was of nothing less than the poorhouse, its inmates consisting of former criminals released from jail, invalids, and people on the brink of death. A wretched company, a depressing future always before one's eyes!

\* \* \*

Back at Saxen, I gathered my things together for my departure. It was with regret that I said goodbye to the home of the daughter who had become so dear to me. The cruelty of the old lady who had come between me and my wife and child infuriated me, and in a fit of anger I raised my hand to the oil portrait of her hanging above my bed. The gesture was accompanied by an unspoken curse.

Two hours later a frightful storm broke over the village. The sky grew black, lightning flashes crisscrossed it, and the rain fell in torrents.

Next morning as I arrived in Klam, where the Rose Room was awaiting me, I noticed a cloud in the shape of a dragon hovering over my aunt's house. Then I was told that the lightning had set fire to a village only a short distance away, and that the storm had devastated our own parish as well, ruining the haystacks and washing away the bridges over the stream.

(On September 10th, a tornado had ravaged Paris, and in very strange circumstances. It had sprung up first, out of a complete calm, behind Saint-Sulpice in the Luxembourg Gardens, crossed over to the Théâtre du Châtelet, the Préfecture de Police, and finally faded out over the Hôspital Saint-Louis, though not before it had smashed down fifty yards of iron railings. It was apropos of this tornado, and of the previous one over the Jardin des Plantes, that my friend the theosophist asked me in a letter: "What exactly are tornadoes? Are they impulses of hate, waves of passion, spiritual emanations?"

(And he added: "Do the Papusists[3] produce their manifestations consciously?"

(Furthermore, by a coincidence that was more than chance I had asked my friend in a letter that crossed the one he had sent me, this direct and precise question, for he was an initiate of the Hindu mysteries: "Can the Hindu wise men *create* tornadoes?"

(I was now beginning to suspect the adepts of the occult of

[3] The Papusists were followers of Dr. Papus (real name Gérard Encausse) who hoped to command the powers by using witchcraft. He later became a Martinist and led the whole occult movement in the direction of Catholicism. See also the footnote to page 161.–EDITOR.

persecuting me because of my gold, or because of my stubborn refusal to become in any way an official member of their societies. Now that I had read Rydberg's *Germanic Mythology*, as well as Hyltén-Cavallius' *Wärend och Wirdarna*,[4] I was aware that witches are wont to appear in tempests or in short but violent gusts of wind.

(I set all this down in order to make quite clear what state of mind I was in at this time before I had any acquaintance with the doctrines of Swedenborg.)

\*    \*    \*

The sanctuary had been prepared, all white and pink, and the Saint was about to take up his abode with his disciple, who had been called from their common fatherland to revive the memory of the most gifted man of modern times.

France sent Ansgar[5] to convert Sweden. A thousand years later, Sweden sent Swedenborg to reconvert France by the intermediary of Saint-Martin, his disciple. The Martinist order, which is aware of the role it played in the formation of a new France,[6] will not minimize the significance of these words, and even less the meaning of the thousand years composing that millennium.

# IX

## Swedenborg

My mother-in-law and my aunt were twin sisters, so completely similar, so identical in character, likes and dislikes, that each appeared to be the other's double. When I talked

---

[4] Gunnar Olof Hyltén-Cavallius (1818–1889) was the leading Swedish ethnologist of his time.–EDITOR.

[5] Saint Ansgar (801–865), called the Apostle of the North, was Frankish missionary to Scandinavia.–EDITOR.

[6] As a young man, the mystic Louis-Claude de Saint-Martin (1743–1803) joined the Freemasons, and it was this affiliation that saved his life when the Revolution of 1789 broke out. In 1795 he wrote his *Lettres à un ami, ou Considérations, politiques, philosophiques et réligieuses sur la Révolution*.–EDITOR.

to one of them while the other was not there, the absent sister immediately knew everything that had been said, so that I was able to relate my confidences by talking to first one and then the other without having to repeat myself. Consequently I confuse them in this narrative, which, after all, is not a novel and has no pretentions to style or literary form.

Thus it was on that first evening that I gave them a sincere account of my inexplicable adventures, my doubts and my torments. With a rather pleased expression on their faces they both immediately exclaimed in unison: "You have had to travel the same road we took."

Starting from an indifference towards religious matters similar to my own, they had gone on to study occultism. From that moment they began to experience sleepless nights, mysterious incidents accompanied by sensations of mortal anguish and, finally, nocturnal attacks that carried them to the brink of insanity. The invisible furies pursued their quarry to the very gates of salvation: religion. But before the two women reached that haven, their guardian angel had already revealed himself, and he was none other than Swedenborg. They supposed, quite wrongly, that I was intimately acquainted with the works of my compatriot, and when they had recovered from their surprise at my ignorance, the good ladies handed me, though with some diffidence, an old volume printed in black letters.[1]

"Take it, read it, and don't be afraid."

"Afraid? Of what?"

Alone in the Rose Room, I opened the book at random and read.

I leave the reader to guess at the sensations I experienced when my eyes fell upon a description of hell in which I recognized the very landscape of Klam, the landscape in my zinc bowl, drawn as though from nature. The valley, the pine-covered knolls, the dark and somber woods, the gorge with the stream running through it, the village, the church, the poorhouse, the manure piles, the puddles of filth, the pig-pens—everything was there.

---

[1] *Les merveilles du ciel et de l'enfer et des terres planétaires et astrales,* par Emanuel Swedenborg. Edited by Pernetty. Berlin, 1782.–EDITOR.

Hell? But I was educated to have a profound contempt for hell, which I was taught to consider as a fantastic notion already thrown onto the rubbish dump of outmoded prejudices. And yet I could not deny that there was one thing that had been changed here, and in that one thing lay the entire novelty of this interpretation of what are termed eternal torments: we are in hell already. The earth is hell—a prison so constructed by a superior intelligence that I cannot take a single step in it without treading on the happiness of others, and in which my cell mates cannot remain happy without making me suffer.

That is how, though possibly without knowing it, Swedenborg describes life on earth in attempting to picture hell.

The fire of hell is the desire for success. The powers that govern us awaken our desires and allow the damned to achieve the goals they aspire to. But as soon as the goal is won and the desires fulfilled, everything seems worthless and the victory is empty. Vanity of vanities, all is vanity. Then, after the first disillusionment, the powers blow out the flames of desire and ambition. And now it is not our unassuaged cravings that torment us most; it is our sated appetites that inspire in us a disgust for all that exists. By the same token, the Devil suffers torment infinitely, for he obtains everything that he desires at the very moment he desires it, and is therefore barred from all possibility of enjoyment.

Comparing Swedenborg's description of hell with the torments in my *German Mythology*, I found an evident correspondence between the two. But the crucial fact of the matter for me personally was the way in which these two books had gained their hold upon me at the same moment in my life.

I was in hell, and damnation weighed heavily upon me. Going back over the past, I perceived that even my childhood had been organized as a place of detention, an Inquisition. And in order to explain why such torments had been inflicted on an innocent child, I was forced into presuming a former existence from which we are expelled into this world so that we might expiate the consequences of sins now forgotten.

With that evasiveness of mind to which I have always been excessively prone, I was able to force the sensations aroused in me by Swedenborg's book back into the deepest recesses of my soul. But the powers were to allow me no further respite.

Taking a walk in the neighborhood of the village, I was led down by the little stream into a sunken road between two cliffs,[2] a place the villagers refer to as the Gorge (Schluchtweg). The approach to this spot, a truly sublime sight on account of the great boulders that have tumbled down into it, attracted me in a very singular fashion. The side of the mountain supporting the ruined castle falls suddenly in a sheer cliff, and this cliff forms the entrance to the ravine at the point where the stream drops down to the mill. Eroded by the play of natural forces, the rock had taken on so striking a resemblance to a Turk's head that not one of the local inhabitants disputed the likeness.

Below this point the miller's wagon stood against the wall of the cliff. On the door handle hung a goat's horn containing grease for the carts. And leaning nearby was a broom.

However natural and ordinary this may seem, I nevertheless wondered what demon had placed precisely in that spot, which I was bound to pass that morning, those two objects so ineradicably associated with witches.

Uneasy, I advanced along the dank, dark path—and was halted in my tracks by the unusual appearance of a wooden building before me. A long, low box with six oven doors. . . . Ovens!

"Great heavens, where am I?"

I was being haunted by an image from Dante's Inferno, the caskets in which sinners are baked red hot. . . . And the six oven doors!!

A nightmare? No, this was merely humble reality, as was made all too clear by the horrible stench, the stream of mud, and the chorus of grunts emerging from a pigsty.

The path grew narrower, forming a strangled corridor between the mountainside and the miller's house as it continued on below the Turk's head.

I went on, but at the far end I perceived an enormous Great Dane with the coat of a wolf. It was identical to the

---

[2] In 1949, the centennial of Strindberg's birth, this road through the Klamm Pass was named Strindberg-Weg.—EDITOR.

monster that used to guard the studio on the Rue de la Santé in Paris.

I recoiled two paces but, recalling the motto of Jacques Coeur, "All things are possible to the valiant heart," I penetrated the dark cleft. The Cerberus made a show of not noticing me, and I continued my advance, now hemmed in on either side by two rows of low, dark houses. A black hen, with a high comb and no tail. A woman, beautiful when seen from a distance, a blood-red crescent marked upon her brow; seen close to, toothless and ugly.

The waterfall and the mill were making a noise that recalled the thrumming in my ears which had pursued me ever since my first restless nights in Paris. The mill boys, white as mock angels, were tending the cogs of the great machine like so many torturers, and the vast wheel, like some mechanical Sisyphus, was endlessly threshing through the water with its heavy blades.

Next came the forge with its blackened, naked smiths armed with their pincers and clamps, their vises and hammers amid the fire and the sparks, the reddened iron and the molten lead—a maelstrom of noise that rocked my brain in its brainpan and set my heart pounding in the rib cage.

Then the sawmill with the great saw screeching its teeth into the giant trunks as they lay in torment on the trestles, while their white, translucent blood oozed down across the viscous earth.

As I continued on my way beside the stream, I found that the sunken road had been devastated by the recent rains and storms. The sharp pebbles, hostile to my slithering feet, had been masked by the flood beneath a layer of gray-green slime. I wanted to cross the water but the footbridge had been carried away, and I stopped below a precipice where a solitary figure of the Virgin, constantly threatened by the overhanging rock, was supporting unaided the whole of that concave and undermined mountainside upon her slender shoulders.

I retraced my steps, plunged in thoughts about this combination of random details that, when taken together, made up one great unity, awe-inspiring without being supernatural.

❊    ❊    ❊

Eight days and eight nights flowed quietly past in the Rose Room. Peace of heart gradually returned with the daily visits of my lovable daughter who loved me, and who was loved by me. And all the while my family took care of me as though I were a spoiled child.

My reading of Swedenborg occupied me during the daytime, and I was overwhelmed by the realism of his descriptions. Everything was to be found there. I recognized my own observations, my own sensations, my own ideas to such an extent that his visions appeared to me to be part of reality, documents of authentic human experiences. It was not necessary to believe blindly; it was enough to read what was set down and then compare that with one's own experiences.

Yet the volume I had at my disposal was in fact no more than an excerpt, and the principal riddles of our spiritual life were not resolved for me until later when the complete work itself, *Arcana Cœlestia,* came into my hands.

\*     \*     \*

Meanwhile, amid the scruples awakened by the conviction that God does exist and that we are punished for our sins, a few lines of Swedenborg had provided me with consolation, and I was immediately prepared to exculpate myself and even to glorify myself.

So, making my usual evening confessions to my mother-in-law, I asked her, "Do you think I'm damned?"

"No, even though I must admit I have never before seen such a human destiny as yours. But you have not yet found the right road to lead you to the Lord."

"Do you recall Swedenborg and his heavenly principles? First comes the desire to dominate, but for some high purpose. That is the main aspect of my character for I have never aspired to the kind of honors and power bestowed on us by society. Secondly, the love of wealth and gold in order to use it for the good of all mankind. You know that I have never concerned myself with profit and have always despised money. If I make gold, or if I should ever make anything like it, I have sworn to the powers that any such gains will be used for humanitarian, scientific, or religious ends. Lastly: married love. Is there any need for me to say that since my earliest youth my affections for women have always been centered on the idea of marriage, of a wife and family? That I should have been fated to marry the widow of a man who was still alive is an irony for which I can find no explanation. But as for the irregularities of a bachelor life, there has been no question of that."

After a moment's reflection, the old woman: "I cannot deny the truth of what you have said, and when reading your work I have always been aware of a mind governed by the highest aims, aims never achieved, however, in spite of all your good efforts. There is no doubt that you are expiating sins committed in another world, before your birth. You must have been a mass murderer in a former life. That is why you will suffer the terrors of death a thousand times before you die, until your expiation has been completed. But now that you have become a believer, set to work at once."

"You mean I should practice the Roman Catholic religion?"

"Naturally!"

"But Swedenborg has said that we are not permitted to abandon the religion of our ancestors, because each one of us belongs to the spiritual territory occupied by the race of which he is a part."

"The Roman Catholic religion is a superior grace granted to all those who truly desire it."

"I am content to remain on a lower rung of the ladder. And if the worst comes, I shall present myself before the throne behind the Jews and the Mohammedans, who are also admitted. I prefer to be modest."

"You are offered forgiveness, and you choose a mess of potage in preference to your inherited rights."

"Primogeniture for the son of a servant? That's too much, much too much."

\*    \*    \*

From that moment, rehabilitated by Swedenborg, I imagined myself once more as Job, the just man without iniquity who was put to the test by the Almighty in order to show the wicked of the world how the man of integrity should bear unmerited suffering.

This idea lodged itself firmly in my mind, and my head

swelled with pious vanity. I bragged of my past adversities
and was never tired of repeating, "See how I have suffered!"
And I lamented the well-being I was experiencing in that
place. The Rose Room became a bitter mockery; I was being
derided for my sincere contrition by being loaded with gifts
and all the trivial pleasures of life. In short, I was one of
the chosen. Swedenborg had said so, and assured of the Almighty's protection, I deliberately provoked the demons. . . .

\*     \*     \*

I had been in the Rose Room eight days when news arrived
that my wife's great-grandmother, who lived on the edge of
the Danube, had fallen ill. She was suffering from a malady
of the liver that was producing vomiting, insomnia, and
nightly palpitations of the heart. My aunt, whose guest I was,
had been called to the old lady's side, and I was invited to
return to my mother-in-law's at Saxen.

When I objected that the ancient woman had forbidden me
the house, I was told that she had withdrawn her order of
eviction and that I was free to reside wherever I wished.

I was astonished by this sudden reversal in one who harbored such ill will towards me, but I scarcely dared attribute
her fortunate change of heart to the calamity that had befallen
her.

The next day we learned that the state of the sick woman
had grown worse. My mother-in-law gave me a bouquet of
flowers from her mother as a sign of reconciliation, and she
confided in me that the old woman imagined she had a snake
crawling in her belly, and other fantasies of the same kind.

We then learned that two thousand francs had been stolen
from the sick woman's house, that the invalid suspected her
private maid, and that the latter, outraged at such unjust suspicions, had flown into a rage and was now bringing a slander
suit against her mistress, with the result that all domestic
peace was completely shattered in the house of this sick
woman who had retired from the world in order to die in
peace.

Every messenger brought us flowers, fruit, game, pheasants,
chickens, fish. . . .

Was it all the work of divine justice, and was the sick

woman aware of it? Did she remember having once driven me out onto the highway that led me to the hospital?

Or was she superstitious? Did she believe me capable of having bewitched her? And were all the presents she was sending merely offerings waved in the face of the sorcerer in an attempt to appease his thirst for vengeance?

By an unfortunate coincidence a volume on magic that arrived from Paris just at that moment provided me with information on the workings of what is called sympathetic magic. The author advised his reader not to think himself innocent simply because he has undertaken no magic procedures with the express purpose of bringing harm to someone. One must also control one's ill will, which is sufficiently strong to affect another person even when absent.

This piece of information had a double application for me. First, to my conscience in the present case, since I once had in a fit of anger raised my hand to the old woman's portrait and pronounced a silent curse; secondly, to my old suspicion, now reawakened, that I might myself be the object of arcane attacks on the part of occultists or theosophists.

Remorse on the one hand, fear on the other. I was now being ground to powder between these two millstones.

❈    ❈    ❈

Here is how Swedenborg describes hell. The damned soul is lodged in a delightful palace, finds life sweet, and believes himself to be among the elect. Little by little the delights of this life begin to fade, and finally disappear altogether, and the wretched man perceives that he is imprisoned in a frightful hovel surrounded by excrement. (See the details below.)

I bade farewell to the Rose Room. And the moment I entered the large room I had been given next to my mother-in-law's I sensed that my stay there would not be a long one.

A thousand tiny inconveniences, combining eventually to make life intolerable, did in fact begin to conspire at this point against the peace of mind essential for my work.

The floor boards rocked beneath my feet, the table wobbled, the chair shook, the washstand quivered, the bed squeaked, and the rest of the furniture hopped when I walked up and down the room.

The lamp smoked, the inkwell was too narrow, and the penholder got covered with ink. It was a country house that reeked of manure, stale, sulfuretted hydrogen, and carbon disulfide. The noises made by the cows, the pigs, the calves, the hens, the turkeys, and the pigeons lasted all day long. By day I was bothered by flies and wasps, at night by mosquitoes.

There was almost nothing to be bought at the little village store. For want of anything better, I was obliged to take the only ink they had, which was blood-red! And then—something so strange—among the hundred or so white papers in a packet of cigarette papers, there was a single rose-colored one. (Rose!)[3]

It was a hell, and I was being roasted over a slow fire. Though accustomed to putting up with great griefs I suffered inordinately from these petty pinpricks, especially since my mother-in-law thought that I was dissatisfied with her hospitality, despite the infinite pains she was taking to make me comfortable.

\*  \*  \*

*September 17.* I awoke in the night to hear the church clock in the village chime thirteen. I immediately felt the usual electric sensation, and there was a noise in the loft above my head.

*September 19.* While investigating the loft I discovered a dozen or so spinning wheels, the wheels of which reminded me of the electric machines. I came upon an enormous chest. I opened it; it was almost empty, containing nothing but five sticks of no discernible use, all painted black and arranged on bottom of the chest in the form of a pentagram. Who had played this trick on me, and what did it mean? I did not dare to inquire further, and the matter remains an enigma.

That night between midnight and two o'clock, there was a terrible storm. Such storms usually exhaust themselves quickly

---

[3] The rose motif is to be associated throughout with Strindberg's erotic wishes. At this point the rose becomes a symbol of disappointed love. His young wife Frida had left him, the middle-aged husband, for good. See Brandell, *Strindbergs Infernokris,* Stockholm, 1950, pp. 84–85.–EDITOR.

and pass on. This one hung over my village for two hours. I took it as a personal attack. None of the lightning flashes aimed at me succeeded in reaching their target.

\* \* \*

During the evenings my mother-in-law told me about all the things that had been happening recently in our district. An interminable list of tragedies, domestic and otherwise, adulteries, divorces, family lawsuits, murders, thefts, rapes, incests, slanders. Every castle, villa, and shack concealed a misfortune of some sort, and I could not walk along any of the roads without being reminded of Swedenborg's hell. The ditches along the main highway were filled with beggars, madmen and madwomen, sick people and cripples, all kneeling at the feet of a crucified Christ, a Virgin, or a martyr.

At night those unfortunate wretches who suffered from insomnia and nightmares would wander through the meadows and the woods hoping to restore their capacity for sleep by dint of physical fatigue.[4] And among the people so afflicted were some of good family, well-born ladies, even a parish priest.

Quite near to our house stood a convent that was used as a place of detention for fallen women. It was a real prison block, with the harshest rules imaginable. In winter when the temperature was thirty or forty degrees below freezing, the inmates were forced to sleep on the icy stone floors of their cells, and since any kind of heating was forbidden, their feet and hands were covered with cracked and bleeding chilblains.

One of these women had fornicated with a monk, a mortal sin. Reduced to despair, lacerated by remorse, she had run to kneel before her confessor only to hear him refuse her both confession and the Holy Sacrament. "For a mortal sin there is no response but eternal damnation." Whereupon the wretched woman lost her reason, imagined she was already dead, and wandered from village to village imploring the

[4] Strindberg may be describing here the effects of the *foehn,* a hot dry wind, sometimes of gale force. Air drawn from the south descends the northern slopes and valleys of the Alps and causes physical discomfort by desiccating the skin. It is also known to have a depressing effect on the nervous system and to cause extreme restlessness and insomnia.–EDITOR.

pity of the clergy everywhere, entreating them to bury her in holy ground. Banished, driven out, she wandered about howling like a savage beast. And those who saw her would cross themselves and exclaim: "There's a soul in damnation!"

No one doubted for a moment that her soul was already burning in the eternal fires while her ghost still roamed the earth—a walking corpse intended as a hideous example for others.

I was also told the story of a man who was so possessed by a demon that the unhappy wretch's personality was utterly changed, and he was forced by the Evil One to pour out blasphemies despite all the repugnance that such behavior still had the power to arouse in him. After a long search for a suitable exorcist, someone discovered a young Franciscan monk who was a virgin and well known everywhere for his purity of heart. Eventually, after the monk had prepared himself for the task by means of fasts and penances, the great day arrived and the possessed man was led to the church to make general confession before the congregation. *Coram populo.* Thereupon the young monk set about his task. Through ceaseless prayers and conjurations that continued from morning till evening, he succeeded in expelling the demon, which fled from the man in such a horrifying manner that the terrified spectators did not dare to describe it. One year later, the young Franciscan died.

Stories such as these, and others worse still, strengthened my conviction that this particular district had been predestined as a place of penance, and that there was a mysterious correspondence between this country and the places depicted in Swedenborg's Hell. Had he visited this part of Lower Austria, and then, in much the same way as Dante used the region to the south of Naples for his descriptions, painted his Hell from nature?

—?
—?

\*     \*     \*

After two weeks of work and study I was once more chased from my lair. It was my mother-in-law's custom when autumn approached to move into her sister's apartment with her, and it was now time for us all to strike camp and move to Klam. In order to remain independent I rented a small house consisting of two rooms and a kitchen, as near as possible to my daughter.

The first evening after moving into these new quarters I experienced an agonizing difficulty in breathing, as though the air were poisoned. I immediately went down to my mother's apartment.

"If I sleep up there, you'll find me dead in bed tomorrow morning. Give a homeless wanderer shelter for the night, good mother!"

Immediately, the Rose Room was put at my disposal. But, good God, how it had changed since my aunt had left! Black furniture, a bookcase with empty shelves, yawning like so many gaping maws, windows stripped of their flowers, a high, cast-iron stove, black and thin as a specter and decorated with hideously fantasticated salamanders and dragons. Everything jarred and conspired to make me feel ill.

Moreover, because I am a creature of fixed habits, unused to doing anything except at my accustomed hours, everything there began to affect my nerves. Despite the efforts I made to conceal how upset I was, my mother was able to read my mind.

"Still unsatisfied, my child!"

She did everything she could—and more—to make me happy, but the spirits of discord were at work everywhere and there was no improvement. Oh, she would remember all my little quirks and fancies, but she always got them confused. For instance, one of the things for which I have a really strong aversion is calf's brains with browned butter.

"Look, I've got something really nice today," she said to me, "cooked specially for you." And she served me a plate of buttered brains. I understood how she had made the mistake, and I ate them, but with a loathing ill concealed by a feigned appetite.

"You're not eating!"

And she refilled my plate. It was too much!

There was a time when I attributed all my bad luck to the malice of woman. Now I recognized that she was innocent and I said to myself: it's the devil's work!

\*     \*     \*

Ever since my youth I have always devoted my morning walk to preparing the day's work ahead. I never allowed any-one to accompany me, not even my wife.

Indeed, in the morning my spirit is filled with a delicious harmony, a sort of expansive mood verging on ecstasy. I don't walk, I fly. My body loses all feeling of weight; all my mel-ancholy evaporates; I am pure spirit. It is my hour of medi-tation and prayer, my divine service.

But now that I was being forced to sacrifice everything, to renounce myself and even my most legitimate pleasures, the powers obliged me to abjure this one also, the last and most sublime of all.

For my little daughter said she wanted to accompany me. I refused her with a very tender kiss, but how could she un-derstand the reasons I gave about having to meditate? She wept. Unable to resist her further, I took her on my walk, making a firm inward decision not to permit any repetition of this abuse of my rights. Certainly children are charming; their originality, gaiety of heart, their gratitude for the slight-est pleasure are captivating, that is, as long as one has noth-ing better to do. But when I was preoccupied with my thoughts, when my mind was absent and wandering else-where, how that tiny thing could lash my spirit with its endless questions, its sudden whims. My little girl was as jealous of my thoughts as a mistress. She waited until that precise moment when her babble would destroy a whole network of skillfully woven thoughts . . . And yet, she was not doing it on purpose.—But I still had the illusion of being preyed upon by the premeditated and malicious tricks of a poor, innocent little child.

I walked up the hill with heavy steps. I no longer flew. My soul was captive, my brain empty because of the efforts I had to make in order to bring myself down to the child's level.

What made me suffer as though at the hands of a torturer were the deep looks she kept giving me, full of reproach be-cause she thought I found her a burden and didn't love her. At such times, the open, frank, beaming little face would cloud over, her eyes would turn away, and I felt myself sud-denly deprived of the light with which this child had been irradiating my darkened soul. I kissed her, I carried her in my arms, I looked for flowers and pebbles. I cut a switch from the hedge, then pretended I was a cow that she must lead to pasture.

She was happy, contented, and life smiled at me.

I had sacrificed my hour of mediation! The hour when I gathered my thoughts. This was my expiation for the harm that I had tried to bring on that angelic head in a moment of madness.

She loved me! I was expiating my crime by being loved!

Truly, the powers are not as cruel as we are!


# X

## *Extracts from the Diary of a Damned Soul*

*October–November 1896*

The Brahmin fulfills his duty towards life by begetting a child. Then he goes forth into the desert and consecrates himself to solitude and abnegation.

\*    \*    \*

MOTHER.    Unhappy man, what did you do in your previous incarnation that destiny should treat you so cruelly?

MYSELF.    Guess! Think back, first of all, to a man who married the wife of another—as I did! Then divorced her in order to marry an Austrian girl—as I did! And then, they tore his dear Austrian bride away from him, as mine has been stolen from me, and their only child was shut away on the slopes of the Bohemian forest, as my child has been. Do you recall the hero of my novel *By the Open Sea?*[1] He died a wretched death on an island in the middle of the sea. . . .

MOTHER.    That's enough! Enough!

[1] *I hafsbandet* (written in 1890), Strindberg's most Nietzschean novel.—EDITOR.

MYSELF. You didn't know that my father's mother's name was Neipperg, did you?

MOTHER. Be quiet, unhappy man!

MYSELF. —or that my little Christine resembles the greatest mass murderer of the century. She's even got his forelock. You only have to look at her, the empress, the man-tamer, just two and a half years old—[2]

MOTHER. You're mad!

MYSELF. Yes!—And you women, what sins you must have committed in the past to make your destiny even crueller than ours! See how right I am in calling women our demons. Each one according to his deserts!

MOTHER. True, it's double hell to be woman.

MYSELF. And a woman is a double demon. As for reincarnation, it's a Christian doctrine that the clergy have cast into the shadows. Jesus Christ said that St. John the Baptist was a reincarnation of Elijah. Is that good authority or is it not?

MOTHER. Certainly, but the Roman Church forbids research into the occult!

MYSELF. And occultism allows it, because no branch of science is forbidden to it.

*　　*　　*

The spirits of discord sprang up on every side, and despite our perfect understanding of their methods and our shared

[2] It was characteristic of Strindberg's turn of mind to see analogues and similarities everywhere, and during this phase of his life he constantly pointed out parallels between his own career and that of others. In 1896 and 1897 we find him in his letters referring to himself ironically and sometimes poignantly as Caesar, Ahasuerus, and Augustus. But his favorite role for a brief time was Napoleon. In letters to his wife he becomes the "Corsican" and she the Empress Marie Louise, while their daughter Kerstin becomes Juno Bonaparte. After divorcing his first wife, Napoleon married Marie Louise of Austria. After divorcing his first wife, Strindberg married Frida Uhl, an Austrian. Count Neipperg, who became the lover and consoler of Marie Louise when Napoleon was shipped off to Elba, was the Austrian ambassador to Sweden from 1811 to 1813. Strindberg's paternal grandmother's name was Neijber. See article by Nils Norman in *Svensk Litteraturtidskrift*, 1959.—EDITOR.

awareness of each other's innocence, there were repeated contretemps that increased the tension.

On top of this, the two sisters now had some suspicion that my ill will had played a part in their mother's illness, and because of the advantage I would necessarily gain by the removal of this obstacle separating me from my wife, they could not rid themselves of the quite natural idea that the old woman's death would inevitably be a source of pleasure to me. The mere existence of this wish made me odious in their eyes, and I no longer dared to make any enquiry concerning the grandmother for fear of being called a hypocrite.

The situation was tense, and my two old friends exhausted themselves in endless discussions about my person, my character, my opinions, and the sincerity of my love for the little girl.

One day I was believed to be a saint, and the deep cracks on my hands were taken to be stigmata. Indeed the marks on the palms did look like holes made by big nails, and in order to eschew all pretentions to saintliness, I said I was the good thief come down from the cross and now on a pilgrimage, hoping to win a place in paradise.

Another day, after speculating on the enigma I represented to them, they decided that I was Robert le Diable.[3] After which, a combination of events began to instill in me the fear that I might eventually be stoned by the populace. These are the bare facts. My little Christine had an excessive horror of the village chimney sweep. One evening when we were all sitting around the supper table, she quite suddenly began to scream. Pointing her finger at some invisible figure behind my chair, she cried: "There's the sweep!"

My mother, who believes in the clairvoyant powers of children and animals, grew very pale. I myself was afraid, espe-

---

[3] In medieval legend, Robert le Diable, who is often identified with Robert the Magnificent, Duke of Normandy from 1027 to 1035, was said to have been sold to the devil by his mother. When Robert learned of what his mother had done, he did penance and cleansed himself of his sins. "Robert le Diable" was the working title for *To Damascus* when Strindberg began writing the play in January 1898.—EDITOR.

cially when I saw that my mother was making the sign of the cross over the child's head.

This incident was followed by a deathly silence that gripped my heart like a vise.

\* \* \*

Autumn was upon us with its storms, its rains, its darkness. The sick, the dying, and the dead became more numerous in the village and in the poorhouse. At night one could hear the little bell of the choirboy walking ahead of the Last Sacrament. By day the church bells tolled out knell after knell. The funeral processions went by, one after another. Life was all gloom, and deadly dull. And my nocturnal attacks began again.

They said prayers for me, told rosaries, and the font in my bedroom was filled with holy water newly blessed by the parish priest.

"The hand of the Lord is heavy upon you!"

It was my mother who crushed me with this apostrophe.

I bowed before the storm, but soon drew myself up again. Armed with a deep-rooted skepticism and possessed of an unusual flexibility of mind, I wrested my soul from these black thoughts, and after reading certain occult works, I imagined that I was being persecuted by elementals, by incubi, by lamias, who were trying to prevent me from completing my great alchemical work. On the advice of initiates, I procured a Dalmatian dagger and felt that I was now well armed against these evil spirits.

A shoemaker in the village, an atheist and a blasphemer, had just died. He had kept a jackdaw as a pet and the abandoned bird had settled on a neighboring roof. During the vigil over the dead body, the jackdaw suddenly appeared in the room, and those who were keeping vigil could not explain how it entered. On the day of the burial the black bird accompanied the funeral procession, and during the ceremony in the graveyard, it perched on the lid of the coffin.

In the morning this creature would follow me along the roads—very upsetting to me, because the villagers were so superstitious. One day—the last—the jackdaw led me through the streets of the village emitting a series of frightful shrieks, interspersed with occasional swear words picked up from the blasphemer. Whereupon two smaller birds, a robin and a wagtail, entered the scene and chased the jackdaw from roof to roof. The jackdaw fled from the village and took refuge on the chimney of a cottage. At the same instant a black rabbit hopped in front of the house and disappeared into the grass.

Several days later the jackdaw was found dead—killed by some of the village boys who hated it because of its penchant for stealing.

\*       \*       \*

Meanwhile, I was working every day in the little house I had rented. But it appeared that I had fallen into disfavor once more with the powers. Often upon entering, I found the air inside thick, as though it had been poisoned, and I was obliged to work with the door and windows open. Muffled up in a thick overcoat and a fur hat, I stayed at my table writing, even though I was forced to struggle continually against the so-called electric attacks, which held my chest in a vise-like grip and stabbed ceaselessly at my back. I often had the impression that there was someone standing behind my chair. When that happened I lunged behind me with a knife, imagining that I was fighting some enemy. This would last until five in the evening. If I stayed after that hour, the struggle became appalling. Exhausted and at the end of my tether, I would light a lantern and go down to be with my mother and the child.

Only on one occasion, after a day spent sitting in an icy stream of air because of the thick, suffocating atmosphere in the room, did I prolong the struggle till six o'clock, and this was in order to finish a chemistry article I was writing. A ladybug (*une bête à bon Dieu*), black with yellow spots, was clambering over a bunch of flowers, blindly trying to find a way out. Eventually it fell onto my paper, where it opened and fluttered its wings just like the weathercock on top of Notre-Dame-des-Champs in Paris. Then it crawled across the sheet of manuscript, reached my right hand, and climbed up onto it. It looked at me, and then flew out at the window.

Glancing at the compass lying on my table, I saw that the insect had made its escape towards the north.

"So be it!" I said to myself. "To the North then! But at my leisure, and when it suits me. Until further orders I am staying where I am."

After six o'clock, it became completely impossible to remain in that haunted house. Unknown forces lifted me from my chair, and I had to shut up shop.

\* \* \*

On All Souls' Day, at about three in the afternoon, the sun was shining and the air was calm. The villagers, led by their priests, went out in procession, with banners and music, to pay tribute to their dead in the graveyard. The church bells began to ring. Suddenly, without warning, without a single premonitory cloud in the pale blue sky, a storm blew up.

The cloth banners began to flap against their poles, the clothes of the men and women in the procession were whipped about at the mercy of the wind, the dust rose up in spiraling clouds, the trees were bent by the blast. . . . It was a true miracle.

\* \* \*

I was afraid of the night ahead, but my mother was prepared for this. She gave me an amulet to wear around my neck. It was the Virgin Mother and a cross carved out of holy wood from a beam in a church more than a thousand years old. I accepted it as a precious gift given out of the goodness of her heart. But a lingering remnant of my ancestral religion prevented me from hanging it around my neck.

At about eight o'clock that evening we sat down to supper. The lamps were lit and a sinister calm reigned over our little company. Outside it was pitch black. The trees were silent. On all sides utter calm.

Then a gust of wind, just one, forced its way through the spaces between the windows and their frames with a wail like the sound of a jew's-harp. Then it stopped.

My mother threw me a terrible glance and hugged the child tightly in her arms.

It was all over in a moment, but I had grasped the meaning of that look. Go away from here; you are damned; your presence is attracting avenging demons and endangering the innocent.

My world crumbled about me. The only happiness left to me, being with my daughter, had been taken away, and in the gloomy silence that followed I inwardly bade farewell to life.

After supper I withdrew to the Rose Room, black now, and prepared myself for a nocturnal battle since I felt that I was threatened, besieged. By whom? I didn't know. But I challenged the invisible presence, whatever it was, Eternal God or vengeful demon, and made ready to wrestle as Jacob did with God.

There was a knock at the door. It was my mother. Sensing the uncomfortable night that lay ahead of me, she invited me to sleep on the sofa in the drawing room.

"The child's presence will protect you!"

I thanked her, assuring her at the same time that there was no danger, and that I was afraid of nothing as long as my conscience was clear.

With a smile, she wished me good night.

Resolving to die fully clothed, I donned my fur hat and boots in preparation for the battle, ready to defy death like a valiant warrior who has braved all that life could offer.

At about eleven o'clock, as the air in the room grew thicker, a mortal anguish began to curdle my courage. I got up and opened the window. A draught of cold air threatened to put out the lamp. I closed it again.

The lamp began to sing, to groan, to whimper. Then silence.

One of the dogs in the village began to howl—traditionally an omen of death.

I looked through the window. Only the Big Dipper was visible. Below, in the poorhouse, there was an old woman bent over her sewing, working by candlelight, waiting for deliverance, perhaps afraid of sleep and her dreams.

I was so tired I lay down on my bed and tried to sleep. Immediately the usual tricks began. An electric current began groping for my heart; my lungs ceased to function; I had to get up or else die there and then. I sat down on a chair, too exhausted to read, and remained there, unable to think, for half an hour.

I decided to go out and walk about until daybreak. I went down into the street. The night was dark and the village was asleep—except for the dogs. The first to scent me called to the others, and as they came crowding around me, with their gaping jaws and glowing eyes, I was forced to retreat.

Back in the house again, as I opened the door of my room, I could sense that it was occupied by living and hostile beings. The room was full of them, and it was like fighting my way through a crowd to reach my bed, upon which, resigned and resolved to die, I eventually collapsed. But at the supreme moment, when the invisible vulture was finally squeezing the breath from me with its talons, someone tore me from the bed where I lay, and the furies began to harry me all over again. Vanquished, routed, beaten to my knees, I quit the battlefield and felt myself weakening in this ill-matched struggle against the invisible powers.

I knocked on the door of the drawing room, on the other side of the passage. My mother, still up and at her prayers, came and opened the door.

The expression that appeared on her face as soon as she saw mine inspired me with a profound horror of myself.

"What do you want, my child?"

"I want to die and then be burned. Or rather, I want to be burned alive!"

Not a word did she reply! She had understood and was struggling against the horror she felt. But pity, her religion and charity won the day. She tucked me in on the sofa with her own hands before retiring to her own room where she slept with the child.

By chance—always that satanic chance!—the sofa was situated opposite the window, and that same chance had seen to it that there were no curtains, so that the black opening of the casement looking out into the darkness of the night was staring me straight in the eyes. And it was through this very window, moreover, that the gust of wind had howled in upon us that evening during supper.

At the end of my strength, I sank back upon my improvised bed, cursing the ubiquitous and ineluctable chance that was pursuing me everywhere with the manifest purpose of awakening a persecution mania in me.

I lay quietly for five minutes, eyes fixed upon the black square ahead. Then the invisible specter slid across my body, and I got up. I remained standing there in the middle of the room for I know not how long, as still as a statue, transformed into a stylite, dozing fitfully where I stood.

But who was giving me the strength to go on suffering? Who was refusing me death while abandoning me to these tortures?

Was it He, the Lord of life and death, the being I had offended when, after reading the pamphlet "The Joys of Dying," I had made those attempts at suicide, believing myself ripe for eternal life?

Was I Phlegyas, condemned for his pride to the anguish and agonies of Tartarus? Or Prometheus, lying a tortured prey to the vulture's beak and claws for having revealed the secret of the Powers to mortal man?

(As I write this, I think of the scene during the Passion of Jesus Christ when the soldiers spat in his face and struck him, some with their hands and some with whips, saying: "Prophesy, who is it that smote thee?")

(Let the companions of my youth recall a certain wild evening in Stockholm when the writer of this book himself enacted the part of the soldier. . . .)

Who had struck him? The unanswered question, the doubt, the uncertainty, the mystery—those were my hell.

Let him show himself and I will fight with him, I will challenge him face to face!

But that is precisely what he took care not to do, in order to afflict me with madness, to scourge me with a bad conscience that makes us see enemies on every side. The enemies were those who had been harmed by my evil intents. And every time I unearthed a new enemy, it was because my conscience had been aroused.

*    *    *

The following day, when I awoke after a few hours of sleep to the babble of my little Christine, everything was forgotten, and I immediately turned my mind to the work I had in hand, which was progressing well. Everything I wrote was being printed immediately, a fact that reassured me as to the state of my mind and intellect.

At about that time there was a rumor reported in the newspapers that an American scientist[4] had discovered a method of changing silver into gold, an occurrence that freed me from all suspicions of black magic, madness, or charlatanism. It was at this moment that my friend the theosophist, who had been subsidizing me till then, approached me with a view to enrolling me as a member of his sect.

Accompanying the copy of Mme. Blavatsky's *Secret Doctrine* that he sent me was a letter which did little to conceal how anxious he was for my opinion of the book; and I too felt some concern, for I suspected that continuance of our friendly relations depended on how I answered.

The *Secret Doctrine,* a collection of all the theories included under the heading occult, a mishmash of every ancient or modern scientific heresy, is absolutely valueless when the lady is expressing her own opinions—which are idiotic—interesting when she quotes little-known authors, and detestable for the deceptions, whether conscious or not, which it contains and also for its stories about the existence of the mahatmas. It is the work of a gynandromorph who has tried to outdo men and is glorying in the thought of bringing low all science, religion, and philosophy in order to raise a priestess of Isis onto the altar of Christ.[5]

With all the reservations and all the considerations due to a friend, I let him know my opinion, adding that the collective god Karma was not to my taste and that, for this reason, I could not become an adherent of any sect that rejected a personal God, who alone was able to satisfy my religious needs. I was being asked for a profession of faith, and although I was convinced that my words would bring about a rupture entailing the withdrawal of my subsidies, I was frank in the matter.

Whereupon this sincere friend, a man with an excellent

[4] Possibly a man named Emmons.–EDITOR.
[5] See footnote to page 185.–EDITOR.

heart, was transformed into an avenging demon, hurling excommunications upon me, threatening me with occult powers, intimidating me with hints about reprisals I should now expect, and vaticinating like a pagan priest intent on a human sacrifice. He ended by summoning me to appear before an occult tribunal, and vowing that I would never forget November 13.

My situation was distressing. I had lost a friend and I was reduced to poverty. And there was another incident too, one that coincided by diabolical chance with our battle of letters.

*L'Initiation* had published an article in which I criticized the present astronomical system. Several days later, Tisserand, the director of the Paris Observatory, had died. In a humorous moment I linked these two facts together, comparing them with the death of Pasteur the day after the publication of *Sylva Sylvarum*.[6] My friend the theosophist did not understand the joke and either because he was monumentally credulous or perhaps because, being even better acquainted than myself with black magic, he began to suspect me of practicing witchcraft.

My terror may be imagined when, after the last letter had passed between us, the most celebrated astronomer in Sweden happened to die of an apoplectic fit.

I took fright—and with good cause. To be suspected of practicing sorcery is a capital crime, and "should the sorcerer be slain, no punishment is meted out to the slayer."[7]

To heap horror upon horror: in the course of that month five more fairly well-known astronomers expired, one after the other.

I was afraid of my fanatic friend, for I believed him to

[6] In the September 1896 issue of *l'Initiation* there appeared an article by Strindberg, "La terre, sa forme, ses mouvements." François-Félix Tisserand, director of the Paris Observatory since 1892, died on October 20, 1896. Tisserand had devoted much of his career to determining the exact orbits of the planets.

Louis Pasteur died on September 28, 1895. About that time the Mercure de France published Strindberg's pamphlet *"Introduction à une chimie unitaire,"* which was intended by Strindberg as part of *Sylva Sylvarum.*—EDITOR.

[7] Strindberg is quoting from the medieval Swedish law, which regarded a sorcerer as an outlaw.—EDITOR.

possess not only the cruelty of a Druid but also the power claimed by Hindu magicians of being able to kill at a distance.

A new hell of anguish! And from that day on I forgot the avenging demons and directed all my thoughts toward the deadly intrigues of the theosophists and their magicians, who are thought to be Hindus endowed with unbelievable powers.

At that point I felt that I was condemned to die, and I took the step of leaving documents denouncing my murderers in a sealed envelope, in case I should meet with sudden death. Then I waited.

\*　　\*　　\*

Ten kilometers to the east on the bank of the Danube stood the little town of Grein, the chief town of the district. Towards the end of November, when it was already full winter there, I was told that a stranger from Zanzibar had come to stay there as a tourist. That was sufficient to awaken all the doubts and black fears of a sick man. I had investigations made about this foreigner. I wanted to know if he really was African, what his designs were, and where he had come from.

Nothing could be learned, and this foreigner who haunted my days and nights remained shrouded in a veil of mystery. And in my extreme distress, I who always stood close to the spirit of the Old Testament implored the protection of the Almighty and invoked his avenging powers against my enemies.

The Psalms of David were what best expressed my hopes, and old Jacob was my God. The eighty-sixth psalm particularly became fixed in my mind, and I repeated endlessly the words: "O God, the proud are risen against me, and the assemblies of violent men have sought after my soul; and have not set thee before them. . . .

"Shew me a token for good; that they which hate me may see it, and be ashamed: because thou, Lord, hast holpen me, and comforted me."

It was this token that I invoked. And mark, reader, how my prayer was answered.

# XI

## *The Almighty Has Spoken*

Winter had come with its yellow-gray sky. Not a single ray of sunshine for weeks on end. The muddy roads made it difficult to go for a walk. The leaves from the trees rotted on the ground. All nature was decomposing in the grip of a contagious gangrene.

The autumn slaughter had begun, and the wails of its victims rose all day towards the black vault above. The butchers waded in blood amid the carcasses.

It was all mortally depressing, and my own sadness added to the burden of the two good sisters of charity who were caring for me like their own sick child. What finally threatened to break my spirit was the necessity of concealing my poverty and my futile attempts to ward off imminent destitution.

Besides, they wanted me to leave. They felt the solitary life was unproductive for a man, and they both agreed that I needed to see a doctor.

I waited in vain for the necessary money to arrive from my own country and marched up and down the main highway, readying myself for a possible escape on foot.

"I am become like the pelican in the desert; I am become like the owl in its lair."

My presence was a torture for my relations. If it had not been for the love of the child, they would have driven me out. Now that there was always mud or snow preventing her going out for walks, I used to carry my little girl in my arms along the roads, climbing hills, scrambling over rocks.

And the old ladies would say, "You are undermining your health, you'll end up consumptive, you'll kill yourself!"

"What a beautiful way to die!"

\*    \*    \*

One gray, dark, loathsome day, the twentieth of November, we were at dinner. Burnt out by a sleepless night spent in continual battle with the invisible powers, I cursed life and complained of the lack of sunshine.

My mother predicted that I would not get well again before Candlemas, before the return of the sun.

"There is my only ray of sunshine," I said, pointing to my little Christine sitting opposite me.

At that precise moment the clouds that had been massed above us week after week parted. A beam of light burst into the room and lit up my face, the tablecloth, the dishes.

"There's the sun! Papa, there's the sun!" cried my child, clasping her little hands together.

I rose from the table, disturbed, gripped by the most contradictory sensations. A coincidence? "No!" I said to myself.

The miracle? The token? But that was too much to expect for a condemned wretch like myself. The Almighty does not trouble himself with the private affairs of a worm!

And yet, and yet—that ray of sunlight shone on my heart, like a great smile in the face of my discontent.

During the two minutes it took me to walk round to my little house the clouds piled themselves up into great masses presenting the most extravagant shapes to the eye. And in the east, where the veil had been lifted, the sky was green, emerald green like a hayfield in high summer.

I remained standing in the middle of my room, waiting for something undefinable, plunged into a deep and calm contrition, freed from all fear.

Then, without any lightning to precede it, a clap of thunder, one single clap, boomed out above my head.

At first I was afraid and stood waiting for the rain, for a storm, as was only natural. But nothing happened. Absolute calm reigned everywhere, and it was all over.

"Why," I asked myself, "do I not throw myself on my face before the voice of the Almighty? Why do I not humble myself before him?"

Because when the Almighty deigns to speak with such majestic gestures to an insect, then the insect feels itself grow bigger, feels itself blown up by such an honor, and pride whispers in its ear that it must be a creature of great and particular worth. To speak quite frankly, I considered myself to be on the same level as the Lord, an integral part of his personality, an emanation of his being, an organ of his organism. He had need of me to manifest himself, otherwise I should have been blasted into nothingness on the spot.

What was the source of this preternatural pride in a mortal? Was it that I could trace my origin to the beginnings of time when the rebellious angels conspired together, rising in revolt against a sovereign who was content to dominate over a race of slaves? Was it for this reason that my pilgrimage on earth had unfolded like a play in which I had been constantly ambushed by lackeys with cudgels, in which the lowest of the low were always delightedly thrashing me, insulting me, and spitting upon me?

There was no imaginable humiliation I had not suffered, and yet my pride still continued to grow, step by step with my abasement! Now what did that bring to mind? Jacob wrestling with the Almighty and emerging from the struggle slightly maimed but bearing all the honors of victory. Job, put to the test, and never ceasing to recognize the justice of the punishments so unjustly inflicted upon him.

I was battered and bruised by so many incoherent thoughts, and my fatigue finally obliged me to loose my hold on them. The swelling of my ego began to abate, my soul to shrivel up, so that what had just happened was reduced to nothingness—a mere thunderclap in late November!

At that moment the rumbling of thunder sounded overhead once more. Back in the grip of ecstasy, I walked over and opened the Bible at random, praying to the Lord that he might speak more clearly, so that I should understand.

My gaze fell immediately upon this verse from Job: "Wilt thou also disannul my judgment? Wilt thou condemn me, that thou mayest be righteous?

"Hast thou an arm like God? *Or canst thou thunder with a voice like him?*"

There could be no further doubt. The Almighty had spoken!

"Almighty Lord, what do you want of me? Speak, for thy servant listens."

No answer?

It was well. I was humbling myself before the Almighty who had deigned to humble himself before his servant. But to bend my knee before the people and the powerful of the earth? Never!

*    *    *

That evening my good mother greeted me in a manner which I still cannot understand. She looked at me out of the corner of her eye as though she were searching my face in an attempt to gauge the effect that this recent and majestic spectacle had made upon me.

"Did you hear it?"

"Yes, it was odd—thunder in winter."

At least, she no longer believed me to be a damned soul.


# XII

## *The Hellhounds Unleashed*


Meanwhile, an issue of *L'Événement* had appeared containing an article calculated to spread confusion as to the precise nature of the mysterious illness that had attacked me. It offered the following information.

"The unfortunate Strindberg, having brought his misogyny with him to Paris, was very soon obliged to make his escape. Since then, his fellow believers have remained silent before the banner of feminism. . . . They have no desire to suffer the same fate as Orpheus, who had his head torn off by the Bacchantes of Thrace."[1]

So it was true that a trap had been set for me on the Rue de la Clef! The attempted murder that had produced the morbid condition of which I was still displaying the symptoms was a reality! Oh, those women! Clearly it was my arti-

---

[1] *L'Événement* for October 26, 1896. The remark about Strindberg appeared in a news article "La veine" by the reporter Émile Goudeau.—EDITOR.

cle on the feminist paintings of my woman-worshipping Danish friend[2] that had been at the root of all this.

At last it was a fact, a palpable reality, and this relieved me of all my terrible suspicions that I might be mentally ill.

I rushed to my mother with the good news. I showed her the proof that I wasn't a madman.

"No, you're not mad; you're simply ill. And the doctor's advice is that you should take more physical exercise. Chopping wood, for example."

"Really? Does that create a favorable disposition towards women, or the opposite?"

This reply was a little too pointed; it drove us apart. I had forgotten that however saintly a woman may be she always remains a woman—which is to say, the enemy of the male.

\* \* \*

Everything else was pushed out of my mind—the Russians, the Rothschilds, the black magicians, the theosophists, even the Almighty. I was the victim, Job, the perfect and upright man, and the women had tried to kill Orpheus, the author of *Sylva Sylvarum*, bringer of new life to the moribund natural sciences. Lost in a forest of doubts, I dismissed the recently formed idea of a supernatural intervention on the part of the powers with some higher goal in view, and I neglected to fill in the details of this attempt on my life and made no inquiry into who had instigated it.

Agitated by a burning desire for vengeance, I was in the process of drawing up an accusatory letter to the Préfecture de Police in Paris and another for distribution to the Parisian newspapers, when a timely change in my situation occurred to bring to an end this tedious drama, which was verging on farce.

One yellow-gray day about an hour after dinner, my little Christine insisted on going with me to my little house, to which I customarily retired for a nap at that hour.

It was impossible to resist her and I yielded to her entreaties.

When we had climbed up to my room, my little Christine

---

[2] "L'exposition d'Edvard Munch," *La Revue Blanche* (Paris), Vol. 10, June 1, 1896, pp. 525–6. This short piece was written to advertise Munch's exhibit at Bing's gallery *L'Art nouveau.*–EDITOR.

demanded crayons and paper. Then she wanted to look at picture books. And I had to be there, explaining the pictures to her, drawing for her.

"Don't go to sleep, Papa!"

Tired, worn out, I could not understand why I continued to obey the child. But there was a certain tone in her voice that I found irresistible.

Then, outside, in front of the door, an organ-grinder began to play a waltz. I suggested to my little girl that she dance with the maid who had come with her. Attracted by the music, the neighbor's children appeared too. The barrel-organ player was invited into the kitchen, and before long my hallway had been transformed into an impromptu dance hall.

The merriment went on for an hour and my sadness vanished.

Looking for something to occupy my mind and still longing for sleep, I took up the Bible that I used as my oracle and opening it at random, I read:

"But the Spirit of the Lord departed from Saul, and an evil spirit from the Lord troubled him.

"And Saul's servants said unto him, Behold now, an evil spirit from God troubleth thee.

"Let our lord now command thy servants, which are before thee, to seek out a man, who is a cunning player on an harp: and it shall come to pass, when the evil spirit from God is upon thee, that he shall play with his hand, and thou shalt be well."

An evil spirit—exactly what I had suspected.

While the children were still amusing themselves in this way, my mother came to take her little granddaughter home, and when she saw them dancing she stood dumbfounded.

She told me that down in the village, at exactly the same time, a lady of the noblest family in the district had succumbed to a fit of madness.

"What sort of madness?"

"She's dancing. And old as she is, the dancing doesn't seem to tire her. She's all dressed up in a wedding gown and she thinks she's Bürger's Lenore."[3]

[3] "Lenore" was a popular ballad, written about 1775, by Gottfried August Bürger. It tells of a young girl who is visited by the specter of her soldier fiancé and carried off to death.—EDITOR.

"She's dancing? What else!"

"She's weeping. She's afraid because death is going to come and take her away."

What increased the horror of this situation even further was the fact that this lady had once lived in the house where I was staying, and that her husband had died in the very room where the children's dance was now in full swing.

Explain that, doctors, psychiatrists, psychologists! Or else admit that your science is bankrupt!

\* \* \*

My little daughter had exorcised the Evil One, and the spirit, driven out by her innocence, had hurled itself upon an old woman who boasted of being a freethinker.

This *danse macabre* went on all night, and the lady's friends kept watch over her to protect her from the attacks of Death. She called it Death, because she denied the existence of demons. There were even times when she claimed that her dead husband was tormenting her.

\* \* \*

My departure was postponed, and in order to recover the strength drained from me by so many sleepless nights, I began sleeping in my aunt's apartment on the other side of the street.

So I left the Rose Room. (Interesting coincidence: In the good old days the Stockholm torture chamber also used to be called the Rose Room. *Rosenkammaren!*)

I spent the first night there in a quiet whitewashed room decorated with pictures of saints. Above my bed, a crucifix.

But during the second night the spirits began playing their tricks again. I lit candles in order to pass the time reading. A sinister silence held sway and I could hear the beating of my heart. Then—a tiny noise that sounded like an electric spark.

Could it be?

An enormous lump of tallow had fallen from one of the candles onto the floor. Nothing more than that. But where I came from it is an omen of death. Death! So be it! After reading for another quarter of an hour I reached for my handkerchief, which I had tucked beneath the bolster. It was not there. I made a search and found it on the floor. I leaned down to pick it up. At that moment something fell on my head. I ran my fingers through my hair and discovered a second lump of tallow.

Far from being frightened, I was unable to suppress a smile, so trifling did the incident appear to me.

To smile at death! How could such a thing be possible if life itself were not ridiculous? So much ado for so little! Perhaps there is even a vague suspicion hidden in the depths of our souls that everything down here is nothing but sham, pretense, counterfeit, and that our sufferings are merely a game for the gods.

*　　*　　*

Above the village at the summit of the mountains on which the castle stood, there was one peak that dominated all the others, and from which it was possible to see the whole of the inferno-like gorge. The way up to it was through a grove of oaks, possibly a thousand years old, and because of the abundant growths of mistletoe on neighboring lime and apple trees it was believed to have been a Druids' grove. Above this wood the path ran up abruptly through a dark pine forest.

I had attempted to reach the summit on several occasions but something unforeseen had always occurred to turn me back—a roebuck breaking the silence with an unexpected leap, a hare with something extraordinary about it, or a shrike with its nerve-shattering call. On my last morning, the day before I was to leave, braving every obstacle, I entered the fir wood—dark, dismal—climbed to the top, and stood on the summit. Spread out before me was a superb view over the Danube valley and the Styrian Alps. The dark hollows below were all behind me and I found myself breathing again for the first time. The sun gave to this landscape an infinity of different aspects, and the white crests of the Alps melted into the clouds. It was as beautiful as paradise! Does this earth perhaps contain both heaven and hell? It is possible that there are no other places for punishments and rewards? Perhaps! And without doubt when I recall the most beautiful moments of my life they seem in memory to be celestial, just as the worst moments seem to have been hellish.

Had the future more of them in store for me, I wondered, any more of those hours or minutes of happiness that are purchased only with anguish and relative purity of conscience.

I stayed up there, feeling little compulsion to descend again into the vale of tears below me. As I walked there on that plateau, wondering at all the beauty of the earth, I noticed how the separate rock that formed the topmost summit of the hill had been sculptured by nature into the figure of an Egyptian sphinx. On top of the giant figure's head there was a little heap of stones, and embedded in those stones was a little stick with a piece of white cloth tied on it to form a flag.

I did not attempt to ponder the significance of this structure, but I was seized by a single irresistible thought: the removal of that flag!

Disregarding all the possible danger, I stormed the rock and took the flag. Immediately and unexpectedly there rang out from the slope facing the Danube below me the strains of a wedding march and a chorus of voices raised in triumphant song. I could tell from the traditional gunshots that it was a wedding procession, although it was invisible from where I stood.

Being enough of a child in spirit and sufficiently poor and miserable to extract poetry from the most common and natural incidents, I accepted this as a favorable omen.

And then, regretfully, with halting steps, I went down once more into the valley of sorrows and death, of insomnia and demons. For my little Beatrice was awaiting me there below, and I was taking back the mistletoe I had promised her, the green branch flourishing amid the snows, the branch that should be gathered with a golden sickle.[4]

\*    \*    \*

For some time the old grandmother had been expressing a desire to see me, perhaps with a view to a reconciliation,

[4] The European mistletoe is better known to English readers as the Golden Bough of legend.–EDITOR.

perhaps for reasons to do with the occult, for she was clairvoyant and saw visions. I had given various excuses for postponing this visit, but once the date of my departure had been
decided my mother said that I must go and see the old
woman and say goodbye to her—probably for the last time
on this side of the grave.

On November 26, therefore, a day of cold, clear weather,
we made our way, my mother, the child, and myself, towards
the Danube on whose banks the family manor is situated.

We got off at the inn, and while waiting for my mother to
return from the house where she had gone to tell the old
woman that I was waiting to see her, I took a walk through
those meadows and woods that I had not seen for the past
two years. I was overwhelmed by memories, and the image
of my wife was everywhere. Everything had been ravaged by
the winter frosts. Not a flower, not a blade of green grass to
be seen where we had wandered together and gathered all
the flowers of spring, of summer, of fall.

That afternoon I was taken to see the old woman, who was
living in the small house adjoining the villa, the very place
where my daughter had been born. Our interview was polite
and cold. They were apparently expecting a scene in the
nature of the return of the prodigal; but I can feel only distaste for that kind of emotionalism.

I restricted myself to reviving all my memories of that
lost paradise. My wife and I had painted the woodwork of
those doors and windows ourselves in honor of the birth of
our little Christine. The roses and clematis decorating the
front of the little house had been planted by my own hand.
The path across the garden owed its existence to my efforts.
But the walnut tree I had planted the day after Christine's
birth had disappeared. "The tree of life," as we named it, was
dead.

Two years, two eternities, had flowed by since we had
last exchanged goodbyes. She had been on the bank, I on the
boat taking me to Linz on my way to Paris.

Who was responsible for the breakup? It was I who had
killed both my own love and hers. Farewell, white house of
Darnach, garden of thorns, garden of roses. Farewell, Danube! I console myself by imagining that you were nothing

but a dream, brief as summer and sweeter than reality, a reality for which I feel no regrets.

\*    \*    \*

That night was spent in the inn where my mother and the child had taken refuge at my entreaty, hoping that their presence would protect me against the dark pangs of death that a sixth sense developed during my six consecutive months of torture warned me were imminent.

At ten that evening a gust of wind began to shake the door of my room leading out to the corridor. I made it firm with wooden wedges. But nothing helped; it continued to rattle.

Then the windows began to whine. The stove howled like a dog. The whole house pitched like a ship at sea.

I could not sleep, and at times I could hear my mother moaning, at others our little girl crying.

In the morning my mother, harrowed by lack of sleep and other things that she concealed from me, said, "You must leave, my son. I cannot bear the fumes of hell any longer."

And I set out to the North to face the fire of the enemy at some new station on my pilgrimage toward expiation.

# XIII

## *Pilgrimage and Expiation*

There are ninety towns in Sweden, and it was in the one I loathed most that the powers condemned me to take up my abode.[1]

I began by visiting the doctors.

Each one tagged me with a different label. The first read "neurasthenia," the second "angina pectoris," the third "paranoia," the fourth "emphysema." . . . These were sufficient to protect me against the threat of being locked up in a lunatic asylum.

Meanwhile, in order to provide for my needs I was obliged

[1] Malmö.–EDITOR.

to write articles for a newspaper. But every time I sat down
to write, all hell broke loose. They had hit upon a new
method of hounding me to madness. As soon as I moved
into any hotel, a frightful noise would begin, much like the
one on the Rue de la Grande-Chaumière in Paris: dragging
feet and moving furniture. I changed hotels—but the noise
was always there, above my head. I would go into a restaurant: as soon as I sat down in the dining room, the din would
start again. And it must be noted that I always asked those
about me if they could hear the same noise as myself. In
every case they replied in the affirmative and gave the same
description of what they heard.

Therefore, it was not an auditory hallucination. So I said
to myself it must be a deliberate plot. But one day the noise
began exactly at the instant when I walked into a shoemaker's shop on an impulse. Since my impulse could not
have been predicted, that meant there was no plot. It was
the devil! Having been driven from hotel to hotel, persecuted
by the electric wires which followed me wherever I went and
which in some cases even ran along the very edge of the bed,
ceaselessly harassed by electric currents that tore me from
my chair or my bed, I set about making formal preparations
to end my life.

The weather could not have been worse, and I sought to
alleviate my misery by drinking with friends.

One day, feeling quite awful, on the morning after such a
bacchanal, I finished the breakfast that had been brought
up to my room, left the tray with its dishes on the table, and
turned my back on the debris.

I heard a dull thud and, looking round, I saw that the
knife had fallen from the tray. I picked it up and replaced
it carefully in such a position that the same accident could
not occur again. The knife rose from the tray and fell.

So there was electricity at work!

That same morning I wrote a letter to my Austrian
"mother," complaining about the bad weather and life in general. As I wrote the words, "The earth is dirty, the sea is filthy,
and the sky is raining mud—" I was amazed to see a drop of
pure water fall on my paper!

No electricity this time! A miracle!

That evening while I was still sitting at my table, I was startled by a noise coming from the direction of the wash-stand. When I looked round, I saw that a piece of oilcloth I used when washing and shaving in the morning had fallen down. As a check, I rehung the piece of cloth in such a way that it was impossible for it to slip off.

It fell again!

Now what was this force?

My ideas turned once more towards the occultists and their secret powers. I left the town, taking my letter of denuncia-tion with me, and made my way to Lund where certain old friends were living—doctors, psychiatrists, even theosophists —people I was counting on to guarantee my temporal sal-vation.

\*     \*     \*

Why and how was I led to settle in that little university town? Lund is regarded as a place of banishment or expiation for students from the University of Uppsala whose dissipa-tions have proved more than their purses and health can bear.

Was it a Canossa where I was to renounce my radical views in the presence of the selfsame youthful body that had once elected me its standard-bearer in the 1880s? I knew the situation there well enough, nor was I unaware that most of the professors had excommunicated me as a seducer of the young, and that the mothers and fathers feared me like the Evil One.

In addition, I had made personal enemies in the place and had contracted debts in circumstances that cast a bad light on my character. It was here that Popoffsky's stepsister and her husband lived, and since they occupied a social po-sition of some prominence, could create serious trouble for me if they wished. There were even some of my own rela-tions in the place, all of whom had disowned me, as well as friends who had repudiated me; that is, they were all ene-mies. In short, it was the worst place I could have chosen for the purpose of leading a quiet life. It was hell, a hell con-structed with masterly logic and divine ingenuity. It was here that I was to drain my cup and rally the younger gen-eration to the cause of the angry powers.

As chance would have it, and very picturesquely too, I had just bought a topcoat in the latest style—puce-colored with a cape and hood and looking very much like the habit of a Capuchin friar. It was in this penitential garb that I made my re-entry into Sweden after six years of exile.

About 1885 a student society had been formed in Lund called "The Young Old Boys," whose literary, scientific, and social views could all be lumped under the general head "radicalism." Their program, which was affiliated to the modern ideas of the time, was at first Socialist, later Nihilist, and finally developed into an ideal of universal disorder expressed by *fin de siècle* attitudes, with admixtures of Satanism and Decadence.

The leader of this group,[2] the most valiant of knight-errants and my friend for many years, though I had not seen him for the past three, came to visit me.

He was dressed like myself in a cape, but his was gray like that of a Franciscan friar, a Cordelier. Aged, thin, he presented the most pitiable appearance. One glance at the expression on his face was enough to reveal his whole story.

"You too?"

"Yes, it's all over!"

When I invited him to take a glass of wine with me, he declined with the somber air of one who has renounced the vine forever!

"And the Young Old Boys?"

"Dead, on the skids, turned philistine, enrolled as members of the damned social establishment."

"Canossa?"

"Canossa all the way down the line!"

"Then my return here was providential!"

"Providential! Exactly the right word."

"Are the powers recognized in Lund?"

"The powers are preparing their return."

"Do people sleep at night here in Skåne?"

"Not too well. Everyone complains of nightmares, chest pains, heart trouble."

[2] Bengt Lidforss. What Strindberg has to say here about Lidforss' "conversion" is sheer fiction.—EDITOR.

"Then I've come to the right place. That's exactly how things are with me!"

\* \* \*

We spent several hours together talking over the marvels that were being made manifest at that time, and my friend told me of several extraordinary events that had occurred in various places. By way of summing up, he expressed the opinion that the new generation was ready and waiting for something new.

"There is a desire for religion, for a reconciliation with the powers (that was the word), for a rapprochement with the unseen world. The naturalistic era, though strong and productive at one time, has had its day. We have no accusations to make against it, and nothing to regret; it was the will of the powers that we should take that path. It was a period of experiment in which the negative results of the experiment as a whole served to prove the vanity of certain theories. A God, still unknown until the new order dawns, has always been present in the world, developing, growing, and only occasionally manifesting himself. During the intervals he seems to leave the world to go his own way, as the farmer leaves the wheat and the tares to grow until harvest time. Each time this God reveals himself he has changed his ideas. He sets up a new administration, incorporating the improvements gained through practice and experience.

"Religion will come back, therefore, but in other forms, and any compromise with the old religions appears to be impossible. It is not a reactionary epoch that lies ahead of us. It is not a return to what has already lived out its time. It is an advance into new territory."

Into what new territory? We must wait and see.

At the end of this conversation, I shot a question at him—an arrow into the clouds.

"Do you know Swedenborg?"

"No, but my mother has all his works. And, you know, some miraculous things have happened to her."

It's only a step from atheism to Swedenborg!

I asked my friend to lend me Swedenborg's books, and

this Saul of the young prophets brought me the *Arcana
Cœlestia.*

At the same time he introduced me to a young man who
had been reprieved by the powers, a former child prodigy[3]
who told me the story of an episode in his life exactly similar
to many in my own. And as we were comparing our trials
and tribulations, the light dawned on us and we were delivered with Swedenborg's aid.

I give thanks to providence for sending me to that small
and despised town where I was to make my expiation and
find salvation.

## XIV

## *The Redeemer*

In acquainting me with my sublime compatriot Emanuel
Swedenborg, the "Buddha of the North," Balzac, in his book
*Séraphita,* had made me aware of the evangelical aspect of
the prophet. Now it was the Law that struck me, whelmed
me and set me free.

One word, one alone, was enough to let the light into my
soul and dissipate all the doubts, all the empty speculations
about imaginary enemies, electrical attacks, and black magicians. That little word was *Vastation.*[1] Everything that had
happened to me I found in Swedenborg: the attacks of pain
(angina pectoris), the constrictions of the chest, the palpita-
tion of my heart, the tightening band that I call the electric
girdle, everything was there. And what the totality of these

[3] Emil Kleen.—EDITOR.

[1] Swedenborg got the term from St. Paul. Vastation, according
to Swedenborg, is the state that generally precedes regeneration.
Besides the hells, there are also vastations. Even a man who has
lived uprightly takes some evils and falsities with him into the other
life. Before he can be taken up into heaven, these must be dis-
sipated, and this dissipation is called vastation. (*Arcana Cœlestia,*
paragraph 698.)—EDITOR.

phenomena constituted in fact was a process of spiritual puri-
fication already known to St. Paul and mentioned in the Epis-
tles to the Corinthians and to Timothy.

"To deliver such an one unto Satan for the destruction
of the flesh, that the spirit may be saved in the day of the
Lord Jesus." . . . "Of whom is Hymenaeus and Alexander;
whom I have delivered unto Satan, that they may learn not
to blaspheme."

While reading Swedenborg's dreams of 1744,[2] the year
that preceded his introduction to the unseen world, I discovered that the prophet had undergone the same nocturnal
torments as myself, and what struck me particularly was the
perfect similarity of the two sets of symptoms, which left me
in no possible doubt as to the character of the illness that had
afflicted me.

I found all the enigmas of the preceding two years explained in the *Arcana Cœlestia* with such overwhelming precision of detail that I retain to this day, even though I am a
child of the latter half of the great nineteenth century, the
unshakable conviction instilled in me by those explanations
that hell does exist, but that it exists here on this earth, and
that I had just passed through it.

For example, Swedenborg provided me with the explanation of my stay in the Hôspital Saint-Louis: alchemists are
subject to leprosy and scrape flakes of skin from themselves
resembling the scales of fish. There you have my incurable
skin disease.

Swedenborg also interpreted the meaning of the hundred
water closets I could see from the Hôtel Orfila: they were the
Excremental Hell. And the chimney sweep my little daughter saw in Austria was also present.

---

[2] Swedenborg's fascinating dream book, which consists of entries
from his diary during the year 1743–1744, was first published in
1859 in a limited edition of 99 copies, edited by G. E. Klemming,
chief librarian at the Royal Library in Stockholm, where Strindberg
worked as a young man. A second edition appeared in 1860. As
Per Erik Wahlund, the editor of the most recent edition (1964),
remarks, the sexual element in the dream book is very strong.
"Swedenborg's main passion, banned from his daily existence, returns in his dreams with searing intensity and graphic vividness."–
Editor.

Among these spirits, there are some that are known by the name of Chimneysweeps because their faces are in fact dirtied by smoke, and because they appear dressed in clothes of a brown, sooty color. . . . One of these Chimneysweep Spirits came to me and entreated me very earnestly to pray and intercede for him in his attempts to gain admission into heaven. "I don't believe I've ever committed any crime that would prevent my being admitted," he said. "I've reprimanded inhabitants of the earth, but I always taught them how to do better after I'd lectured them and punished them." . . .

The Spirits whose task it is to admonish, correct, or instruct man place themselves on his left side while they lean over his back and there, inspecting the tables of his memory, they read through all his past actions and even his thoughts. For when a spirit insinuates itself inside a man it seizes control of his memory. When they come across a bad action, or the intention of committing a bad action, they punish him with a pain in his foot, in his hand [!] or in the epigastric region, and they do so with unparalleled dexterity. Their arrival is signaled by a shudder.

Apart from the pains they inflict in the limbs, they also employ a painful pressure around the navel, which is rather like the tightening of a spiked belt, and at other times a tightening of the chest that may even go so far as to produce the sensation of *angina pectoris*, or a distaste lasting several days for all food except bread.

Other Spirits attempt to sway me to the opposite of what is told me by the Instructive Spirits. These contradictory spirits had been banished from the society of men while on earth because of their wickedness. Their approach is signaled by a flickering flame that seems to move downwards in front of one's face; they take up their position at the base of one's back and from there they affect his limbs.

(I had observed these floating flames or sparks on two occasions, and both times I had been in a state of revolt, rejecting and denying everything as idle dreams.)

They preach that man should put no faith in what the angels are telling him through the agency of the Instructive Spirits, and not to behave according to the teachings of these latter, but to live in all licence and freedom, and always to yield to the impulse of the moment. Ordinarily, they come immediately the Instructive Spirits have left. Men know them for what they are and are not much disturbed by them; but from them they learn what good and evil are, for we recognize the quality of goodness by its opposite, and every conception or idea of a thing is formed by reflecting on the differences between contraries regarded in different ways and from different points of view.

The reader will recall the human faces like antique marble statuary that I saw formed by my white pillow slips at the Hôtel Orfila. This is what Swedenborg says about them.

There are two signs that let us know when they (the Spirits) are visiting a man. The first is an old man with a white face. This sign warns them that they must always tell the truth and do nothing but what is just. . . . I have myself seen an aged human face of this kind. . . . A face of shining whiteness and great beauty radiating sincerity and modesty at the same time.

(In order not to alarm the reader I have deliberately concealed until now the fact that all the quotations above refer to the inhabitants of Jupiter. It may be imagined what surprise I felt one day last spring, when someone brought me a magazine in which there was a reproduction of a drawing by Victorien Sardou depicting Swedenborg's house on the planet Jupiter. To begin with, why Jupiter? What a singular coincidence! And had the revered French dramatist observed that the left-hand façade, if looked at from a sufficient distance, forms an antique human face? The appearance of this face is very similar to the one made by my pillow! But in M. Sardou's drawing there are several silhouettes of human figures created by the contours. Can it be that the artist's hand was guided by another hand, so that he had given us more than he was conscious of?)

\*    \*    \*

Where did Swedenborg see these hells and heavens? Are they visions, intuitions, inspirations? I cannot say, but the analogies between his hell and those of Dante and those in Greek, Roman, and Germanic mythologies lead one to believe that the powers have always employed more or less similar methods for the realization of their aims.

And those aims? The perfection of the human species, the procreation of the higher man, the Superman cried up and urged on us by Nietzsche, our scourge and rod of chastisement worn out before his time and cast into the fire.

Whereupon the problem of evil reappears, and the moral indifference of Taine proves utterly inadequate to man's new needs.

The demons follow as a matter of course. What are the demons? Once we have admitted the immortality of the soul, the dead are nothing but surviving beings who still maintain relations with the living. Evil genii are not malicious, therefore, since their aim is benevolent, and it would be better to employ Swedenborg's term—disciplinary spirits—in order to remove man's fear and despair.

The devil in the sense of an autonomous power equal to God ought not to exist, and the undeniable apparitions of the Evil One in his traditional guise must be no more than a scarecrow set up by the unique and benevolent Providence that governs this universe through the agency of an immense administration staffed by the spirits of the dead.

Take consolation, therefore, and be proud of the grace that has been granted to you, all you who are afflicted and obsessed by sleepless nights, by nightmares, by apparitions, by palpitations and agonies of heart! *Numen adest.* God yearns for you.

# XV

## Tribulations

And so, imprisoned in this little town of the Muses, without any hope of escape, I joined in fearful battle against the enemy—myself.

Every morning as I took my walk on the ramparts, beneath their shady line of plane trees, the huge, red building of the lunatic asylum provided me with a daily reminder of the danger I had escaped and of what lay in store for me should I relapse. By enlightening me as to the nature of the horrors I had met with during the previous year, Swedenborg had freed me from the electrical machines, the black magicians, the sorcerers, the envious foes of the gold maker, and from madness. He had pointed out my only road towards salvation: to seek out the demons in their lair, inside myself, and to kill them by . . . repentance. Balzac, the prophet's second-in-command, had taught me in his *Séraphita* that "remorse is merely a feeling of impotence in him who will transgress anew. Repentance alone is a force and power that can put an end to things once and for all."

Repentance then! But did that not mean repudiating providence, which had chosen me as its scourge? Was that not saying to the powers, "You have guided my destiny ill; you have caused me to be born with a vocation for retribution, for overthrowing idols, for rebellion, and now you are withdrawing your protection, you are leaving me to recant, to make myself a laughingstock! To kneel at the altar rail, to make my apologies!"

A strange, vicious circle, already foreseen at the age of twenty when I wrote my play *Master Olof,* and now become the tragedy of my life. What is the good of having dragged out a painful existence for thirty years simply in order to live through an experience I had already predicted? As a young man I was a sincere believer, and you made me a freethinker. From a freethinker you turned me into an atheist, and from an atheist into another kind of believer. Inspired by the humanitarians, I advocated socialism. And five years later you demonstrated to me the absurdity of socialism. Everything for which I have felt enthusiasm you have undermined. And if I were to devote myself to religion, I am certain that in ten years time you would refute my beliefs.

How can one not help believing that the Gods are playing a joke on us, on us mortals? And that is why we down here, snickering because we have found that out, can laugh even at the moments when we are most tormented!

How can you expect anyone to take seriously what is so manifestly a magnificent joke!

*    *    *

Jesus Christ, the Saviour—what did he save? Look around at the most Christian of all Christians, our Scandinavian bigots, these pale, cruel, terrified people who don't know how to smile! They have the faces of men obsessed! They look as though they are carrying the devil in their hearts. And take note how all their leaders have ended up in prison, like so many malefactors. Why did their Lord deliver them into the hands of the enemy?

Is religion a punishment and Christ an avenging spirit?

All the ancient gods became demons in the age that followed. Those who dwelt on Olympus became evil spirits: Odin, Thor, the Devil himself. Prometheus-Lucifer the light-bearer degenerated into Satan. Has Christ—God forgive me! —also been transformed into a demon? For he is in fact the killer of reason, of the flesh, of beauty, of joy, of all the purest affections of humanity. The destroyer of virtues: honesty, valor, glory, love, and pity!

*    *    *

The Mills of God, the Mill of the Universe—two phrases that are now part of our everyday language.

Have you ever heard that rumbling in your ears that sounds like the noise of a watermill?

Have you noticed in moments of solitude, during the night, or even in broad daylight, how your memories rise from the past, trembling as though newly resurrected, one by one and two by two? All the faults you have committed, all the crimes, all the stupid actions, they come and force the blood even to the tips of your ears, they make the sweat burst even from your scalp, they make the shivers course through the length of your spine. You relive your past life, from your birth until the present day; you suffer all over again every suffering you have ever endured; you drink again all the bitter cups you have already drunk so often; you crucify your very skeleton, because there is no flesh left to mortify; you immolate your soul because your heart has already been reduced to ashes.

Do you know what I'm talking about?

Those are the mills of God that grind so slow and so ex-
ceeding small. You are reduced to powder and you think that
it is all finished with. But no, it will begin again, and you will
pass between those millstones a second time. Be happy! That
is hell here on earth. Luther recognized it, Luther who esteemed it a particular sign of grace to be ground to powder
this side of the empyrean.

Be happy, contented, and grateful.

\*    \*    \*

What can one do? Humble oneself?

If you humble yourself before men, you will awaken pride
in them, because they will think themselves better than you,
however great their own wickedness.

Humble yourself before God then! But it is an outrage to
drag the Supreme Being down to the level of a plantation
owner who must keep the whiphand over his slaves!

Pray!—What? Arrogate to oneself the right to deflect the
will and the decrees of the Almighty by flattery, fawning,
and bootlicking!

I seek God and I find the Devil! My experience in a nutshell.

I did penance, I corrected my faults, and as soon as I began resoling that soul of mine, the toe cap would need attention. No sooner did I replace the heel than the upper
would burst a seam. There was no end to it.

I stopped drinking; I walked soberly home at nine o'clock
in the evening to drink my bedtime milk. The room was
crammed with demons that ripped me from my bed and tried
to suffocate me with the bedclothes. Whereas if I got home
at midnight, drunk, then I went right off to sleep like a baby
and woke up next morning as strong as a young god, ready
to work like a galley slave.

I eschewed women and was assailed at night by morbid
dreams.

I accustomed myself to thinking nothing but good of my
friends, I entrusted them with my secrets and my money.
They immediately betrayed me. If ever I rebelled against a
perfidious deed, it was always I who suffered.

I tried to love all men in general. I made myself blind to

their faults. With inexhaustible forbearance I ignored all their infamous actions and slanders. One fine morning I woke to find myself their accomplice. If I came to the conclusion that certain companions were bad, and therefore ceased to associate with them, I was immediately attacked by the demons of solitude. And if I sought out new friends they always turned out to be worse than the old ones.

And then, even after I had overcome my bad impulses and achieved some measure of peace of soul by such abstinence, I began to experience a feeling of self-satisfaction that raised me above my fellow men. And there I was committing a mortal sin—self-love—for which I was immediately punished.

How is one to explain the fact that every lesson learned in our training in virtue gives rise to a fresh vice?

Swedenborg resolves the paradox by saying that vices are punishments inflicted upon men for sins of a higher order. For example, ambitious men are condemned to the hell of sodomy. If we admit that there is some truth to this theory, then we must bear our vices as best we may and somehow enjoy the remorse that accompanies them. For what other recourse have we, if we wish to be left with sufficient funds to pay our Final Reckoning? Attempting to be virtuous is therefore tantamount to attempting to escape from prison and its tortures. This is what Luther meant in his Article XXXIX against the Papal Bull, in which he proclaims that "souls in Purgatory sin continually because they seek for rest and flee from penalty."

And again, in Article XXXIV, he says: "To make war against the Turks is nothing else than to strive against God, Who is punishing our sins by means of the Turks."

It is therefore clear that "all our good works are mortal sins" and "that the world must necessarily be criminal before God and must recognize the fact that no one can become righteous without grace."

Let us suffer therefore, my brothers, without hope of any lasting joy from life, for we are in hell.

And let us not accuse the Lord because we see innocent children suffer. No one will ever know why, but divine justice gives us to suppose that this suffering is an expiation for crimes committed before their arrival on this earth.

Let us rejoice in these tortures, which are so many debts paid in advance, and let us believe it is out of pity for us that we are kept in ignorance of the primordial causes of our sufferings.

# XVI

## Towards What Goal?

Six months have gone by, and I am still taking my daily walk on the ramparts, allowing my gaze to wander over the walls of the lunatic asylum, straining my eyes to catch the blue line of the sea in the distance. It is from over there that the new age will come, the new religion that the world is dreaming of.

The dark winter is buried now, the fields are springing green, the trees are in flower, the nightingale is singing in the Observatory garden. But the sadness of winter still weighs upon our spirits because of all the sinister events, all the inexplicable facts that are disturbing even the most skeptical. Sleeplessness is increasing here, hysterical attacks become ever more numerous, there are frequent visions, and true miracles have been performed. Something lies in the offing.

* * *

A young man came to see me.

"What must one do to sleep peacefully at night?"

"What has happened to stop you from sleeping?"

"On my word, I don't know, but I have conceived a horror of my bedroom, and I'm moving out tomorrow."

"Young man, atheist and naturalist that you are, tell me what happened?"

"Devil take it! Last night as I opened the door to my bedroom, on my way to bed, someone seized my arm and shook me."

"There was someone in your bedroom?"

"No! I lit the candles and saw no one."

"Young man, there was someone there whom you can't see by candlelight."

"Who might that be?"

"The invisible, young man! Have you taken sulfonal, potassium, morphine, chloral?"

"I've tried everything!"

"And the invisible won't budge, will he? Well, you wish to sleep peacefully at night, and you've come to ask me how to do it. Listen, young man, I am neither a doctor nor a prophet. I'm an old sinner who has done penance. Don't expect either sermons or prophecies from a criminal who needs all the time he has, and more, to read sermons to himself. I too have suffered from sleepless nights and despair. I wrestled with the invisible hand to hand, and in the end I won back the power to sleep and recovered my health. Do you know how? . . . Guess!"

The young man guessed what I meant and lowered his eyes.

"You have guessed! Then go in peace, and sleep well!"

*      *      *

A friend asked me, "What goal are we heading for?"

"I can't say, but as for myself, it seems that the stations of the cross are guiding my steps back to the *faith of my forefathers.*"

"Roman Catholicism?"

So it seems to me. Occultism played its part by providing a scientific explanation of miracles and demonology. Theosophy opened the way to religion, but it had outlived its usefulness once it had re-established a universal order of punishments and rewards. Karma will become God and the mahatmas will reveal themselves as regenerated powers, as corrective spirits (daimons) and instructive spirits (sources of inspiration). The Buddhism advocated by the younger generation in France has introduced the idea of resignation and recognizes the need for suffering, thereby setting us on the path of Calvary.

As for the nostalgia I feel in the bosom of the Mother Church, that is a long story, and I should like to give it here in condensed form.

When Swedenborg taught me that it is forbidden to abandon the religion of our ancestors, he pronounced a clear sentence against Protestantism, which constitutes a betrayal of the mother religion.

More, Protestantism is a punishment inflicted upon the Barbarians of the North. Protestantism represents the Exile, the Babylonian Captivity, but the return to the promised land seems now to be in the offing. The immense progress being made by Catholicism in America, in England, and in Scandinavia heralds the great reconciliation. At the same time, the Greek Orthodox Church has just stretched out a hand towards the West.

This is the socialist dream of a United States of the Occident, but interpreted in line with its true spiritual meaning. Having said that, I must now entreat you not to believe that I have been brought back towards the Roman Church by any political theories.

It is not I who went seeking for Catholicism; it was Catholicism that finally imposed itself upon me after pursuing me for years. My child, though she in fact became a Catholic against my own will, taught me the beauty of a form of worship that has continued intact since its beginning, and I have always preferred the original to any copy. The long period I spent in my daughter's country led me to admire the high sincerity of its religious life. A similar effect had also been produced by my stay in the Saint-Louis Hospital, and, lastly, by all that I have experienced in the course of these last few months.

After this examination of my past life, which delivered me up to the whirlwind like certain damned souls in Dante's Inferno, and after my recognition of the fact that my existence in its totality had had no other end than that of humiliating and sullying me, I resolved to take the wind from my torturers' sails and administer the tortures myself. I wished to live in the midst of suffering, disgust, and agony, and with this end in view I prepared to apply for a post as a male nurse at the hospital of the Frères Saint-Jean-de-Dieu in Paris. This idea came to me on the morning of April 29 after an encounter I had that day with an old woman whose head looked like a skull. When I got home, I found my copy of *Séraphita* open on my table. On the right-hand page was a sliver of wood pointing to the following sentence:

> Do for God what you once did for your own ambitious schemes, what you do when devoting yourself to creating a work of art, what you did when you loved one of his creatures more than Him, or when you were tracking down a secret of human knowledge! Is God not knowledge itself. . . .[1]

That afternoon I received a copy of the newspaper *l'Éclair*, and—what a coincidence!—the hospital of the Frères Saint-Jean-de-Dieu was mentioned twice in its columns.

On May 1, for the first time in my life, I was reading Sâr Peladan's *"How to Become a Magus."*[2]

Sâr Peladan, whom I had never encountered until that moment, appeared before me like a great storm, a revelation of the superior being, of Nietzsche's *Superman,* and with him Catholicism made its solemn and triumphal entry into my life.

Had "he who shall come" come already in the person of Peladan? Was the poet-prophet-philosopher really he, or was there still another that we must wait for?

I did not know. But after passing through these propylaea to a new life, I began writing this present book on May 3.

On May 5, a Catholic priest, a convert, came to see me.

---

[1] From Balzac's *Séraphita,* Chapter VI: "The Road to Heaven." —EDITOR.

[2] Joseph Peladan (he called himself Joséphin) (1859–1918) was as a young man a disciple of Barbey d'Aurevilly and Richard Wagner. When Stanislas de Guaita restored the Cabalistic Order of the Rosy Cross in 1888, Peladan soon became an adept and illuminatus. In 1892 he founded the Salon de la Rose-Croix, and about the same time he bestowed the title Sâr on himself. It was probably at his *soirées estétiques* that Yeats came under the influence of the Rosicrucians. Peladan's most ambitious literary work was a cycle of nineteen novels called *le Décadence latine,* begun in 1884. Among his works of criticism are *Comment on devient mage,* 1892 (1891?), *Comment on devient fée,* 1893, and *l'Art idealiste et mystique,* 1894. In all his works he ceaselessly wages war on the materialistic modern world, which he sees as the product of Masonic anticlericalism and Judaic business-as-usual.—EDITOR.

On May 9, I saw Gustavus Adolphus[3] in the embers of the fire.

On May 17, I read in Sâr Peladan:

> A belief in witchcraft was acceptable in the year 1000. Now as we approach the year 2000 an observer cannot help noticing that there are certain individuals who have a capacity for causing harm and bringing misfortune to those who cross them. You turn them down when they ask a favor of you, and the next day your mistress becomes unfaithful. You browbeat and threaten them, and it is you who fall ill. All the evil you wish on them turns back and strikes you, with interest.
>
> No matter; chance can explain all these inexplicable coincidences. Chance satisfies all the requirements of modern determinism.

On May 21, I read a work by the Danish writer Jørgensen,[4] a Catholic convert, on the monastery of Beuron.

*May 28.* A friend I had not seen for six years had just arrived in Lund and rented an apartment in the house where I am living. You may imagine the emotion I felt upon discovering that he had recently become a convert to Catholicism.[5] He has loaned me a Roman Missal, since I lost my own a year ago, and as I read those hymns and Latin canticles again I feel I have come home.

*June 17.* After a series of conversations on the subject of the Mother Church, my friend has written a letter to the Belgian monastery where he was baptized requesting permission for the author of this book to make a retreat there.

[3] Gustavus II Adolphus (1594–1632), King of Sweden, led the Swedish armies in the Thirty Years' War, ostensibly to protect the oppressed Protestants.–EDITOR.

[4] The career of Johannes Jørgensen (1866–1956) paralleled that of Strindberg to a certain extent. In the 1880s he read Georg Brandes and became a naturalist and materialist. In 1892 he listened to the lectures of the French Catholic writer Léon Bloy and became a Symbolist. In 1894 he lost a great deal of money and had a nervous breakdown. In 1896 he was converted to Catholicism. The following year he wrote *Beuron,* a description of monastic life, and settled accounts with the past in the novel *Den yderste Dag* (Judgment day).–EDITOR.

[5] Dr. Gustaf Brand, who had been converted to Catholicism at the monastery at Maredsous, Belgium.–EDITOR.

*June 18.* There is a rumor abroad that Mrs. Annie Besant has become a Catholic. Not confirmed.

∗   ∗   ∗

I am still awaiting an answer from the Belgian monastery. By the time this book is in print I shall have received a reply. And then? After that?—Another joke of the Gods, who roar with laughter as we weep hot tears?

*Lund, May 3 – June 25, 1896.*

## Epilogue

I had ended this volume originally with the exclamation, "What a joke, what a dismal joke life is!"

However, after some reflection, I found the sentence unworthy and scratched it out.

I still felt doubtful, and I turned to my Bible for the enlightenment I desired.

Here is the answer given me by that sacred book endowed with a prophetic faculty more miraculous than that of any other.

"And I will set my face against that man, and will make him a sign and a laughingstock,[1] and I will cut him off from the midst of my people; and ye shall know that I am the Lord.

"And if the prophet be deceived when he hath spoken a thing, I the Lord have deceived that prophet, and I will stretch out my hand upon him, and will destroy him from the midst of my people Israel."

EZEKIEL 14:8–9.

Here then was what my life adds up to: a sign, an example destined for the improvement of others: a laughingstock set up to demonstrate the vanity of celebrity and fame; a laugh-

---

[1] ". . . make him a sign and a proverb" in the King James version, but *jouet*, a plaything or laughingstock in the French Bible. —EDITOR.

ingstock to teach the young what ways of life they should avoid; a laughingstock that believed itself a prophet and found itself unmasked as an impostor.

Yet it was the Almighty that deceived this prophet and made him an impostor. It was the Almighty that caused him to speak those things. And so the false prophet feels freed of all responsibility, since he has only played the role that was assigned to him.

And there, brothers, you have the fate of one man among so many others. Now admit that a man's life may bear every appearance of a practical joke.

*     *     *

Why has the author of this book been punished in so extraordinary a fashion? Let those who ask that question read the mystery play that serves as epilogue to *Master Olof*. That mystery play was composed thirty years ago before the author had even heard of the Stedinger heretics,[2] that sect excommunicated in 1232 by Pope Gregory IX for its Satanist doctrine: "Lucifer, the good God, cast out and stripped of his power by 'The Other,' will return. He will return when the wretched rule, the cruelty, and the injustice of the usurper, presently referred to as God, have brought the contempt of all mankind upon him and he has been convinced of his own incompetence."

The Prince of this world who condemns mortals to their vices and punishes virtue with the cross, the stake, insomnia, and nightmares, what is he? The torturer into whose hands we have been delivered for unknown or forgotten crimes committed in another world!

And what are the disciplinary spirits of Swedenborg? Guardian angels that protect us from spiritual evils!

What Babylonian confusion!

---

[2] The Stedingers were a group of peasants in the region north of Bremen who rebelled against their lords and refused to pay tithes to the church. They appointed mock popes and bishops. In 1232 Gregory IX ordered a crusade against them and in his bull described them as "heretics who worshipped demons, indulged in magic, and crucified priests." They were finally put down in 1234 after six thousand Stedingers had been slain.–EDITOR.

St. Augustine declared it imprudent to harbor any doubt as to the existence of demons.

St. Thomas Aquinas stated clearly that demons stir up storms and call down thunderbolts. He also said that they can confer these powers to mortals.

Pope John XXII complained of the illicit means employed against him by his enemies when they tormented him by pricking portraits of him with needles (bewitchment, or *envoûtement*).

Luther was of the opinion that all accidents, broken bones, falls, fires, and most diseases, are the effect of diabolic intervention.

Furthermore, Luther expressed the opinion that certain individuals find their hell during their lives here on earth.

Is it not with good reason therefore that I have christened my book *Inferno?*

If any reader rejects my opinion in this matter as overly pessimistic and as a matter for doubt, let him read my autobiographies *The Son of a Servant* and *A Madman's Defense.*

And let him who is inclined to regard this book as a piece of fiction consult the diary that I have been keeping daily since 1895, and of which this book is merely a reworked version, augmented and arranged.

## Bibliography

For the guidance of readers who are not initiate in the occult sciences.

Papus. *Magie.*
————. *Science occulte.*
Guaita. *Le serpent de la Génèse.*
————. *La clef de la magie noire.*
Mulford. *Vos forces et le moyen de les utiliser.*
Lermina. *Geheimlehre.*
Sawyer. *Le livre des augures.*

*L'Initiation: Revue philosophique des Hautes études.*
*Le voile d'Isis: Revue hebdomadaire.*
Sâr Peladan. *Comment on devient Mage.*
————. *Comment on devient Fée.*
————. *Comment on devient Artiste.*
Jollivet-Castelot. *Comment on devient Alchimiste.*
Balzac. *Séraphita.*
————. *Louis Lambert.*
Swedenborg. *Arcana Cœlestia,* and other works.

(Most of these works can be obtained at Chamuel, Rue de Savoie 5, Paris.)

# Jacob Wrestles

## (Jakob brottas)

## A Fragment

Translated by David Scanlan and Evert Sprinchorn

After finishing *Inferno* at the end of May 1897, Strindberg spent most of the summer in Lund awaiting its publication in French and Swedish editions. At the end of August, however, he left for Paris and took a room there in a modest hotel on the rue de Saints-Pères. For some weeks he had been dallying with the idea of making a retreat to the Benedictine monastery of Solesmes in Belgium, which was well known in literary circles and which Huysmans was to visit in the fall of 1897 in order to work on his confessional novel *La Cathédrale*. Evidently the Higher Powers were still taking a personal interest in Strindberg; some inner voice made him hesitate. Then came the scandalous news that the abbot of Solesmes had been removed because of immoral acts at the monastery. Among the more sensational disclosures was that the abbess of the Solesmes cloister took her role as vicarious Virgin so literally that she encouraged the monks to suckle at her breasts at Christmas. Perhaps Huysmans dreamed of drinking at these Pierian springs; Strindberg, however, remained in Paris and received his inspiration from the fountains in the Luxembourg Gardens.

His principal reason for being in Paris seems to have been to get his *Inferno* manuscript revised for French publication. The Swedish translation had been prepared by Eugene Fahlstedt, a college friend of his, and was scheduled for publication in the fall, but Strindberg's original French manuscript needed to be edited by someone whose French was perfect. For this purpose he secured, either through the publisher Mercure de France or through his friend Paul Herrmann, the services of Marcel Réja, a medical student who had aspirations as a poet.

Strindberg, Herrmann, and Réja frequently formed a nocturnal triumvirate, making the rounds of the cafés and walking the streets of Paris. Strindberg was much more abstemious than during his Black Pig days in Berlin, and he seems to have sworn off (except for a few lapses) the absinthe that

provided fuel for the flames of his Inferno. Five or six whis-
kies with water (*grogs américains*) and it was time to go
home. He always preferred to sit at a sidewalk table rather
than inside. Extremely shy (and he grew shier as his fame
and notoriety spread), Strindberg impressed the young Réja
as a man always on his guard, aloof and reserved.

"Bright, piercing eyes flashing under an inordinately large
forehead, a lion's mane on top, the whole forming a flaming
punch bowl of gray hair—this was Strindberg," as Réja saw
him. "A small mouth with a shy smile continually suggesting
hidden thoughts without end, a life full of mystery from
whose depths were flung up now and then aperçus of cruel
precision—this, too, was Strindberg, but the living Strindberg,
relaxing with friends whom for the moment he could trust.
. . . Man or woman, every stranger was to him a kind of
enemy who . . . had to undergo a sort of moral quarantine
before being accepted openly."

Herrmann was one of the few people with whom Strindberg got along extremely well, though they cannot be said
to have been close friends. They were more like good acquaintances with compatible personalities.

Herrmann, too, suffered from insomnia and went to bed
when the sun rose. In him Strindberg saw himself in an earlier
stage of his development.

"I hate!" exclaimed Herrmann, "hate everything and everybody—myself excluded."

"That's strange," replied Strindberg, "I hate myself."

"Not me. I love myself. But I hate all the others." (Letter
from Strindberg to Geijerstam, October 1897.)

During these months in Paris the Inferno syndrome manifested itself again. Strindberg lost weight and suffered from
neuralgia, as he renewed his efforts to "brew" gold. The occult continued to obsess him, and he began to collect material for a sequel to *Inferno*. Convinced that the current of
the 1890s was carrying man to the shores of a new religion,
Strindberg wanted to show that his Inferno experiences were
not unique and that many others had felt the invisible hand
of the Higher Power. Everywhere Strindberg looked he found
people who were suffering from insomnia, angina pectoris,
and anxiety, all symptoms of what Swedenborg calls vasta-

tion, the spiritual desolation that precedes the awakening. The epidemic of conversions and the outbreak of mysterious occurrences were further indications of the great change that was taking place in European culture in the wake of scientific progress. From one point of view there was a genuine resurgence of religious interest; from another point of view, the intellectuals were simply attaching greater significance to the subconscious workings of the human mind.

Strindberg felt called upon to "bridge the gap between naturalism and supernaturalism by teaching how the latter is only a development of the former." In his new book, *Legends*, written in September and October of 1897, he employed the parable or miracle to record the origin and growth of the new religious feeling. Originally a *légend*, in the French sense of the word, was a work relating the life of a saint, or the lesson in the liturgy devoted to the saint of the day. Later it came to mean a fictional story based on historical fact. The murals of Puvis de Chavannes, extraordinarily popular in the 1890s, were called legends because of their allegorical content, and it may have been the articles written about Puvis on the occasion of his death in October 1897 that led Strindberg to choose the title *Legends*.

The unwitting latter-day saints of Strindberg's book were nearly all from his circle of friends in Lund. With a sovereign disdain for facts, Strindberg, obviously taking the word legends in its more modern sense, attributed to many of these freethinkers experiences they had never had, anxieties they had never felt, and conclusions they had never reached. The result is a work that is quite unreliable as regards Strindberg's "brothers in misfortune," but very revealing to Strindberg students as a kind of author's sketch book.

In contrast to the freethinking climate of Lund, that of Catholic Paris with its flourishing Symbolist movement was much more hospitable to religious speculation. *Legends* ends with Strindberg's return to Paris in the summer of 1897. Toward the end of the year he sought once again to render his religious struggle in allegorical form. This third part of the Inferno story, *Jacob Wrestles* (or second part of *Legends*), is set exclusively in Paris, and rarely was Strindberg so successful both in evoking the atmosphere of a real place, the Left Bank of Paris, and in bringing his own imaginative world before our eyes.

Though *Jacob Wrestles* is only a fragment, it occupies a major position in the Strindberg canon. Not only does it provide a good summing-up of his quarrel with the Higher Powers but it reveals a further development of his style in the direction of speech-like utterance and untrammeled subjectivism. *Jacob Wrestles* is actually a one-sided dialogue between a questing Strindberg, the old rebel torn between arrogance and humility, and a highly approachable God, whose voice comes as often from within Strindberg as from without. Yet behind them both one can sense the creative Strindberg, the cool ironist with the shy smile and the would-be scientist who conducted experiments on himself. "I split myself in two," he wrote at the beginning of *Legends*, "and show the world the naturalist occultist, while my inner self keeps and preserves the seeds of a creedless religion. The exoteric role often wins the upper hand; I mix my two natures together so that I can laugh at my newfound faith, (which makes it easier for my theories to worm their way into the most resistant minds)."

Strindberg felt that *Jacob Wrestles* was a failure, a work that did not come off and had to be abandoned when his thoughts about religion dissolved into utter chaos. To the modern reader it is this sense of chaos, of skepticism and questioning, of dissatisfaction with all the answers, that makes it so stimulating. Nor does it seem a fragment when it is placed in the context of the other autobiographical writings. Near the end of *Jacob Wrestles*, when Strindberg loses faith in Swedenborg, the story that began with the first chapter of *Inferno* draws to a close. "My religious struggles come to an end [in *Jacob Wrestles*]," wrote Strindberg in a letter of March 2, 1898, "and the whole Inferno story is complete. It also has its natural end . . . when I say thanks and goodbye to Swedenborg and *The Imitation of Christ*."

In January 1898 Strindberg broke off the writing of *Jacob Wrestles* and returned to the drama after an absence of nearly six years. One of the greatest miracles in a decade of strange and wonderful occurrences was the transformation of the Inferno story into the first two parts of the Damascus trilogy—*To Damascus,* Parts I and II. It was in them that his religious experiments produced their finest results.

AFTER MY RETURN to Paris toward the end of August 1897, I found myself suddenly isolated. My friend the philosopher,[1] whose daily company had become my only moral support and who had promised to follow me to Paris and spend the winter here, is delayed in Berlin. He cannot explain to me what keeps him in Berlin when Paris is the final destination of his journey and he burns with desire to see the City of Light.

I have waited for him for three months and it now seems to me that Providence wishes to keep me to itself in order to detach me from the world, to harry me into the desert where the chastising spirits can try my soul at their leisure. And Providence has done the right thing, for solitude has educated me by forcing me to renounce the unimportant pleasures of human society and by divesting me of a friend's support. I have grown used to talking with the Lord and confiding only in Him. The need for human company has almost ceased, a condition which has always seemed to me the ideal one for personal freedom. Even the monastery, where I enjoyed the support of religion and the community, is taken from me. The life of a hermit has been inflicted upon me and I have accepted it as punishment and instruction, in spite of the great difficulty of reforming the established habits of forty-eight years.

I occupy a small room, narrow as a cell, with a high barred window that looks out onto a courtyard surrounded by a wall covered with a huge ivy. There I remain, after my morning walk, until six-thirty in the evening. They bring my lunch on a tray.

In the evening I go out to dine without the preamble of apéritifs, which disgust me. Why I have chosen the little restaurant on the Boulevard St. Germain is difficult to explain. It may well be that I am bewitched by the memory of two terrible evenings spent here last year in the company of my occult German-American friend. The fascination is so intense that any attempt to dine elsewhere provokes extreme discomfort and I am forced to return to this restaurant I ab-

[1] Axel Herrlin, docent at University of Lund.–EDITOR.

hor. The reason: my former friend has left debts here and they recognize me as his companion. Because of that and because they overheard us speaking German I am treated like a Prussian—that is, very badly served. It does me no good to make such mute protests as leaving behind my card or some envelopes bearing Swedish postmarks. I must suffer and pay for the guilty one. No one but I perceive the logic of this affair or understand that it is an expiation for a crime . . . It is, quite simply, Justice taking its course, and for two months I masticate this horrible food that smells of the anatomy laboratory.

The proprietress seated on her throne behind the counter, pale as a corpse, salutes me with a triumphant air and I force myself to think: "Poor old woman, she must have had to eat rats during the siege of 1871."

But then it seems she pities me when she sees my silent submissiveness and my persistence. There are times when it seems to me that she turns pale upon seeing me enter alone, always alone, and always a bit thinner. That is simply the honest truth. When I went to buy new collars, after two months, I had to buy size 43 instead of my usual size 47—a loss of four centimeters. My face is lined and my clothing hangs in folds.

Now the service improves and the proprietress smiles at me. At the same time the place ceases to be bewitched and I go my way holding no grudges, as if relieved of some onus, certain that the expiation is complete for my own account and perhaps for that of my absent friend. In case this is a product of my imagination—this abusive treatment I've been exposed to—and in case the woman is not to blame, I ask her pardon, and then it is I who punished myself and administered the well-deserved discipline. "The chastising spirits take possession of the imagination of the guilty one and by this means work to raise him from wretchedness by making everything appear to him in distorted shape." (Swedenborg.)

How often it has happened to me in going to a sumptuous dinner that all the dishes disgusted me as if the food were spoiled, while the rest of the company joined in eulogies to the grand repast!

The "perpetual malcontent" is under the scourge of the

invisible Powers and is shunned by others for good reason. He is condemned to be a party spoiler who atones for secret deeds, condemned to solitude and its sufferings.

Consequently I go my way alone, and when, after not having heard my own voice for weeks, I visit someone I overwhelm the unfortunate soul with such a torrent of words that he tries to escape and unwittingly lets me know that he would prefer not to see me again.

There are other times when the temptation of seeing a human being forces me to seek out bad company. But then, in the middle of a conversation, a depression accompanied by a migraine headache seizes me; I grow silent, incapable of offering a word. I have to leave the group, which never fails to show its satisfaction at being rid of an insupportable intruder, who had no business being there in the first place.

Condemned to isolation, banished from human society, I take refuge with the Lord, who has become a personal friend to me. Often He is angry and then I suffer; often He seems absent, occupied elsewhere, and that is worse still. But when He extends His grace my life is sweet, especially in solitude.

By a strange coincidence I have settled in the Rue Bonaparte, the Catholic street. I live opposite the École des Beaux-Arts and when I go out I walk down a street lined with shop-windows in which Puvis de Chavannes' legends, Botticelli's madonnas, Raphael's virgins guide me to the upper part of the Rue Jacob, where the Catholic libraries with their prayer books and missals accompany me to the Church of St. Germain des Prés. From there the shops dealing in religious objects form an unbroken line of Saint-Saviors, Virgins, Archangels, Angels, Demons, Saints, the fourteen Stations of the Cross and the Christmas crèche—all on the right; and on the left books of holy pictures, rosaries, vestments, and sacred chalices, right down to the Place Saint-Sulpice where the four lions of the Church, dominated by Bossuet, guard the most devout temple in Paris. After passing in review this repository of sacred history, I often enter the church to fortify myself by contemplating Eugène Delacroix's picture of Jacob wrestling with the Angel. This scene always gives me pause and inspires impious thoughts, in spite of the orthodoxy of the subject. As I go out past the kneeling worshippers I keep thinking of the wrestler who remains on his feet in spite of his wounded thigh.

Then I pass the Séminaire des Jésuites, a kind of formidable Vatican, which emits currents of immeasurable psychic force whose effects can be felt at some distance, according to the theosophists. At last I arrive at my goal, the Luxembourg Gardens.

Since my first visit to Paris in 1876 this garden has attracted me in a mysterious way and it was always my wish to live near it. This dream was realized in 1893 and since that time, except for certain intervals, this garden has become incorporated into my memories, assimilated into my person. Although its actual size is not great, to my imagination it seems immense. Like the Holy City of the Apocalypse it has twelve gates, and to increase the resemblance: "On the east three gates; on the north three gates; on the south three gates; and on the west three gates" (Revelation 21:13). Each entrance gives me a different sensation according to the disposition of the gardens, the buildings, the statues, or to the personal memories associated with it.

Entering by the first gate on the Rue Luxembourg on the Saint-Sulpice side, I experience a lightness of heart. Set amid duckponds and paulownias the ivy-covered cottage of the caretaker is like a stone idyll. Farther on there is the museum of contemporary art with its canvasses of bright sunlit colors. The thought that friends of my youth—Carl Larsson, the sculptor Ville Vallgren, Fritz Thaulow—have placed bits of their souls therein strengthens and rejuvenates me and I feel the radiance of their spirits piercing the walls and inviting me to have courage because I have friends nearby.

Farther along there is Eugène Delacroix, whose laurels have been blighted by Time and Posterity.

The second gate, which opens on the Rue de Fleurus, brings me onto the lists, the racecourse, broad as a hippodrome, ending on the flower terrace with a marble Victory as a goal post, and in the distance the Panthéon surmounted by the Cross.

The third gate, at the end of the Rue Vanneau,[2] leads me

---

[2] Strindberg seems to have Rue Vavin in mind.–EDITOR.

down a somber path that on the left emerges into a kind of Elysian Fields. The children have here a playground containing wooden horses who march in pairs with the lions, the elephants, and the camels as in Paradise, and farther on, the tennis courts and the Guignol Theater among the flower beds, the Golden Age, Noah's ark. It is springtime that greets me here in the autumn of my life's course.

On the south side, toward the Rue d'Assas the orchard and the nursery bring me summer. No more blossoms—it is the season of fruits! The apiary on the one side, with its bourgeois inhabitants who gather gold dust against the approach of winter, heightens the feeling of ripeness.

The second gate opposite the Lycée Louis le Grand opens on an Eden-like landscape—green velvet lawns always young, here and there a rosebush, and a single peach tree that I shall never forget, for once in the spring, bedecked with dawn-colored flowers, it lured me into remaining for half an hour in contemplation—I should say adoration—before its slender, youthful, virginal form.

The Avenue de l'Observatoire stops before the main gate, a truly royal entrance with golden fasces. Since it is too majestic for me I remain outside—in the morning to admire the palace, in the evening to observe the lights of Montmartre above the rooftops. In fine weather I can see the Big Dipper and the North Star circling above the large grated gate that serves as a quadrant for my astrological observations.

On the eastern side only the gate at the Rue Soufflot tempts me. It was by that gate that I discovered my garden—a sea of verdure, the enchanting contours of giant plane trees, and in the blue hazy distance, full of secrets then unknown, lay the Rue de Fleurus, that later became so precious to me as the propylaeum to a new life. Here I used to give a backward glance over the course I had already traveled, intersected on one side by the artificial pond and on the other by the little David who has broken his sword. One morning in autumn the water fountain created for me the spectacle of a rainbow, which led my thoughts back to the dyer's shop on the Rue de Fleurus where the rainbow appeared as a sign of my alliance with the Eternal Lord. (See *Inferno.*) As I approach the end of the terrace I pass by a row of statues of women—queens and sinners, more or less—and pause at the great stairway which in springtime is crowned with the pink hawthorn that surrounds this great circus of flowers. In the autumn the pomegranates and the rosebay (Nerium)—very old, centuries old, almost prehistoric—the palm trees lining the immense beds of chrysanthemums where the butterflies hover, the turtledoves coo, and the children laugh, remind me of illustrations in a book of fairy tales.

And above the sycamores rise the twin spires of Saint-Sulpice, which are unlike any others and not even like each other.

The northern side has three gates but I use only two since the third is guarded by a soldier. The doors of the Odéon are like the overture to an opera. That singular and ancient house where all the muses meet beneath the arcades fills with true joy the hearts of those avid for beauty and knowledge. And then the corner of the poets of my youth—of Murger and Banville—inspire juvenile reveries, dreams of the student of twenty I once was.

The Medici Fountain, an Ovidian poem in white marble, appearing in a new version by the pond where the carp hover mutely in front of the young lover sprawled immodestly beneath the eyes—he has two—of the black Cyclops, and the whole engarlanded in Virginia creeper and shaded by the most beautiful plane trees in France.

Beautiful! Ecstatic! A Paean! Pagan! Worthy of Orpheus! And sad at the same time, melancholy like some elegy of love that shall turn out badly for Galatea whose Acis shall be crushed with a rock thrown by some Polyphemus.

The last door, the one by the museum, gives a rather mixed impression. A vulture is perched for no apparent reason on the head of the Sphinx, and Hero kisses the brow of Leander, dead before his time, and through an accident that might easily have been foreseen. Now I make a little landfall by skirting the museum of contemporary art and entering the bay of roses where I am engulfed by ten thousand of them.

That is my morning walk and in choosing my gate of entry I can tune my state of mind to whatever key I want. I return on the Boulevard Saint-Michel, navigating by the steeple of the Sainte Chapelle that steers me between the reefs and shoals of vanity, on show in the shop window displays and exposed on the sidewalks in the form of prostitutes and women of the world. When I arrive at the Place Saint-Michel I feel protected by the sublime Archangel, the slayer of the dragon. It is not the lizard's tail that creates the feeling of evil in this work of art, nor is it the ram's horns, nor the lifted eyebrows. It is the mouth, which does not close at the corners while the lips are drawn together over the four front teeth. The tusks cannot be hidden and the ferocious sidelong smile depicts immortal evil, still grinning although the lance is in its heart.

I have encountered such a mouth only three times in my life, once in an actor, once in a female painter from Sweden, and once in a certain Norwegian lady—and it has never deceived me.

After a glance at Notre Dame, I follow the Quai des Augustins along a street lined with bookstalls and plane trees to the foot of the Rue Dauphine where it joins the Pont-Neuf.

This is a very colorful corner and gives me such pleasure that I would like to seat myself at a table on the terrace of the wine shop and there sit out the end of my days. A bit of open country with the most beautiful plane trees in France; Henri IV, the incarnation of France; the stalls of the naturalists—replacing the bookstalls—with their butterflies, shellfish, precious or at least sparkling stones, signboards in lively colors, bottles and vegetables, and above all, the knowledge that this is Pont-Neuf, the sublimest bridge in Europe with its masks of sylvan gods, dryads, satyrs—all this hypnotizes me to the spot. Or perhaps the happy days of time past have chosen this corner as a rendezvous and the laughter still rings in the air, ricocheting from the ground and walls that enshrine these waves of sound.

L'Hôtel des Monnaies, noble, solemn, silent, palatial, closed in upon itself, reveals no hint of the base gold piled in its cellars.

L'Institut, reaching its arms toward the Louvre, resembles a summer pavilion or the fortress of a giant with its high casements; and the palace on the other side of the water is not a building but a chain of mountains where the giant, a descendant of the Atlantides, sleeps and gathers strength for the Resurrection Day. The other evening as I passed the Palais Mazarin the sun was setting below Passy and the last rays were reflected in the windows of the Louvre. And as I walked I watched the windows of the Tuileries light up, one after the other, all the way to the Flore Pavilion. The magical effect made me imagine that the brothers Barberousse of France had awakened, that Saint Louis celebrated his coronation with a gala feast to which all the monarchs of the earth were invited, dressed in penitential sackcloth and serving the repast on their knees.

I have now arrived at the mighty mouth of the Rue Bonaparte. This ravine serves as an outlet for the quarters of Luxembourg, Montparnasse, and part of the Faubourg Saint-Germain. It takes skillful maneuvering to get through the flow of pedestrians and vehicles with the terra firma represented by only a yard of sidewalk. Nothing however makes me quite as apprehensive as the omnibuses drawn by three white horses. I think I have seen these creatures in a dream —and moreover, these white horses may even remind me of a certain "pale horse" mentioned in the Apocalypse. In the evening especially when they come three abreast, one after the other, with red lanterns above their heads, I imagine that they turn their faces to me and, looking at me with their malevolent eyes, declare: "Just wait, we'll soon get you!"

There, in short, is my *circulus vitiosus*, which I travel twice a day. My life is fixed in that orbit so firmly that if I permit myself another route I lose my bearings, as if I had lost bits and pieces of my self, my memories, my thoughts, even my affections.

*   *   *

One Sunday evening in November I went out to eat dinner alone. Two small tables stand in front of the restaurant on the Boulevard Saint-Germain. Flanking them are two oleanders in green pots and two fiber mats that form a hanging enclosure. The air is warm and calm. The street lamps reveal a cinematographic scene that becomes especially animated when the omnibuses, the berlins, the cabs return from the parks with their holiday crowds, singing, blowing horns and hailing the pedestrians.

As I begin my soup, my friends, two cats, take their accustomed places at my side to await the meat course. Since I have not heard my own voice for several weeks I deliver a little speech to them, but receive no response. I rebel inwardly against the injustice of being thus condemned to dumb and hungry company because I have avoided the evil company in which my ears were wounded by impious and filthy talk. As a matter of fact, I detest animals, cats as well as dogs, just as I have the right to hate the animal in myself.

Why is it that Providence, which is taking such pains with my education, relegates me to evil company when the example set by good company would be more apt to improve me?

At that moment a black poodle wearing a red ribbon comes onto the scene, chases away my feline friends, and, after swallowing their tidbits, expresses his gratitude by watering the leg of my chair; after which the ungrateful cynic deposits himself on the pavement and turns his back on me. Out of the frying pan, into the fire! I must not complain or I might find myself in the company of swine, as did Robert le Diable and St. Francis of Assisi. One must ask only a little of life. So little—yet for me, too much.

A flower woman offers me carnations. Why carnations? which I detest because they look like raw meat and smell like a drugstore. Finally in order to please her I take some and since I pay her generously the old woman thanks me with: "God bless you, Monsieur, you have treated me well this evening." Although I know their game, the blessing reverberates in my thoughts for some time; I have need of it after so many curses.

At seven-thirty the newsboys shout *"La Presse! La Presse!"* like cries of distress, and that is the signal for me to rise from dinner. If I stay to indulge myself with a second dessert and an extra glass of wine I am certain to be tormented in one way or another, either by a bunch of cocottes who take a table right in front of me or by roving street-urchins who insult me. No doubt I have been put on a diet. If I take more than three courses and a carafe of wine I am punished. After my first attempts at revolt were repulsed, I no longer dared to let myself go at dinner and I finally had to content myself with reduced rations.

So I rise and head for the Rue Bonaparte and from there to the Luxembourg.

At the corner of the Rue Gozlin I buy cigarettes and go on past the Faisan d'Or restaurant. At the corner of the Rue du Four a strikingly realistic statue of Jesus Christ causes me to stop. The art of the religious-minded, in spite of their war on Zola literature, has not been able to resist the spirit of realism, and with the aid of this Beelzebub the other will be driven out. It is impossible to pass these pictures without pausing to look at them, done in realistic detail and decked out with glaring impressionist colors.

The shop is closed, steeped in shadows, and the Saviour stands there in a royal robe, lighted by the street lamps, offering his bleeding heart, the crown of thorns on his head. For more than a year He has persecuted me, this Saviour whom I do not understand and whose help I would like to dispense with by carrying my cross myself, if that were possible—due to a remnant of male pride that is offended by the cowardice of casting one's faults on the shoulders of an innocent person.

I have seen the Crucified One everywhere: in toyshops, at picture-sellers', in bookstalls, at art exhibits especially, in the theater, in literature. I have seen His image in the indentation on my pillowcase, in the glowing ashes of the hearthfire, in the snows of Sweden, and in the rocks of the Norman coast. Is He preparing His return, or is He already here? What does He want?

Here in the windows of the Rue Bonaparte He is no longer the Crucified. He comes from heaven in triumph, dressed as the Victor, resplendent in gold and jewels. Has He become aristocratic like the lower classes? Is He the "good tyrant" of whom the young dream, the pacifist enlightened hero?

Having discarded the cross, He has taken up the scepter and as soon as His temple on the Mont de Mars (formerly the Mont des Martyres) is erected, He will come to rule the world Himself, dethroning the unfaithful vicar who finds himself too narrowly lodged in the 11,000 rooms of *infamia Vaticana loca,* who complains of his luxurious captivity and kills time with his little indulgences in poetry.

Leaving the Redeemer I am astonished to find, when I

arrive at the Place Saint-Sulpice, that the church is an enormous distance away. It has withdrawn at least half a mile and the fountain with it. Have I lost my sense of distance? As I proceed along the seminary wall, I cannot seem to reach the end of it, so immense does it appear this evening. It takes me half an hour to cover this part of the Rue Bonaparte that usually requires only five minutes. And someone is walking in front of me, someone I seem to recognize. I quicken my steps, I run, but the unknown figure advances at whatever speed I travel in my attempt to close the distance between us. At last I reach the Luxembourg gate. The garden, which has been closed since sunset, reposes in solitude, the trees bare, the flower beds devastated by frost and autumn storms. But it smells good, it gives off an odor of dry leaves and fresh earth. I follow the garden wall along the Rue Luxembourg preceded still by the unknown figure, who begins to interest me. Clad in a traveler's cloak resembling my own but opal white, slender and taller than myself, he proceeds when I proceed and stops when I stop so that he seems to be dependent on my movements; I seem to be leading him. There is one thing that particularly attracts my notice—his cloak is fluttering in a spirited breeze that I cannot feel. In order to be certain, I light a cigarette. Observing the smoke rising straight into the air without a waver, I am convinced that no wind is blowing. What is more, the trees and bushes in the garden are motionless.

I turn right past the Rue Vavin and instantly find myself transported from the sidewalk into the garden without being able to say how, since the gates are closed.

About twenty paces beyond me stands my walking companion, facing me. His beardless and dazzling face gives off a luminous nimbus in the shape of an ellipse whose center is occupied by the Unknown. Signaling me to follow him, he proceeds and takes his nimbus with him so that the bare, somber, dirty garden is illuminated in the wake of his progress. And now the trees, the bushes, the plants grow green and flower in an area corresponding to the reach of his aureole, and fade when he has passed. I recognize clearly the great canes with leaves like the ears of elephants above the statue of the family of Adam, the bed of *salvia fulgens,* sage the color of fire, the peach, the roses, the banana plants, the aloes—all my old acquaintances and each one in its place. But it appears that the seasons are confused so that the spring flowers have bloomed simultaneously with the autumn flowers.

And what astonishes me even more is that nothing astonishes me, everything seems reasonable and quite natural. As I walk beside the apiary a swarm of bees buzzes about the hives and attacks the neighboring flowers, but in an area so precisely determined that the insects vanish the moment they fly out of the light and the illumined portion of the sage is covered with leaves and flowers while the shadowed part remains withered, black and blighted with hoarfrost.

Under the chestnut trees the spectacle is especially enchanting—beneath the foliage an empty dove's nest is suddenly occupied by a cooing pair of doves.

At last we have arrived at the Fleurus gate where my guide signals me to wait. And in a second he is at the other side of the park, at the Gay-Lussac gate, a distance which seems to me immense although it is only half a kilometer. In spite of the distance I can see the Unknown surrounded by his luminous oval aureole. Without saying a word the Unknown tells me by small movements of the muscles of his mouth to advance. I believe I grasp his intention as I cross the interminable avenue, the hippodrome I have known for years, bounded at the end by the cross of the Panthéon that stands out blood-red against the black sky.

The Way of the Cross and perhaps the fourteen Stations if I am not mistaken. Before setting out I make a sign that I would like to speak, to ask questions, to get things clear; and my guide responds with an inclination of his head that tells me to speak.

At the same moment the Unknown changes position without the slightest motion or noise. The only thing I notice as he moves toward me is that he emits a balsam-like scent that swells my heart and lungs, inspiring me with the courage to do battle.

I begin my interrogation.

"It is you who have been persecuting me for two years. What do you want with me?"

Without opening his mouth, the Unknown answers me with a kind of smile full of superhuman goodness, forbearance, and urbanity.

"Why do you ask me since you know the answer yourself?"

And as if from within myself, I hear a voice saying:

"I wish to raise you to a higher life in drawing you out of the mire."

"Born of the mire, created out of mud, how can I be delivered from the dirt except by death? Kill me, then! You won't? Then the inflicted pain must be an educating agent. But I assure you that humiliations make me prideful, that denial of small pleasures awakens concupiscence, that fasting evokes gluttony, which is not my besetting sin, chastity stimulates lubricity, enforced solitude gives birth to love of the world and unhealthy pleasures, poverty engenders avarice, and the evil company to which you consign me makes me contemptuous of mankind and will awaken in my soul the suspicion that justice is badly administered. Yes, it sometimes appears to me that Providence is rather ill-informed by the satraps to whom it has delegated the government of humanity, that its prefects and subprefects are guilty of misappropriation, falsehood, and unfounded accusations. Thus it has happened to me that I have been punished when others sinned and there have been trials in which I was not only innocent but the defender of the right and the prosecuter of crime—and nevertheless the punishment fell on me while the criminal triumphed. Allow me a frank and direct question: Have women been admitted into the administration? For the present regime seems to me annoying, paltry, unjust—yes, unjust! Is it not true that each time I pleaded a just and honest cause against a woman, she—however infamous her character—was acquitted and I condemned? You will not answer that, will you? And you require that I love the guilty, the soul-murderers, the spirit-poisoners, the falsifiers of truth, the perjurers! No, a thousand times no! 'Eternal, should I not hate them that hate Thee? Should I not abhor them that rise up against Thee? I hate them with a perfect hatred: I count them mine enemies.' Thus the Psalmist; and I add: I hate the wicked as I hate myself. And my prayer is this: Punish, Lord, those who persecute me with lies and injustice as you have punished me when I was unjust and untruthful. Have I now blasphemed, have I offended the Eternal, the Father of Jesus Christ, the God of the Old Testament and of the New? Of old he heard the complaints of mortals and let the accused defend themselves. Listen to the complaint of Moses before God when the Israelites tired of manna: 'Wherefore hast Thou afflicted Thy servant? And wherefore have I not found favor in Thy sight, that Thou layest the burden of all this people upon me? Have I conceived all this people? Have I begotten them, that Thou shouldest say unto me, Carry them in thy bosom, as a nursing father beareth the sucking child, unto the land which thou swearest unto their fathers? Whence should I have flesh to give unto all this people? For they weep unto me, saying, Give us flesh, that we may eat. I am not able to bear all this people alone, because it is too heavy for me.' Is this not the plain speaking of a mortal? Is it unbecoming, this language of an angry servant? And consider that his Master does not strike the rebel with lightning, but that He listens to reason and lightens Moses' burden by selecting seventy chieftains to share his responsibilities. At the same time, the manner in which the Eternal grants the prayers of the people who hunger for flesh is also slightly malicious, like the false heartiness of a father who condescends to the wishes of his unreasonable children: 'Therefore the Lord will give you flesh, and ye shall eat. Ye shall not eat one day, nor two days, nor five days, but even a whole month, until it come out at your nostrils, and it be loathsome unto you.' That is a God according to my ideal, the same that Job invokes: 'Oh that one might plead with God as a man pleadeth with his friend.' But without waiting for such permission, the afflicted one takes the liberty of demanding explanations for the bad treatment he has been receiving. 'I will say to God, Condemn me not; show me wherefore Thou goest against me in judgement. Doth it please Thee to oppress me, to overthrow the work of thine own hands, and to further the devices of the wicked?' These are reproaches and imputations that the good God accepts without anger and to which He will respond without recourse to thunder. Where is He, the good-natured Father of Heaven Who knows how to smile at the folly of His children and how to pardon after punishing? Where is He hiding, the Master who keeps the house in order and who oversees the overseers in order to prevent injustice? Has He been removed by the Son, the Idealist, Who occupies Himself only with worldliness? Or did He deliver us up to the Prince of this world, called Satan, when He hurled His curse on the world after the fall of our first parents?"

During this incoherent harangue the Unknown watched me with the same indulgent smile, without a trace of impatience. But as I came to the end of my argument, he immediately vanished, leaving about me a suffocating cloud of carbon monoxide, and I found myself alone in the gloomy, dirty, autumnal Rue de Medici.

As I walked down the Boulevard Saint-Michel I was angry with myself for having missed the opportunity of saying everything. Oh, how many shafts I still had in my quiver if only the Unknown had deigned to respond or to accuse me!

But as soon as the crowd presses upon me in the glaring light of the gas lamps and all the reality of the merchandise on display reminds me of the trivialities of life, the scene in the park seems like a miracle and I hasten in fear to find my way home, where my meditations plunge me into an abyss of doubt and anguish.

Something is happening in the world and mankind is waiting for something already partly visible. It is the Middle Ages, the age of faith and creed, that is coming again to France, introduced by the fall of an empire, of an Augustus, just as in the time of the decadence of Rome and the barbarian invasions. One has seen Paris-Rome in flames and the Goths crowned in the Capitol-Versailles. The great pagans Taine and Renan have descended into nothingness, taking their skepticism with them, while Joan of Arc has been resurrected. Christians are persecuted, their processions dispersed by the gendarmes and the dragoons, while Saturnalias are celebrated on feast days and display their shame in the streets, protected by the police and subsidized by the government that solaces the malcontents with *circenses*, with or without the putting to death of ferocious beasts by the gladiators. *Panem et circenses*—bread (costly) and circuses! Everything can be bought: honor, conscience, country, love, justice—deep and infallible symptoms of the dissolution of a society from which virtue, as a word and as a thing, has been banished for thirty years.

Middle Ages in the dress and hair-do of primitive women. Young men don the monk's cowl, cut their hair in tonsures, dream of the monastery, write legends, perform miracle plays, paint madonnas, and model Christs, all drawing their inspiration from the Magician who has enchanted them with Tristan and Isolde, Parsifal and the Grail. The Crusades begin again, against the Turks and against the Jews; the anti-Semites and the philhellenists are in charge. Magic and alchemy have already insinuated themselves and we await only the first proven case of magic before the building of a pyre that always follows a witchcraft trial. The Middle Ages! Pilgrimages to Lourdes, Tilly-sur-Seine, Rue Jean Goujon! And heaven itself gives signs to the sluggish world to prepare itself. The Lord speaks through waterspouts, cyclones, floods, and bolts of lightning.

Medieval also is the return of leprosy against which the doctors of Paris and Berlin have just formed an alliance.

The beautiful Middle Ages when men knew how to rejoice and how to suffer, when strength and love, beauty in color, line, and harmony were revealed for the last time before they were drowned and overrun by that renaissance of paganism known as Protestantism.

❊    ❊    ❊

Evening has come and I burn with desire to renew my conversation with the Unknown, well-prepared as I am this time to confess all and to defend myself against damnation!

My melancholy dinner over, I go up the Via Dolorosa of the Rue Bonaparte. The street has never appeared to me so immense as it does this evening and the shop windows gape like abysses in which Christs are multiplied, sometimes suffering, sometimes triumphant. And I walk, I walk, sweating large drops, the soles of my boots burning the soles of my feet—without progressing a step. Am I the Wandering Jew who refused the Redeemer a drink of water, and now that I wish to follow Him and imitate Him am incapable of approaching Him?

Finally, and without knowing how, I find myself before

the Fleurus gate and a moment later inside the damp, silent, gloomy garden. Immediately a gust of wind shakes the skeletons of the trees, and the Unknown materializes before me in his shell of light and summer.

With the same soft smile as last time, he invites me to speak.

And I speak!

"What do you want with me and why do you torment me with your Christ? The other day you placed in my hands with deliberate intention the *Imitation of Christ* and I read it as I did in my youth when I learned to despise the world. How have I the right to despise the Creation of the Eternal, the beautiful earth? And where has your wisdom led me? To such neglect of my affairs that I have become a burden to my neighbors and have ended up as a beggar. This book, which forbids friendship and proscribes worldly intercourse, which demands solitude and denial, is written for a monk, and I haven't the right to become a monk lest I allow my children to perish. See where the love of solitude has led me? On the one hand, you ordain for me the solitary life, but as soon as I retire from the world the demons of madness attack me, my affairs become disordered and, isolated as I am, I have no more friends to ask for help. On the other hand, in seeking out people I meet the worst kind, who annoy me with their arrogance, and that in proportion to my humility. For I am humble, treating all as equals until the moment they trample me underfoot, when I behave like the worm who lifts his head but cannot bite. What do you want of me, then? To go to any lengths to torment me so that I do your will even though I despise it? Will you make me a prophet? It is too great an honor for me and I lack the vocation. Besides, I cannot pose as such a person. All the prophets that I have known have ended up unmasked as semi-charlatans, half-mad, and their prophecies have always misfired! And so, if you have a vocation for me, you must endow me with the graces of election and deliver me from all the deadly passions that debase a preacher. You must begin by supporting my career in life instead of soiling me with the misery that degrades me and ties my hands. It is true, and I confess it, that contempt for the world has led to contempt for myself and disdain for glory to the neglect of my reputation. I admit that I have cared badly for my own person, but this is due to the superiority of my better self that despises this dirty sheath into whch you have stuffed my immortal soul. Since infancy I have loved purity and virtue, yes. And yet my life has been dragged through indecency and vice so that it often seems that my sins have been inflicted as tortures intended to engender in me a permanent disgust with life itself. Why have you condemned me to ingratitude, which I detest more than all the other vices? You have set traps for my naturally grateful nature in order to reduce me to the necessity of seeking obligations from whomever I could find. Thus entangled in dependency and servitude—for benefactors always demand in return one's thoughts, desires, inclinations, affections, in a word, one's soul—I have always been forced to retreat, debt-ridden and ungrateful, in order to preserve my individuality and human dignity, forced to break the ties that threaten to strangle my immortal soul. And all this with the pangs of conscience and remorse of a thief who makes off with the goods of another.

"And now that I begin to conform my soul to the ordinances of the *Imitation* is it reasonable to demand of a man that he take God Himself for a model, that he imagine himself to be in a condition to acquire the perfection of the Perfect? It will only inspire him with delusions of grandeur. Or, seeing the impossibility of imitating the Savior, he will see the absurdity of his intentions, fall into despair, and end by consoling himself with the accomplishment of worldly tasks and with intellectual pleasures. If the wisdom of this world is contemptible, why do you send us to schools in which we are urged to venerate great scholars, to glorify the heroes of literature, art, and science? No, to imitate the Eternal is sacrilegious and woe unto him who allocates to himself such a privilege! It is more becoming to remain a man and to seek to model oneself on the best of mortal sinners than to dream of making oneself equal to God. Then at least one is not involved in the sin of pride, which is the worst sin. The Imitation of Jesus Christ makes me a hypocrite. For in suppressing my hatred of wicked people I become indulgent toward wickedness and thus toward myself while I still retain deep in my heart my justifiable indignation. To give good for evil is to encourage vice and pride. The Apostles have taught me that we must correct one another and I assure you that the others have never spared me.

"At bottom, as a consequence of following the royal road of the Cross I have become so entangled in the thorns and prickles of theology that the most horrible doubts imaginable have seized my spirit and whispered in my ear that all evil, all injustice, and all the consequent work of salvation is only an enormous ordeal that must be resisted. There are moments when I believe that Swedenborg with his terrible Hells is only an ordeal by fire and water through which one must pass, and in spite of my unpayable obligation to this prophet who saved me from madness I feel reborn in my heart a burning desire to reject him, to defy him as an evil spirit who desires to swallow my soul in order to make him his slave after having pushed me to despair and suicide. Yes, he has slipped between me and my God whose place he wishes to take. It is he who subjects me to terrors in the night and who threatens me with madness. I hope that he has finished his task of leading me back to the Lord and that I can bow before the Eternal! May his Hells be to me only as scarecrows. I accept them as such but I no longer believe in them; I have no right to believe in them without offending the good God Who demands that we forgive because He knows how to forgive Himself. If the evil and afflictions that have fallen upon me are not punishments, then they are initiation tests to which I must submit. I am inclined to interpret them as such, and Christ must be my model since He has truly suffered—although I do not understand the good of such sufferings unless they are intended as a background to throw future blessedness into relief. I have spoken. Answer me!"

But the Unknown, who had listened with admirable patience, answered only with a look of ironic deference and then disappeared, leaving me alone in a stinking atmosphere of carbolic acid.

Back in the street I was furious as usual at having forgotten my best arguments, which always occur after the fight, and now a whole new argument occurs to me while my heart swells and my courage mounts. The formidable and sympathetic Unknown had, after all, listened without blasting me. He had heard my reasoning and he would ponder on the injustice of which I have been the victim. Perhaps I had even convinced him, seeing that he stood there without answering?

The old illusion that I am Job insinuates itself into my mind. Have I not lost my goods, have they not taken my furniture, books, means of livelihood, wife, children, and hunted me from country to country into the solitude of the desert? Is it I who have written these lamentations or is it Job? "My kinsfolk have failed, and my familiar friends have forgotten me. My breath is strange to my wife, though I entreated for the children's sake of my own body. Yea, young children despised me. He hath made me also a byword of the people; and aforetime I was a tabret. Are there not mockers with me? And doth not mine eye continue in their provocation? When I lie down, I say, When shall I arise, and the night be gone? My *skin is broken* and become loathsome. When I say, My bed shall comfort me, my couch shall ease my complaint; then Thou scarest me *with dreams,* and *terrifiest me through visions.*"

Decidedly, it is I: the broken skin, the dreams and the visions, all these things confirm it. Yet there is something that gives me the edge. I endured the final torture when the Powers arranged those circumstances that strangled me by forcing me to neglect the first duties of a man—the care of his children. Job retired from the game with his honor intact but for me all was lost, even honor—and I nevertheless overcame the temptation to commit suicide, I had the courage to live dishonored.

In the last analysis I am not so reprehensible and if I do not deserve grace I will be able to profit from mercy. Having served for twenty-five years as a hangman, I have proven my ability as such by executing myself before the public, who greet my act of self-knowledge with unanimous applause.

If, in the adversities and the storms that have battered me from all sides, I have found not kindness but malevolence, am I really worse than that Upright Servant of the Eternal? With the rest of us mortals love and kindness manifest themselves in affectionate and tender acts and words and the good father brings up his children with tenderness, not with the most refined kinds of cruelty!

How stupid to have forgotten to say all these things to the Unknown. But next time I will make up for it.

※　　※　　※

For three months I try in vain to make personal contact with the Swedenborg Society in Paris. Every morning for a week I go past the Panthéon to reach the Rue Thouin where the chapel and library of the Swedish prophet are situated. Finally I find someone who informs me that the librarian is there only in the afternoon, which is my resting time, a time when I am too tired to go out. Nevertheless, I make several attempts to reach the Rue Thouin. The first time I am overwhelmed, as I set out, by a feeling of depression, which at the end of the Saint-Michel bridge develops into such anguish that I am forced to return home. A second time it is Sunday and the Divine Office is to be said. I arrive an hour early and haven't the strength to wait in the street. A third time I find the Rue Thouin torn up and workmen blocking the way with their scaffolding and their apparatus. Then I consider the possibility that it is not Swedenborg who is destined to conduct me on the right path, and mulling this over I return home. But when I get home the idea occurs to me that I am wrong or that I am being abused by the invisible enemies of Swedenborg and that I must fight them. I make my last attempt in a carriage. This time the street is barricaded as if expressly to frustrate my plans. I descend from the carriage and climb over the obstacles, but when I arrive at the door of the Maison Swedenborg they have removed the sidewalk and the steps. In spite of everything, I gain the entryway, ring the bell and—a stranger informs me that the librarian is ill.

It is not without inner relief that I leave the dark shabby chapel, its windows dulled and soiled by rain and dust. This building in the severe, barbarous, sinister Methodist style—whose lack of beauty reminds me of the Protestantism of the North—has always repelled me. It was only after a serious struggle with my pride that I could bring myself to seek entrance there. It was an act of pious devotion to Swedenborg, nothing more.

As I regain the street with a light heart, I notice on the sidewalk a piece of tin in the shape of a cloverleaf and superstitiously pick it up. Immediately a memory stirs in me. It was last year, the terrible year 1896, on the second of November as I took my morning walk in Klam, Austria, that the sun rose behind a cloud in the shape of a cloverleaf arch surrounded by blue and white rays. This cloud resembled my piece of tin as two drops of water resemble one another and the sketch I made in my Diary will easily confirm the fact.

What does it mean? The Trinity, that is clear. And what else—?

I leave the Rue Thouin happy as a schoolboy who has escaped a difficult lesson because the teacher was ill. As I pass the Panthéon I find the temple open, the great gate wide open, crying out an invitation to me, Come in. In fact, in spite of my long residence in Paris I have never visited this church, mainly because I was told lies about the paintings, told that they treated certain contemporary subjects that I do not like. Imagine then my great pleasure when I enter that shower of light falling from the central dome and find myself in the midst of a golden legend, the sacred history of France that ends just before Protestantism. The meaning of the ambiguous inscription, "Aux grands hommes," had deceived me. An insignificant number of kings, still fewer generals, and no deputies at all—I breathe more easily. Instead: Saint-Denis, Sainte-Geneviève, Saint-Louis, Sainte-Jeanne (d'Arc). I had never imagined that the Republic was so Catholic. Only the altar and the tabernacle are missing, and in place of the Crucified and the Heavenly Mother an undistinguished and worldly woman has been set up by the gynolaters. But I console myself with the thought that this celebrity will end up in the gutter like so many others, and more glorious ones at that. It is sweet and beautiful to wander in this temple dedicated to sanctity, but sad at the same time to think of the beheadings and the burnings alive of the virtuous and beneficent.

Must not one imagine, out of respect for the honor of God, that all this evil treatment of the just and miserable is only done in pretence and that, as discouraging as the path of virtue seems, it leads to a good end that is hidden from our understanding? Otherwise, these infernos, these scaffolds, these stakes reserved for the saints, while the executioners triumph, invite blasphemous ideas about the goodness of the supreme Judge Who only appears to hate and persecute sanctity here below in order to reward it above so that "Those who sow in tears shall reap in joy."

Meanwhile, as I leave the church I look again at the Rue Thouin and am astonished that the road to Swedenborg has brought me to the temple of Sainte-Geneviève. Swedenborg, my guide and my prophet, has prevented me from going to his humble chapel. Is it because he has disowned himself and, now better instructed, has become a Catholic? When studying in depth the works of the Swedish seer I was struck by his antagonism to Luther who advocated faith alone, and in fact Swedenborg is more Catholic than he might have wished to appear when he preaches faith *and* works, just as the Roman Church does.

If that is so, then he is fighting himself and I, his disciple, will be crushed between the anvil and the hammer.

*　　*　　*

One evening, after a day filled with remorse and scruples of conscience and after my melancholy dinner, I betook myself to the garden that attracts me like a Gethsemane where unknown sufferings await me. I foresee tortures and I cannot flee, I almost desire them as a wounded man wishes for the cruel operation that will bring him health or death.

Upon reaching the Fleurus gate I find myself immediately on the racecourse bounded in the distance by the Panthéon and the Cross. Two years ago this temple signified to my worldly mind the glory of "great men." Now it means: "To the martyrs and the sufferings they have undergone"—so much has my point of view changed.

The absence of the Unknown makes me uneasy and I feel a constriction in my chest. Although ready for battle, I feel myself weaken due to the absence of a visible adversary. To wrestle with phantoms, with shadows, is worse than with dragons and lions. Terror seizes me and urged on by the courage of the fearful, I advance with firm steps over the slippery ground between the plane trees. A stifling odor of spoiled codfish mixed with tar and tallow suffocates me; I hear the slapping of waves against a pier and the hulls of ships; I emerge into the courtyard of a yellow brick building, I ascend the stairway, pass through immeasurably large rooms and innumerable galleries, between showcases and glass cabinets filled with animals stuffed and preserved in glass jars. Finally an open door invites me into a hall of strange appearance, gloomy, poorly lighted by patches of light reflected from a multitude of coins and medals arranged in a display case. I stop before a case by the windows and among the gold and silver medals my eye is attracted by one cast in a metal dull as lead. It is my face, of the criminal and ambitious type, with hollow cheeks, bristling hair, a hateful mouth. And the other side of the medal displays the motto: "The truth is always ruthless." Oh, truth, hidden from mortals—that I had the insolence to believe I had exposed Holy Communion by mocking and ridiculing it, whose miracle I now acknowledge.[3] An impious memorial erected to the dishonor of impiety by blasphemous friends. The truth is I have always been ashamed of that glorification of brutality, that I did not take the trouble to save this commemorative coin, that I threw it to the children to play with, and that it has disappeared with no regret on my part. Similarly, a fatal "coincidence" ordained that the artist who designed the coin should go mad soon thereafter, having deceived his publisher and committed forgery. O shame! indelible, ineffacable, since the law demands the preservation of this accusing object in the museums of the state. *Voyez la gloire!* But how can I complain when Providence has answered the sacrilegious prayer I addressed to it in my youth? It was about my fifteenth year when—exhausted by futile struggles against the demands of my young blood that sought the fulfillment of its passions, harassed by religious conflicts that devastated my soul, eager to know the secret of existence, surrounded by pietists who tortured me under the pretext of wishing to bend my spirit in the direction of divine love—I hurled that phrase into the face of a long-time lady-friend who had moralized

[3] See footnote page 252, *A Madman's Defense.*—EDITOR.

me to death: "I reject morality in order to become a great talent admired by the world." Later, Thomas Henry Buckle confirmed me in my opinion by teaching that morality is nothing, since it does not develop, and that intelligence is all. Later in life, about my twentieth year, I learned from Taine that good and evil are indifferent things with innately unspiritual and irresponsible qualities no different from the acidity of acid and the alkalinity of alkali. And this idea, quickly seized on by Georg Brandes, left its immoral mark on Scandinavian literature. A sophism, that is to say, a bad and faulty syllogism, has seduced a whole generation of advanced thinkers! What weakness! For in analyzing Buckle's epigram—morality does not develop, therefore it doesn't matter—one easily discovers that a better inference could be drawn: the fact that morality remains unshaken proves its divine and eternal origin.

At last my wish was fulfilled. I was the renowned and admired genius—and the most despised man of the century in my country, banished by good society, scorned by the smallest of the small, disavowed by my friends, receiving my admirers at night and in secret! Yes, the whole world bows before the moral code while only a minority reverence genius—which gives rise to interesting thoughts about the nature of morality!

And the other side of the medal is worse still. Truth! As if I had never given in to falsehood in spite of my reputation of being more truthful, more sincere than the others. I bypass the petty faults of childhood because they matter so little, stemming for the most part as they do from fear, from the incapacity to distinguish between reality and imagination, and because they were counterbalanced by wrongly inflicted punishments, based on the false accusations of comrades. But there are other graver ones due to the evil consequences that result from following bad examples and excusing serious faults. There is the false description in my autobiography *The Son of a Servant* concerning the crisis of puberty. When I wrote that confession of an adolescent it appears that the liberal spirit of that period lured me into using all too bright and happy colors—the pardonable end of freeing from fear young men who had fallen into precocious sin.

At the end of these bitter reflections the coin-case contracts and the medal retreats into the distance, diminishing to the size of a lead button. I see myself in a garret in the country on the banks of Lake Mälar in a dormitory for boys at the house of a sexton in 1861. Children born of illegal unions, children of exiled parents, badly raised children who were encumbrances in oversized families, all live together, piled into the attic, two to a bed, tyrannizing over one another, maltreating one another in vengeance against the cruelty of life. A hungry troop of little malefactors, poorly fed, poorly clothed, the terror of the peasants and especially of the gardeners. Finally, the oldest of the band plays the role of seducer, and vice makes its entrance into the young congregation. . . .

The fall—yes, the fall—is immediately accompanied by remorse and I see myself in a nightshirt, seated at a table, a prayerbook before me, in the feeble light of a summer dawn. Shame and remorse in spite of complete ignorance of the nature of sin. Innocent because unaware, but all the same guilty. Seduced and then seducer; repentance and relapse; doubts about the truth of my accusing conscience! Doubts about the grace of a God who spreads the most difficult temptations before an ignorant boy, a child who accepts as a pleasure offered by the generosity of nature what divine law punishes with death. Faultless before himself and at the same time tortured by scruples that compel the unfortunate toward religion, which neither pardons nor consoles but condemns to madness and to hell the poor innocent, the victim deprived of the strength to resist in an unequal struggle with all-powerful nature. Meanwhile, the infernal brazier is lit and will burn until the grave, whether it flames alone under the cinders or is nourished by the fuel of a woman. Try to extinguish this fire by abstinence and you will see passion become corrupt and virtue chastised in strange ways. Try to extinguish the pyre with gasoline and you will have an idea of permissible sex!

Truly, if a young man now asked me nearing my fiftieth year: what must one do?—I would have only one answer after so much experience, so much discussion: I don't know! If a young man were to ask me about the preferability of celibacy or marriage I would say to him: That depends upon your taste. If you prefer the hell of boyhood, choose it. If you like hell of marriage better, choose that. For my own part, I adore Gehenna with a spouse at my side because it is followed by a paradise—artificial but charming—in which there are reminders of the Golden Age. I am thinking of the child.

I would like to accuse myself as a seducer of the young but I cannot, since the aim of my confession was to liberate them from fear. Liberation, freedom, yes, that was the watchword of Scandinavian literature throughout the 1880s. And I took part in the work of liberation. I liberated women with the result that family women have become the equals of prostitutes and have turned on their liberator, striking him with their broken chains. I freed the miserable and the oppressed so that society is governed by the worst of the oppressors, who have now attained to power. I wanted to free youth from remorse and madness, and the young men, having fallen into vice and crime, now accuse me of being a Cataline, and the fathers and mothers put me on the Index. Consequently, one should refrain from setting people free since life is a prison house, something I didn't know and which excuses me to myself for I acted in good faith and good will, desiring only to follow the example of the Savior who acquitted the thief and the woman taken in adultery. Only—and this is the main point—I lied in denying the terrible remorse that accompanied the fall of a boy, and that is the *mea culpa* that makes me blush before the inscription on the commemorative coin—an inscription I had nothing to do with!

To my son I would like to say: try to remain chaste, and, failing that, avoid women of bad morals because they will poison your life; they are *possessed* unfortunates whose evil spirits transplant themselves in a pure soul and that is why these women, accepted merely because they exist, constitute temptations that a young man must count himself honor-bound to resist. And finally, my son, never yield to the temptation of a married woman for she will puncture your male vanity by calling you Joseph! It is not, after all, to Potiphar's wife that honor is due but to Joseph whose honorable name was passed on to the man who had the courage to act as foster-father to the Savior without putting up the slightest resistance to what is a compromising situation for a man to be in.

And to my daughters, one word, one only: the marriage altar or the veil! That is all! Free love has always existed for women, and free women are coquettes and whores and they will be that as long as the world exists. And the unfaithful wife is their equal, or rather their inferior since she assassinates a man and ruins her children's future!

I burn with desire to accuse myself and to defend myself at the same time but there is no tribunal and no judge and I eat out my heart here in solitude.

As I cry out my despair to the four corners of heaven a shadow envelops me and when I begin to see clearly once more my head is leaning against a chestnut tree in the Rue de Fleurus. It is the third tree from the entrance. The street is furnished with forty-seven on each side and nine benches are placed between the trees like so many relay points. I still have forty-four steps to go before the first station.

For a moment I stand there, weighed down before the long path of tears. Then under the leafless trees there comes a ball of light carried by a pair of buzzard's wings. It stops before me at the level of my eyes and in the light that surrounds the ball I see a white card decorated like a menu. At the top in smoke-colored letters I read: "Eat!" And below it in an instant all my past life unrolls like a micrographic reproduction on an enormous placard. Everything is there! All the horrors, the most secret sins, the most disgusting scenes in which I play the principal role . . . I could die of shame seeing depicted these scenes that my enlarging eye perceives instantaneously without having to read or interpret! But I do not die. On the contrary, in a minute that lasts forty-eight years I review my whole life from early infancy to this very day. My bones dry up to their marrow, my blood coagulates and, devoured by the fire of remorse, I fall to the ground crying: "Mercy! Mercy! I renounce justifying myself to the Eternal and I will stop accusing my neighbor. . . ."

When I regained consciousness I found myself in the Rue Luxembourg. Looking through the gates, I saw the garden in bloom—and a chorus of little mockingbirds greeted me from behind the bushes and trees.

As I went down the Rue Bonaparte I felt as if I had been lashed, shame gave way to anger, and my recalcitrant spirit began to stir and struggle. I have sinned, I confess it, and I have been punished! Is not that enough to wipe the slate clean? A good father knows how to forgive after punishment. And there are some who know how to render mercy without demanding an eye for an eye and a tooth for a tooth, and there are those who never punish except with soft words, and who, once the affair is cleared up, mention it no more. But I have never known anyone who kept a detailed ledger of the sins and peccadilloes of his children!

The spirit of rebellion, the feeling of human-divine worth and dignity, rises again and says to me: "Weakling, you fell, you abased yourself, when you denied the justifiable rights of your ego against those of others. The struggle of life consists precisely in resisting the temptation to bow down before others, for the moment you do so you have made yourself judge over the Lord who is master of your fate and dirt beneath the feet of others." If I had been a ruler I would have hated the rebel but I would have respected him as much as the humble and submissive. Strength of soul is beautiful, and what is beautiful is godlike. I shall kneel before a God, the wisest, the kindest, the most beautiful, but I have no right to bend my knees before wretched, miserable human beings who are no better than myself. I have always esteemed the great souls, and it is a blatant lie to say that I am incapable of admiring anyone, although I have never been able to admire small souls. I have openly expressed my esteem for men like Linné, who saw God, for Bernardin de Saint-Pierre, for Balzac, for Swedenborg, for Nietzsche who was crippled in his thigh and in his brain in the battle of the Titans. . . . But the little Gauds of Nowadays wanted to break me and force me to kneel before all that that was mean and petty, before everything that was physically, morally, and intellectually inferior. But I have not been a tyrant. On the contrary, I allied myself with the less fortunate and spoke in their behalf. I joined with them and fought in the war of liberation for the oppressed—because I did not understand at that time that their place in life had been assigned them by Providence. I don't know whether it was intended to show me the consequences of this slave war, but fate always placed me in the hands of someone with the soul of a slave who became my lord and master and who walked all over me with clogs or high heels. I always had to carry straw and bricks for some coarse Egyptian man or woman, who lived off my flesh and blood and fed me what was left over to keep me alive. Finally, made wise by the great teachings, I broke out of bondage, and all that was left for me then was the freedom of the wilderness where truly no manna and no quails were offered me. I was doomed to solitude; and whenever I asked for someone to speak to, I was sent an Egyptian man to spit on me, an ignoramus to tell me how much more the ignorant knew than the wise men, a proud incompetent to tell me that I was the proudest of all, a profligate to preach virtue at me!—Who persecutes me, who humiliates me more than he humiliates others? If he is all-wise, then he knows that I was less haughty and that I was proud only on behalf of Him Whose mouthpiece I took myself to be. And He well knows how evil and envious people can be, who no matter what I say or do are ready to find something wrong with me. If I say my thoughts are my own, I am blamed for being arrogant; if I say I have got them from God, I am guilty of blasphemy. If all men are equal, why has Providence established a hierarchy of social classes in which some are better off than others and possess the right to order around the others, who are told to be subservient to their earthly authorities? Why are some entrusted with high positions of honor and power while others are condemned to be reverent, worshipful, and obedient down below? Is this equality? Does this indicate we were all created alike? I can see no law of equality either in the natural world in which the racehorse has a name and a reputation, a family tree and a staff of servants, eats from marble troughs and wears an alpaca blanket, while the workhorse gets to pull the street sweeper, or in the social order in which even the journeyman has his apprentice whom he can treat like a dog. Then why must I be forced, against all human and divine order, to admit a fact that is confuted regularly every hour of the day, a fact that doesn't even exist? Is God divided against Himself or have His satraps fallen into conflict with each other? Is every period of history here on earth a reflection of what is going on up there? Are they, the power-hungry and the democratic agitators, forming political parties up above too? Now and then it would seem so, with so many voices raised at one time. A leader of the people gets a message from on high and leads the masses with holy fervor to plunder and murder; and he succeeds so well at times one could believe a mighty protector is keeping him safe. Another time the destroyer of the people, the scourge and conqueror, invoking the protection of heaven, leads his consecrated troops against the masses, and his enterprises are crowned with success, as if unearthly powers had led him to victory. Pity the poor children of this earth when the Principalities and Dominions have had a falling out! You had better have discriminating ears when the voices of the unseen ones ask for your obedience; you had better know how to pick the right course, for the victor is always right. Is Ragnarök in the offing? Or is it already upon us? Are not all the aroused divine powers fighting in the heavens for control? Pan was on top for a while and seemed to be running the show. Jehovah has protected his own people, and Christ has remained true to his faithful flock. Allah has only recently shown us at Thermopylae that he could topple the Olympians.[4] And Buddha was making inroads with a violence that seriously threatened the Nazarenes for a moment! Everyone invokes the One and Only True God but no one can say who it is. Is He the one who plays with thunder and whirlwinds? But Zeus and Thor did that too; and the theosophists swear that the unseen gods in the Far East know how to conjure these natural forces, forces which Jehovah, the priests of Osiris, and the black magicians are said to have mastered. The people demand signs and miracles, and signs do appear and miracles do occur, but no one knows who causes them, for the black powers are as potent as the white. Who is the Lord who can command the people nowadays? Or who is my Lord? Doesn't the human ant have a right to know whom he is to serve and obey— and how—before he is rejected as deaf and unhearing? How often have I not called upon the unknown one to speak more

[4] An allusion to the Greek war with Turkey, 1897, in which the Greeks were annihilated.—EDITOR.

clearly, and when he finally answered me, he answered with
a sunbeam, a thunderbolt and a water drop. The Lord of
Nature! Well, well, I recognize him. But it wasn't he who
was to give me a new disposition and rid me of desire, hate,
and pride. . . .

That's how the mills of conscience turn round and round.
The same accusations, the same defenses. Sisyphus rolling his
stone, the Danaïdes drawing water with their sieves. The
punishment seems indeed to be eternal!

Back home in my cell I see that it is only nine o'clock, and
I open the Bible to find some enlightenment and peace of
mind. But when I come across in David's psalms those horrible curses he in his prayers calls down on his enemies, I
feel I've had enough. I have only one enemy—myself. The
others who torture me have a right to do so and they have
always done so for my own good. And have I not learned
that one should forgive one's enemies? And the theosophists
have even told me that praying is black magic and that to
call down evil on one's enemies is *envoûtement* or putting a
hex on someone, a crime punishable by burning at the
stake! My old friend Job no longer consoles me either, in part
because I am no upright man, as is well known, and in part
because I find his criticism of the Lord's methods just as god-
less as my rebellious thoughts and utterances.

Then I flip over to the New Testament where I meet Paul,
who has been a Saul like me, and who should therefore have
much to say to me. I can find some of my faults and failings
in him, but that is not why I turned to him. And I *still* don't
understand how he has the gall to preach punishment and
consign others to Satan when he stands with both his feet in
the swamp of sin. His fervor makes him childish, and therefore sympathetic at moments—for instance, when he begins
one of his letters to the Corinthians by admitting, "I Paul
who in presence am base among you, but being absent am
bold toward you." I cannot listen to this man's words and
believe they come from God. He has all my failings, the
ones I want to rid myself of with his help. How shall I attain
humility when my teacher spends two long letters bragging
about himself? "For I suppose I was not a whit behind the

very chiefest apostles." Or when he says, "Let no man think me a fool; if otherwise, yet as a fool receive me, that I may boast myself a little." And then he draws up a list of all that he has suffered (exactly as I have done, only I finally came to realize that my sufferings were well deserved). "I am more: in labours more abundant, in stripes above measure, in prisons more frequent, in deaths oft. Of the Jews five times received I forty stripes save one. Thrice was I beaten with rods, once was I stoned," and so on and on.

I find in him all my besetting sins, and worse, I find excuses for them. "I am become a fool in glorying; ye have compelled me; for I ought to have been commended of you: for in nothing am I behind the very chiefest apostles, though I be nothing." The last words expose the preposterousness and speciousness of the much vaunted humility that arrogance employs to brag about itself. And there flared up in me again the revulsion that I felt as a youth for this colporteurs' prophet whose style they imitate so well. So I turned from the pupil to hear words of wisdom from the Master Himself. But I don't know what demon on this evening when I was alone and depressed turned the pages and distorted my vision in such a manner that this book that holds the answers to all problems and the cures for all ills did nothing but mock me and fleer at me. When I read how Christ let the woman caught in adultery go free, I felt a profound sense of doubt and skepticism rising from the dead past. Back in 1872 I let the reformer free the prostitute Magdalena with approximately the same words in my youthful drama *Master Olof*. What was the result? A deluge of forgiveness for sin that set everyone free from all moral responsibilities. It poured forth from books and plays and stories and undermined everything, family, morals, honor, faith. And this remission of sin and guilt based on the noblest of human motives and in complete accord with the commandment of Christ: Judge not—this is now disavowed and abjured by the "powers" who strike the redeemers and deliverers with fear and new torments! Imitation of Christ? No, not even of the Bible, or Christ, or humanity, or—anything.

I'm done for! I have no way to turn. Denied the company of my fellow man without knowing why, deprived of my interest in science that formerly made life bearable by the excitement of solving great riddles, evading the consolation of religion since it only teaches what is evil and false, I have nothing left but the thin rind of an empty ego. Sitting in my chair, regarding the starry heavens through the bars of my window, I contemplate nothing, feel nothing, dream nothing. Finally I begin to wonder what my speaking voice will sound like when I get to hear it again after three weeks of silence. I long for the company of a human being, even the most unsympathetic person who would only have to open his mouth to cut me to the quick. I ponder the thought that the purpose of this isolation is to teach me that we all need each other, although I know well enough that bad company should be avoided and that there are those who have needed me more than I needed them. When I look at the clock, I see that it is only half past nine, and I don't dare go to bed before ten out of fear that my night will be restless. I have waited all my life for my great dreams to come true, and now I'm sitting here waiting for a half hour to pass. I can't read, for when I open a book I feel I've read it all before. Nothing interests me, nothing gladdens me, nothing hurts me. I have over a thousand francs in my pocket, but they are worthless because there's nothing I want. Always in the past when I lacked money, I was full of wishes: books, instruments, payment of debts. And this desire for something made life interesting. It was a putting off, a stretching forward of the will, an easily raised anchor that didn't tie one to one place.

At long last the clock struck ten. After my habitual ablutions I went to bed and soon fell asleep, dead tired from utter idleness and boredom.

\*        \*        \*

Up to 6 P.M. the following day was like the previous one. Then there was a knock at the door and in stepped that American painter whom I in my book *Inferno* made identical with Francis Schlatter. As we had parted from each other quite indifferently, neither friends nor enemies, our meeting was rather cordial.

I notice that he is somewhat altered. He seems physically

smaller than I remember him. He looks more serious and I cannot get him to smile, as I used to, at life's tribulations and at past sorrows, which weigh so lightly once they have been endured. And he treats me with a surprising respect that contrasts sharply with his former camaraderie. In any case, his showing up rouses me from my lethargy, partly because I have someone I can speak to who understands every word I say, and partly because he forms a link with the period in my life when I developed myself most, lived most intensely, believed and grew. I feel as if the clock has been set back two years, and I have an urge to cut loose, to spend half the night at the sidewalk cafés in good talk with our glasses before us. Agreeing to have dinner in Montmartre, we set off on our stroll. The street noise somewhat interrupts the flow of conversation and I notice I am having unusual difficulty in hearing and understanding his words.

At the entrance to the Avenue de l'Opéra the press of the crowd is so great that we are constantly being separated. A man carrying some cotton wool happens to stumble against my companion and covers him with white fluff. My head full of Swedenborg's symbols, I try to recall what this is supposed to "mean," but all I can think of is the opening of the grave at St. Helena when Napoleon's body appeared to be spun in white down.

By the time we reach the Rue de la Chaussée I am already so tired and nervous that we decide to take a carriage. Since it is dinner time, the street is crammed, and when we have driven for a few minutes the carriage suddenly stops with a jerk. At the same time I receive such a jab in the back that I rise from my seat and feel a moist panting on my neck, and as I turn around I see three horses' heads right on top of me—an omnibus with a shouting driver on top of it. This puts me out of humor, and I ask myself if it is meant to be some kind of warning.

We get off at the Place Pigalle and dine there. Here I am reminded of my stay in Paris in the 'seventies when I was young. But it makes me feel sad and melancholy for so much has changed. My hotel in the Rue Douai is no more. Chat Noir, which opened then, is now closed; and Rodolphe

Salis was buried this year.[5] The Cafe de l'Ermitage is only a memory, and the Tambourin has changed its name and character. My friends of those days are all dead, married, scattered all over, and the Swedish colony has moved to Montparnasse. I feel that I have grown old.

Dinner turns out to be less gay than I had expected. The wine is of that bad sort that depresses one. My having got out of the habit of listening and speaking makes the conversation disjointed and exhausting. Having our coffee out on the sidewalk in the hope of recovering our former cheerful mood doesn't work out, and soon there settles on us that terrible silence which betrays a mutual desire to break up.

For a long while we struggle against the growing embarrassment but in vain. It's only nine o'clock when we part, and my companion, guessing my mood, goes his own way under the pretext of having an appointment. As soon as I am by myself I feel an indescribable sense of relief. My lethargy disappears, my headache vanishes, and I feel as though the convolutions of my brain and the network of my nerves that had become entangled with someone else's were slowly unraveling themselves. In truth, solitude has made my personality so sensitive that I cannot bear the contact of a stranger's effluvium. Feeling calm, but with one illusion the less, I return home, glad to be in my cell again. But I have just settled down when I sense that the room is different, that some change has taken place, that an atmosphere of tedium has penetrated to every corner. Though the furniture and bric-a-brac are all in place they nevertheless create a strange impression. Something alien has penetrated the walls and left traces of itself everywhere. I can't stand the room any longer.

Again the next day I notice the change and I have to get out to meet people, but nobody is around. The third day I keep my appointment with my artist friend to see his etchings. He lives in Marais. I ask the porter if he is home. He says yes, "but he's sitting down in the café with his lady friend." Having nothing to say to her, I leave.

[5] With the assistance of a group of bohemians, Louis-Rodolphe Salis (1852–1897) opened in 1882 on the boulevard Rochechouart the Chat Noir, the most brilliant of French cabarets. It was closed in 1897 when Salis died.–EDITOR.

The next day I head for Marais once again, and since he is home this time I proceed to mount the six flights of stairs. When I have managed three of them, which wind like steps in a tower, the memory of a dream and of a real experience begins to stir within me. The dream, which often recurs, has to do with just such a narrow corkscrew stairway up which I crawl till I am stifled as they close in on me. The first time I recalled this dream was in the tower at Putbus, and I immediately went down again. Now I stand here trapped, panting, my heart palpitating, but determined to climb on.[6] I force myself up, and I enter the studio and meet my friend with his girl. After I have been sitting there for five minutes I get a severe headache deep inside my skull. "My good friend," I say to him, "it seems as though I am not meant to see you. Your steps will be the death of me. I have the distinct impression that if I climb them once more, I'll die."

He answered, "But you climbed up Montmartre and all the steps at Sacré-Coeur not long ago."

"Yes, that's the strangest thing of all."

"All right, then I'll come to see you, and we'll have dinner together in the evening."

[6] Leaving his wife Frida Uhl in London to promote his books, Strindberg sailed to Germany to continue his chemical experiments in the summer of 1893. From Rügen, where Frida was supposed to join him later, Strindberg wrote toward the end of June:

> I am living confined to an attic room, once again. My dream, the most abhorrent possible, back again—again—*sous les toits!* I crawl, crawl, and find myself up there, *sous les toits.* And the old ladies are waiting for me, always waiting. And they have warned me—Don't do that, don't do that! But done it is, and done again.
>
> Oh, what I live through in my dreams. . . .

In *The Cloister* in a passage describing his stay in Rügen, Strindberg elaborates further:

> He had found himself an attic room, and a foot above his head the sun burned on the tin roof. Sixteen years earlier he had left a similar tin-roofed cell five flights up to marry and live in an apartment. Ever after in a recurring nightmare he saw himself crawling up the five flights to his old digs where all the misery and filth of a bachelor's existence awaited him. Now he found himself in an attic room once again; and a bachelor, though married.

The next day we do indeed have dinner together and fall
into the relaxed and pleasant mood that is usual on such occasions. We treat each other with respect, avoid saying unpleasant things, find that we have much in common, appreciate each other's point of view, and delude ourselves into
thinking that we are of one mind on all important issues.
After our meal, and since the evening is mild, we carry on
with our conversation as we walk over the bridge and proceed
to the boulevards, hopping from one sidewalk table to another, until we finally reach the top of the rise at the Café du
Cardinal. It's midnight by this time, but we are far from tired.
And now begin those wonderful hours when the soul sheds
its shrouds. The spirit energies that would ordinarily be used
in dreams are now devoted to conceiving ideas clearly and
wakefully, to penetrating the past and the future. It is during these night hours that my spirit seems to hover over and
outside my body, which sits there like a complete stranger.
Drinking is a secondary matter that serves to keep sleep away,
and perhaps also to open the floodgates of memory whence
all the stored-up experiences of my life can flow forth, so
that at any moment I can pour out facts, dates, scenes, words.
This is the joy that intoxication offers me, this is the feeling
of power that it gives me. But an occultist I know, quite religious, has told me that this is a sin because it is a way of
enjoying bliss in advance, bliss consisting in the liberation of
the soul from matter; and that's why anyone who resorts to
this little trick is punished by the terrible qualms of the
morning after, which are intended to remind us of damnation.
However that may be, signs of closing time at the sidewalk
cafés begin to disturb us, but since the night still seems young
to me, I mention the name Baratte and my friend takes me
up on it at once.

Café Baratte near les Halles has always exerted a miraculous drawing power on me, without my knowing exactly why.
It may be the proximity of les Halles. When it is night on the
boulevards, it is morning there—morning all night long, as a
matter of fact. The long sad idle night with its disturbing
dreams doesn't exist there. After its drunken spree in the im-
material worlds, the soul wants to get down to the physical
world of food and dirt, vice and noise. For me this smell of

fish, flesh, fruit, and vegetables and the sound of garbage crunching beneath my feet forms a divine contrast to the rarefied subjects I've been dealing with. Here is the muck out of which we are created and re-created three times a day. And when you step from those half-dark streets, full of dirt and shady characters, into the cozy café, you're greeted by light, warmth, music, mandolines, and guitars. The whores and their companions will be sitting there, but at this time of night all class distinctions are wiped out. Artists, students, writers are all thrown together here, drinking at long tables, lost in their dreams, or perhaps trying to flee those dreary sleepness nights. It's not a place of wild parties; the atmosphere is narcotic. To me it's as if I had entered the realm of shadows where spookish characters lead a half-real life. I know an author who used to sit here writing through the night. I have seen people who looked to me like princes and princesses in disguise drinking champagne here, and I don't really know whether all these maskers are truly mere mortals or whether they are the "astral bodies" of sleeping people that have come to hallucinate the groggy, sleep-drunk persons sitting here. The remarkable thing is that there is nothing coarse or vulgar about all these people packed together in this narrow café. The gloom of sleepless nights prevails and gives a melancholy aspect to what goes on there. The songs are mostly sentimental ones, the bittersweet guitar soothing the little wounds made by the sharp, steel-stringed mandoline jabbing at the heart muscles.

I just remembered a night I spent in this café with this same friend two years ago. We had been discussing the hidden riches of the soul, and using various arguments, I denied that the brain's function was that of a thinking machine.

"It's an intestine or a gland, can't you see that?"

"Don't believe it! Come on, let's walk out and buy one."

We walked down to les Halles and asked for a brain. We were shown down into a cellar, through corridors and crypts. At last we found ourselves in a room decorated with bloody carcasses, guts and innards. We waded forward through the blood and arrived at the brain room. Blood-covered men wielded blood-covered clubs and iron bars on decapitated animal heads so that the skull cracked open and the brain popped out. We bought one and carried it up to the light, but the vision of the horrible setting accompanied us to the café table where the supposed thought machine was demonstrated.

Now tonight after having gone through my long cure in solitary during the past weeks, I feel right at home among all these people. Human warmth, sympathy, friendliness emanate from them. For the first time in a long time I feel a sentimental compassion for these unfortunate women of the night. Next to our table a half dozen of them are sitting, alone, depressed, without having ordered anything. They are ugly for the most part, despised, probably unable to order anything. I suggest to my friend, whose interest in them is as impersonal as mine, that we invite two of the ugliest ones to our table. He agrees, and I speak to those two, asking them if they would like something to drink and adding that I don't want them getting ideas—and insisting upon propriety.

They seem to understand their part and ask first for food. My friend and I continue our philosophical discussion in German, once in a while addressing a word to our ladies, who are diffident and seem more interested in food than attention.

For a moment I think, what if someone I know should see me now? I know what he would say, and I know what I would answer. You've kicked me out of society, condemned me to solitary confinement. I'm forced to buy human companionship, that of pariahs, outcasts like myself, hungry as I have been. It gives me a little pleasure to provide these despised women with something to brag about, an apparent conquest on their part, to see them eat and drink, to hear their voices, which are female voices at any rate. Besides, there's been no payment or transaction; I haven't even fed them a moral.

I simply find it pleasant to sit with some human beings and to be able to give them something when my pockets are temporarily full; next month I may be as poor as they. . . .

It's morning. The clock says five when we get up to leave. My lady asks fifteen francs for keeping me company, which I find understandable from her point of view since my company is worthless, as worthless as any protection I can offer her against the police. The fifteen francs don't feed my ego; quite the reverse.

In any event, I stroll back home with a clear conscience after a night well spent. I sleep till ten, wake up feeling rested, and pass the day in work and meditation. But when night comes I suffer one of those disgusting attacks that Swedenborg describes in his *Dreams*. This was my punishment. For what? For "eating and drinking with prostitutes and publicans while John preached in the wilderness. . . ." Yes, with prostitutes because he was allowed no other company. . . . Nothing makes any sense to me any more. I had really thought that this was meant to be a lesson in the art of getting along with people, that I was being taught that all men eat from the same plate; and for a moment I actually imagined that my role at the café was that of a lover of mankind rather than a debauchee and profligate—or at any rate neither one thing nor the other, morally speaking.

The following days I was very despondent and heartsick, and one evening in particular I felt instinctively that the night that lay ahead would be a terrible one. About nine o'clock I was reading in Cicero's *Natura Deorum* and was so caught by Aristotle's view that the gods ignored our world and would pollute themselves by having anything to do with it that I decided to copy it out. In doing so, I noticed that blood had broken out on the back of my right hand without any apparent cause. When I wiped away the blood, I found no sign of a scratch. But I put this incident out of my mind and went to bed. About half past twelve I woke up experiencing all the symptoms of what I call the "electric girdle." In spite of the fact that I knew its nature and its inner significance, something instantly compelled me to look for the cause outside myself: "Here they come again!" They??? Who? I forced myself to make an effort of some sort, sat up and turned on the lamp. Since the Bible lay next to the bed, I decided to consult it for advice.

And it said to me, "I will instruct thee and teach thee in the way that thou shalt go; I will guide thee with Mine eye: be not like to horse and mule, whose mouths must be drawn with bit and bridle, else they will not come near thee."

There was my answer indeed, and I went back to sleep again, satisfied that it was not the voice of spiteful people that spoke to me but a benignant power, although rather ambiguously.

After I had quieted myself with a few days of solitude, I went out again one evening with the American and a young Frenchman who corrects my manuscripts. It got to be rather tedious, and I returned home shortly before midnight with a bad conscience. Drawn into a heated conversation, I had felt compelled to speak evil of someone absent. What I had said was said in self-defense, and against a liar, and absolutely true. Nevertheless about two o'clock I woke up and heard someone stamping in the room above me and then come down the stairs and go into the room next to mine. The same tactics as at Hôtel Orfila! Am I being watched? Who else would reserve two rooms in this hotel, one above me and one next to mine? The same thing had happened in this hotel last September when I lived on the fourth floor. So it cannot be an accident. And if indeed my unseen mentor wishes to punish me, as seems probable, what a subtle technique it is to keep me uncertain whether they are human beings who persecute me or not. Although I have been completely convinced that no one is persecuting me, I have to be drawn into that old vicious circle of thinking that there is someone. And when I ask who it can be, my guesses begin their round dance, slowed up and interrupted by my conscience, which indicts me even when I have in pure self-defense sought to clear myself of the unjust accusations hurled at me. I feel as if I were put in pillory with all passers-by having a legal right to spit on me without fear of punishment. But when I spit back, I'm gagged, flayed, and hunted by furies. The whole world, including the lowest scoundrel, has rights he can exercise against me! If I only knew why! The strategy behind this smacks of female behavior so much that I cannot stop thinking about it. For instance, a woman who for years on end has nagged her husband and done him one injustice after another until he, who as a born gentleman has never lifted his hand to threaten her, finally flicks his hand at her as if he were chasing away a fly, then this woman lets out a shriek, yells for the police and complains, "Officer, this man is defending himself!" Or to take another kind of example: in school when an unreasonable teacher goes after a pupil who, having been baselessly accused, seeks to defend himself out of an injured sense of justice, what does the teacher do? He resorts to corporal punishment, exclaiming, "Don't you talk back to me!"

Well, I have talked back. And that's why I am being tortured. And it goes on for a week, night after night. The result is that I become downhearted and gloomy and poor company indeed. My American friend grows tired of me and gradually withdraws; and when he has settled back into his domestic routine, I find myself once again alone. However it is not entirely a mutual irritability that has separated us this second time. We have both noticed during our last meetings that strange things were happening that could be attributed only to the intervention of conscious powers who deliberately intended to make us irritate each other. This man, who knows virtually nothing of my past life, seems during our last visit to have had the express purpose of touching all my sore points. It seemed as if he knew all my innermost thoughts and intentions, which I had never revealed to a soul. And when I remarked on this, a light dawned on him.

"It's the Devil!" he broke out. "I knew there was something wrong. All evening long you couldn't open your mouth without saying something that hurt me, but I could tell from your face and your friendly expression that you had nothing malicious in mind."

We attempted to defy the powers. But for three days in a row he took the long way to my place and missed me each time. I wasn't home, I wasn't at my usual eating place, I wasn't anywhere.

Thus loneliness closes in on me again like a black night. Christmas is not far off, and being without a home and a family depresses me. Life becomes repulsive to me, and quite inevitably I look heavenward to see what's up there. I buy a copy of the *Imitation of Christ*.

This is not the first time this wonderful book has come my way, but this time the ground is prepared for it. The theme of the book: to die to the world while still alive, to die to the contemptible, wearisome, filthy world. The unknown author has the remarkable faculty of neither sermonizing nor condemning. He speaks kindly and gently, convincingly, logically, invitingly. He chooses to see our sorrows not as punishments but as tests, and thereby instills in us the will to endure.

Now Jesus is with me once again, not Christ this time, and He steals in to me softly and surely as if He came on velvet sandals. The Christmas displays in the Rue Bonaparte create the right atmosphere for this. There is the Christ child in the manger, the Jesus child with royal mantle and crown, the Child redeemer on the Virgin's arm, the Child playing, and lying, and on the cross. The Child! Him I understand. The God who heard the lamentations of men over the misery of mortal life for such a long time that He finally resolved to descend, to let Himself be born and live in order to prove to himself how difficult it is to lead an earthly life. Him I comprehend!

One Saturday morning I passed by the Church Saint-Germain. The intimate nature of this building has always attracted me. The porch with its paintings has an inviting air, and the size and proportions are such that one is not overwhelmed or overawed. Inside I am greeted by soft light, colored pictures, wax candles. Whenever I enter a Catholic church, I remain standing at the door, feeling embarrassed, ill at ease, beyond the pale. When the gigantic Swiss guard approaches with his halberd, my conscience bothers me and I expect him to drive me out as a heretic. Here in the Saint-Germain l'Auxerrois I am troubled by a certain anxiety, for I am reminded that it was in this tower that the bell for some unknown reason began to toll during the night of the massacre of St. Bartholomew, at two o'clock. (At two o'clock in the night!) Today my position as a Huguenot makes me more uncomfortable than usual, having read a couple of days ago in the *Osservatore Romano* the congratulations that were sent by the Catholic priests to the persecutors of the Jews in Russia and Hungary, followed by a passionate comparison with the great days of the St. Bartholomew massacre, which the writer hoped would return as soon as possible.

The organ, out of sight, plays music I have never heard before, music that rises in my mind like memories from olden times, from the ages of my ancestors, or still further back. When I hear great music, I always ask myself where the composer got it from. Not from nature nor from life, for in music there are no models as in the other arts. The only other explanation is to consider music as the recollection of a condition that every man in his best moments longs for, and to long for something shows a vague consciousness of having lost something that one formerly possessed.

There are six lighted candles on the altar. The priest, arrayed in white, red, and gold, says nothing, but his hands hover over a book with the graceful movements of a butterfly. Two little children dressed in white come up behind him and bend their knees. A little bell rings. The priest washes his hands and prepares to do something or other that is unfamiliar to me. Something rare, beautiful, and sublime is taking place there in the distance among gold, incense, and candlelight. . . . I understand none of it, but I feel an inexplicable awe and reverence, and I suddenly have the sensation that I have experienced and participated in this before. . . .

But then comes the shameful feeling of being a heathen, an outcast who doesn't belong here. The whole truth dawns on me bright and clear: a Protestant has no religion. Protestantism is freethinking, schismatizing, revolt, dogmatism, theology, heresy. And the Protestant is excommunicate. This is the curse that weighs on us and makes us dissatisfied, sad and restless. At this moment I feel the curse, and I understand why the conqueror at Lützen died at his moment of victory and why his own daughter renounced her father's faith,[7] understand why Protestant Germany was pillaged and ravaged while Austria remained untouched. And what did we gain? The freedom to be cast out, the freedom to split and schismatize and split and schismatize until we finally ended up with no creed at all.

The congregation surges out through the doors, but I remain standing where I am to endure, as it seems to me, their looks of disapproval. I am standing in the dark near the door but I see all those who pass out touch the holy water in the

---

[7] Gustavus Adolphus, King of Sweden, allied himself with the oppressed Protestants of Germany in the Thirty Years' War. He conquered most of northern Germany but was killed during his final victory, the battle of Lützen in 1632. His daughter Christina became Queen of Sweden but later abdicated the throne, renounced Protestantism, and became a convert to the Catholic faith.–EDITOR.

stoup and cross themselves, and since I am standing directly in front of it, it looks as though they were crossing themselves because of me—a not unknown experience for me: in Austria I saw those who met me as I walked the roads cross themselves against the Protestant me.

When I am finally alone, I approach the font, out of curiosity or for some other reason. It is made out of yellow marble, shaped like a conch shell, and over it hangs the head of a child—with wings behind it. The cherub's face is vividly real, and radiant with an expression that one sees only in good, sweet, beautiful, well-cared-for three-year-olds. The mouth is open, the corners of the lips suppressing a smile. The large beautiful eyes are lowered, and one can see how the little rogue contemplates his image in the water, under cover of his eyelids however, as if he knew he were doing something wrong but still were not afraid of his chastiser whom he knows he can disarm with a single glance. Here is the pure child who still bears the impress of our distant origin, a gleam of the superman whose home is heaven. Does this mean it is possible to smile in heaven, to do something besides bear the cross? How often have I not in my hours of self-accusation when the eternal punishments have loomed before me as objective realities asked myself a question that many would consider irreverent: Can God smile? Smile at man's folly and arrogance? If He can do that, He can also forgive.

The sweet baby face smiles at me and looks at me through his eyelids, and the open mouth says to me teasingly, "Come on, try it, the water won't hurt you."

I dip two fingers in the water, and a ripple runs across the surface as if—I believe it could be the pool at Bethesda. And now I move my finger from my forehead to my heart and then from left to right as I have seen my daughter do. In the next instant I find myself outside the church, for the little one laughed at me and I was—I will not say ashamed, but I wish that no one had seen it.

Outside a church is a notice of some sort that informs me today is Advent! In front of the church an old woman is sitting, asleep in the terrible cold. I gently place a silver coin in her lap without her noticing it, and although I would very much like to see the expression on her face when she wakes up, I go my way. It's an inexpensive but solid pleasure to act as middleman in granting boons and answering prayers, and for once to give after having been on the receiving end for so long.

*     *     *

I'm studying the *Imitation* and Chateaubriand's *Le Génie du Christianisme*. I have taken the sign of the cross and I carry a medal that I was given at Sacré-Coeur in Montmartre. But the cross is for me the symbol of sufferings patiently borne and not a token that Christ suffered in my stead; that is something I'm sure I must tend to myself. I have even framed a theory that goes like this: when we unbelievers refused to hear any more talk about Christ, He left us to our own devices, His vicarious satisfaction ceased, and we were left to get along as best we could with our miseries and our guilt feelings. Swedenborg says expressly that Christ's sufferings on the cross were not a redemption but a test imposed by the godhead on itself, an ordeal of shame rather than of physical pain.

Along with the *Imitation of Christ* I get hold of Swedenborg's *Vera christiana religio* in two thick volumes. With a force and power that defies all resistance he drags me into his gigantic mill and begins to grind me up. At first I put the book aside, saying this is not for me. But I pick it up again because there is so much in it that chimes in with my observations and experiences, and so much worldly wisdom that interests me. A second time I put him to one side, but he will not let me be until I pick him up again. And the terrible thing is that when I read him I have the definite impression that here is the truth but that I can never attain it. Never! Because I don't want to. Then I begin to revolt, telling myself that he is mistaken, that the spirit of falsehood pervades the book! And then comes the fear that I am the one who has gone astray.

And what do I find in Swedenborg that can be the living word of truth? I find the whole system of grace and eternal hell—childhood memories of the hell of childhood with its eternal anxieties! But now he's got me. My head is in the snare and I can't get out. All day long and through half the night my thoughts revolve around one point: I am damned. Everything points to it. Among other things, I cannot speak the word Jesus without adding Christ, and according to Swedenborg this is the shibboleth that betrays the devils.

An abyss opens within me. The mild and gentle Christ of the *Imitation* has become a demon torturer! I feel keenly that if this goes much further I'll end up as a pietist, and that I don't want! That I don't want!

Three days have passed since I put Swedenborg away, but this evening as I was busy studying the physiology of plants, I remembered having seen in *Vera christiana religio*, of all places, something particularly ingenious regarding the position of plants in the chain of creation. Carefully I begin to look for the remarkable passage but can't find it. Instead I find everything else—the call, the enlightenment, sanctification, conversion. And no matter how I turn the pages and try to skip over the words, my eye is arrested by terrible passages that sting and burn. Twice I work my way through the two volumes but what I am looking for has vanished. It's a bewitched book and I'd like to burn it. But I don't dare for night is upon me and the clock may strike two. . . . I can sense that I am beginning to dissemble, and I promise myself that if I can just get a good night's sleep tonight I shall fight this soul destroyer, I shall examine his weaknesses under the microscope, I shall pluck his thorns from my heart even if I tear it to shreds, and I shall forget that he once saved me from one madhouse—only to lead me into another!

❋    ❋    ❋

Having gotten some sleep during the night, although I had expected to be slain, I set to work the following morning—not without scruples, however, for to take up weapons against a friend is the saddest of all enterprises. But it had to be. It was a matter of saving my immortal soul from annihilation.

As long as Swedenborg in the *Arcana* and the *Apocalypse* confined himself to revelations and prophecies, he had a religious effect on me, but when he began to reason about dogmas, as he does in *Vera religio*, he became a freethinker and a Protestant. If he misfires with his reason, he has no one to blame but himself. He had his choice of weapons. I want religion to be a quiet accompaniment to the monotonous melodies of everyday life but with him it is a matter of professional religion and pulpit controversy—in brief, a struggle for power.

Already while reading *Apocalypsis revelata*, I had come across a passage that repelled me by betraying a human vanity which I do not like to see in a man of God. But out of respect I let it pass, not, however, without making a note of it. In heaven Swedenborg meets an English king to whom he complains that the English journals have not thought it worth while to review some of his writings. He expresses his indignation especially with certain bishops and lords who had received copies of his works but had taken no notice of them. The king (George II) is astonished and turning to the unworthy recipients he says, "Go your ways! Woe betide him who can remain so indifferent when he has an opportunity to hear about Heaven and the eternal life." (I may remark in passing I find both Dante and Swedenborg unsympathetic for the way in which they send their enemies and friends to hell while they themselves scale the heights: and if I, like Paul, were to permit myself a little self-praise, this would be the moment to note that in contrast to the great masters I have placed myself alone among the glowing coal heaps in *Inferno* and have at least set the rest above me in Purgatory.)

Things are even more unpleasant in the *Vera religio* where one finds Calvin in a brothel for having taught that faith is everything and works nothing (compare the thief on the cross). And Luther and Melanchthon, in spite of their Protestantism, are exposed to coarse scorn and mockery.—Enough! it disturbs me to seek out these flaws in an exalted spirit. And I hope it has fared with Swedenborg in his spiritual development as he says it fared with Luther: "From his first entry into the spiritual world, Luther was a most vehement disseminator and defender of his own dogmas," but since these were not embedded in his internal spiritual man but only imbibed from childhood, he soon saw more clearly and finally shared in the new heavenly faith.

Is my teacher angry with me for having written this? I cannot believe it. Perhaps he shares my views now and has found out that up there they do not argue about theology.

His description of life in the spirit world with lecterns and audiences, opponents and respondents, has prompted in me the sacrilegious question, "Is God a theologian?"

* * *

By now I had locked up Swedenborg and taken leave of him, thanking him for being the one who had, albeit with horror pictures, frightened me like a child into running back to God. And behold, the Black Christ no longer torments and threatens me with unblessedness; instead the White Christ, the child who can smile and play, approaches me at Advent time, and brings with him a happier outlook on life that lasts at least as long as I keep watch over my acts, words, and even my thoughts, which it seems cannot be kept secret from the unknown guardian and avenging angel who follows me everywhere.

Strange and mysterious things continue to happen but they are no longer so ominous as before. I have abandoned Swedenborg's Christianity because it was spiteful, revengeful, petty and slavish, but I hold on to the *Imitation*, with certain reservations; and a calm compromise-religion has set in after that state of unblessedness which always accompanies the search for Jesus. I am sitting at dinner one evening with a young French poet who, having just read *Inferno*, would like an explanation from the occultist point of view for the attacks I had to endure.

"Don't you have a talisman?" he asks. "You should have a talisman."

"Of course. I have the *Imitation!*" I answered.

He looked at me. A little embarrassed at being a defector, I took out my watch in order to busy myself with something, and in so doing the medal from Sacré-Coeur with the Christ picture fell off the chain. I became even more embarrassed but said nothing.

Soon after we got up and went to a café in the Place du Châtelet for a glass of bock. It was a spacious room and we took a table exactly opposite the door. We sat there for a while and the conversation touched on Christ and what He means to us.

"Well, He certainly didn't suffer for us," I said. "If He had, our sufferings would have been lessened, but they're just as intense as ever."

At this moment a waiter began to make a noise and to clean the floor with broom and sawdust between us and the door. No one had entered that door since we came in, but on the white inlaid floor was a circle of red drops. Sweeping away, the waiter mumbled to himself and looked snidely at us as if we were the guilty party. I asked my companion what it was and he said it was something red.

Then we must have done it because no one came in after us, and the floor was clean when we walked in.

"No," said my friend, "we can't have. It's not footprints. It looks as if someone had been bleeding, and we're not bleeding."

It was uncanny, and not a little unpleasant, for we were attracting the attention of the other guests.

My poet friend read my thoughts, but he hadn't seen the incident with the medal. Therefore, and also to ease my own mind, I concluded, "Christ is persecuting me."

He said nothing, although he would have liked to have found a natural explanation, but that he couldn't do.

Before I leave my American friend, whom I tentatively identified with the therapeutist Francis Schlatter, I must relate some incidents that increase my suspicion that this man had a "double."

When we recently renewed our acquaintanceship, I told him straight out what I thought on the subject, and I showed him the issue of *Revue Spirite* containing the article about "my friend H—."[8] He seemed to be of two minds, but more inclined to be skeptical.

When he came to dinner, after some days, he was in a rather confused and disturbed state of mind, and with a certain amount of emotion he told me that his mistress had disappeared without leaving any information about herself and without a word of farewell.

She was gone for a few days and then returned. On being questioned she finally admitted that she was afraid of her

---

[8] "My friend Herrmann" was the German-American painter Paul Herrmann whom Strindberg called the double of Francis Schlatter. See *Inferno*, Chapter VI.—EDITOR.

lover, who employed her as a housekeeper. After further persistent questioning, he found out that when she woke up at night and he was asleep, she saw his face appear as white as chalk and quite unrecognizable, and this frightened her indescribably.

Moreover, he did not dare to go to bed before midnight for if he did he would be tortured, stuck on a skewer and slowly turned round and round, until he finally had to get up from the bed.

After he had read the first part of *Inferno*[9] he told me, "You didn't have a persecution complex. You were really being persecuted—but not by people."

Stimulated by the experiences I had set down he searched through his memory and came up with several inexplicable events that had occurred in his life during the past few years. For instance, there was a certain spot on the Pont Saint-Michel where he would experience a cramp in one leg that would compel him to stop in his tracks. This happened regularly and he had even let some of his friends witness it. He had also noticed other strange incidents and had learned to use the word "punished" in describing them.

"If I smoke, I'm punished for it. And if I drink absinthe, I'm punished."

One evening, having met before it was time for dinner, we went to the Café de la Frégate on the Rue du Bac for a drink. Talking energetically, we grabbed the first decent place we saw and ordered absinthe. We went on talking until all of a sudden my friend broke off, looked around and exclaimed, "Have you ever seen such a collection of bandits? They all look like criminals."

And when I too looked around, I was amazed. This was not the usual crowd that gathered in that café but the scum and dregs of humanity, most of whom looked as if they were in disguise and making faces. Because of the lack of space, my comrade had propped himself up against an iron pillar, which thus appeared to be growing out of his back, and at the

[9] Strindberg apparently means the whole of what is now known as *Inferno*. *Legends,* of which *Jacob Wrestles* is the concluding section, was intended as Part II of *Inferno.*—EDITOR.

height of his throat the pillar swelled out to form what looked like an iron collar.

"And you're clapped in the pillory!" I burst out.

By now we felt that everyone was staring at us. We grew restless, felt depressed, and left without finishing our drinks.

That was the last time I drank absinthe with him. However, I tried it again later on my own, an experience that I never repeated. Waiting for my dinner companions, I took a table in a sidewalk café on the Boulevard Saint-Germain directly opposite Cluny, and ordered an absinthe. Pretty soon three figures appeared from I don't know where and stood in front of me. Two fellows with torn clothes spattered with filth as if they had just been hoisted out of the sewer, and next to them a woman, bareheaded with tousled hair, some vestiges of beauty, drunken, dirty. And all three of them looked at me, mockingly, insolently, cynically, as if they knew me and expected to be invited to my table. I have never seen such types in either Paris or Berlin, although perhaps I have at the approach to London Bridge where the crowd really does have an occult appearance. I thought I would outface them and wear them down. I kept on lighting cigarettes, but it didn't work. Then the thought struck me that these were not "real" people but half-visions, and recalling my former adventure at the Brasserie des Lilas, I got up. And never again have I dared to touch absinthe.

*    *    *

In the midst of all this vacillating only one thing seems certain to me, and that is that an invisible hand has taken charge of my education. For it is not the ordinary logic of cause and effect that is at work here. It is not logical, for instance, that because I drink absinthe a fire should break out or that nonexistent figures should appear before me. The logical result would be that I got sick. Nor is it logical that I should be dragged out of bed at night because I have spoken evil of someone during the day. All these events betray the existence of a premeditated design, a conscious, thinking, allknowing design with good intentions behind it, but one which I nevertheless find it difficult to follow and obey because my experiences with good intentions and unprejudiced plans have all been bad. In any event, the design has incorporated in it a complete system of signals, which I am beginning to understand and whose reliability I have tested.

For example, for six weeks I had not bothered with my chemical experiments and my room was free of the smoke from the forced fire. One morning I tentatively took out my apparatus for making gold and prepared the chemical solutions. Almost at once the room was filled with smoke. It rose from the floor, behind the mantelpiece mirror, everywhere. When I called the landlord, he said it was incomprehensible because it was coal smoke and coal was not used anywhere in the house. Ergo: I am not to occupy myself with alchemy.

The wooden concertina that I have often mentioned signifies peace. I have found this out because when it is not around there is always some trouble brewing.

The whimpering voice of a child, which I often hear in the chimney and which cannot be explained by natural causes, signifies: "You must work hard" and "You must write this book and not occupy yourself with anything else."

If I am rebellious in my thoughts, my speech, or in my writing, or if I approach forbidden subjects, I hear a hoarse base note that sounds as if it came from an organ or from a mad, trumpeting elephant.

Let me mention two bits of evidence that indicate these are not merely subjective impressions on my part.

We were dining in the Place de la Bastille, the American, the French poet, and myself. For about two hours the conversation had turned on art and literature, but during dessert the American wandered off into the subject of bachelor life. Almost immediately the trumpeting of the elephant could be heard in the wall. I pretended not to hear it, but my dinner companions noticed it and looked up, and then changed the subject, feeling a bit uneasy. Another time I was having breakfast with a Swedish friend in an altogether different place. He was talking, also at the end of the dessert course, about Huysmans' *Là bas* and was about to describe the Black Mass. At that instant the trumpeting was heard, but this time from the middle of the room, which was absolutely empty.

"What was that?" he interrupted himself.

I didn't answer him, and he went on with the disgusting description.

Once again the trumpeting was heard, this time so loud and violent that the Swede got confused and nervous, spilled first some wine and then a whole pitcher of cream on his clothes, after which he abandoned the subject that tortured me.

## Afterword

Having probably seen through my efforts, the reader will realize that this second part of *Legends*, called *Jacob Wrestles*, is an attempt at a metaphorical description of the author's religious struggles, and as such it is a failure. Therefore it has remained only a fragment and, like all religious crises, dissolved into chaos. The inference to be drawn from this seems to be that all attempts to storm heaven meet with confusion, and that all efforts to approach religion by the way of reasoning lead to absurdities. The reason for this must be that religion like science begins with certain axioms, and axioms do not need to be proved and *cannot* be proved. Consequently if anyone tries to prove the self-evident and indispensable premises, he runs into an impossible situation.

When the author in 1894 abandoned as a matter of principle his skeptical attitude, which threatened to make havoc of all intellectual life and began, as a kind of experiment, to adopt the point of view of a believer, there opened before him a new spiritual life, which is depicted in *Inferno* and these *Legends*. In the course of things, the author, abandoning all resistance, found himself assailed by various influences, forces that threatened to overwhelm him, and feeling himself about to drown, he grasped whatever light objects were around that might keep him afloat. But even these began to give way, and it was only a question of time when he would sink to the bottom. It is at moments like this that a piece of straw becomes a floating log in the eyes of the terrified man, and it is then that the faith he is forced to grasp lifts the drowning man out of the waves and lets him walk on water. *Credo quia absurdum:* I believe because the impossible situation that arises from reasoning shows me that I was trying to prove an axiom. And with that the final link to what is above and beyond us is forged.

\* \* \*

During the 1880s a French author[1] wrote a book against the Jesuits, and just recently I came across the following sentence in it: "In 1867 in a review-article called 'Providential Atheism' I predicted that God was about to go and hide Himself in order to make people seek Him all the more eagerly."

1867! The same as in Sweden, for it was about then that all religious reasoning ceased among the cultured classes and God vanished from literature. Now when He is coming back, we cannot be certain that He is the same as He was before, that He like everything else hasn't grown and developed. And should He have become even harsher and more demanding, He still must forgive the agnostics and the investigators of the hidden world for not finding him, since it was He who was either not at home or not receiving visitors.

*August Strindberg*
*Lund, April 23, 1898*

[1] Jean Wallon.—EDITOR.

# Alone

## (Ensam)

Translated by Evert Sprinchorn

Though Strindberg was only fifty-four when he wrote it and had nine more productive years ahead of him, *Alone* is the last regular volume in his autobiographical writings. To fill out the story of his life the reader must turn to his Occult Diary and to his correspondence, both of which Strindberg wanted to include in his complete autobiography.

The inspiration for *Alone* came indirectly from Strindberg's third marriage. In 1900 he cast a young, virtually unknown Norwegian actress, Harriet Bosse, as the Lady in his play *To Damascus*. During rehearsals he fell in love with her; four months later, in March 1901, he proposed to her ("Would you like to have a baby with me?"—"Yes, thank you."); and in May he married her. The relationship was filled with friction from the start. He was nearly thirty years older than she. He had already lived a full life, while she was just beginning her career. He wanted a quiet life with regular hours, a devoted wife and a smiling child, ringed in by a small circle of friends. She wanted to go to parties and to meet people. In June she went on her honeymoon—alone, while Strindberg stayed at home to work on a play. From then on Harriet frequently lived apart from her husband. However, during the period when Harriet was pregnant and during the weeks following the birth of the child, that is, from the autumn of 1901 to the following summer, they lived together. A year later, in March 1903, Strindberg set to work on *Alone*, which he finished in June. Two months after that Harriet took her child and moved into a separate apartment. But she and Strindberg still continued to see each other, and during the short periods of reconciliation they lived together as man and wife, even after they had agreed on a divorce.

None of this is mentioned in *Alone*. Like his previous autobiographical volumes, it is a mixture of fact and fancy. Strindberg had not been living in the provinces for ten years as has the narrator of the story, though Strindberg had spent a number of years outside Sweden. Nor was Strindberg a widower, as the narrator is; he was only an intermittent husband. Moreover, the whole episode concerning his son's return from America is entirely fabricated, the germ of it having been planted in the author's mind when he was confronted with the possibility that his son in his first marriage might come over from Finland to Stockholm to visit him.

As usual, Strindberg was creating a state of mind and touching up reality to make it accord with his feelings, in the same way that a landscape painter alters nature to suit his purposes. Strindberg wrote *Alone* to inure himself to the anguish of being forever separated from his wife. Thus, masochistically, he could suffer the pain of isolation twice—first in anticipation and secondly in reality. The benefit of this approach, as every masochist knows, is that the pain is less intense than if it comes without preparation. And it is clear, too, that the writing of *Alone* was motivated by a desire to savor the quiet pleasures of a life of solitude. After the Inferno crisis Strindberg became more and more wrapped in himself as his art grew increasingly subjective. In the earlier half of his career Strindberg could appropriately view himself as a reflector catching and focusing the rays from the world around him. In the latter half the relationship was reversed; the real world became a mirror reflecting his emotions and thoughts. The impressionist became an expressionist.

Though all the autobiographical writings are valuable for the light they shed on Strindberg as artist, *Alone* is unique among them because it ushers us into the artist's inner sanctum—or very nearly. Like most artists, Strindberg kept his trade secrets fairly well locked up, but in *Alone* we are permitted to see the role that seemingly trivial incidents, chance occurrences, and events without any apparent purpose whatsoever, play in the creative process.

Much of Strindberg's creative work was carried out on his morning walks. It was then that he scanned the outer world for some motive that would trigger a reaction within him, and mentally culled from his notes and readings the thoughts that might serve his work best. Returned from his stroll, he would spend two or three hours at his desk, writing feverishly when inspired, and utilizing certain recurrent and affecting experiences as building blocks, which like a child's set of blocks could be arranged and rearranged in countless patterns.

Since much of *Alone* is devoted to these matutinal promenades (a fact that makes it resemble Rousseau's *Rêveries d'un promeneur solitaire*), the reader is given a vivid picture of the Stockholm of 1900, a city that like so many others was undergoing a radical change under the impact of industrialization. Having grown up there, Strindberg identified himself with the city, and the transfiguration of Stockholm in the course of a generation reflected, perhaps inversely, the transformation that had taken place in Strindberg. Stockholm was the arena in which he had fought his first battles, and many of its streets and buildings were haunted with memories for him. The young rebel had become the grizzled veteran, still quarreling with the world and with heaven, still the troublesome Loki whose lips the gods tried to sew together. And when, at the climax of *Alone,* a fire breaks out in Stockholm, it is with the howling wolves, pent in their zoo cages, that Strindberg associates himself.

By returning us to the city of his birth and by recapitulating the outcast theme, *Alone* rounds off perfectly the story of Strindberg's life. But in allowing us a glimpse into the artist's workshop, it serves to remind us that such an autobiography is false to many facts, that the events in a life so remarkable as Strindberg's had to be toned down as often as they were lit up for the artistic effect of the whole, and that his whole mode of creation consisted in playing roles. Truth and poetry, fact and fiction, life and art were inextricably mingled in Strindberg, and his creative energies seemed to have been devoted largely to blurring the distinctions between the two in order to make the two one. Therein lies the extraordinary fascination of the man and his work.

AFTER TEN YEARS in the provinces I find myself back in the city of my birth, sitting down to dinner with my old friends. We are all pretty much in our fifties, with the younger fellows in the group being over forty or thereabouts. We're all a little surprised that we haven't aged since we last saw each other. Of course there are a few gray streaks in our beards and here and there at our temples. But on the other hand there are some among us who have grown younger since the last time we saw each other, and they confess that when they turned forty a remarkable change took place in their lives. They felt old and tired, could see their lives coming to an end; they discovered they had sicknesses that didn't exist. Their shoulders felt stiff and they found it difficult to pull on their overcoats. And the world seemed old and tawdry; the same old notions kept coming back with monotonous regularity. The younger generation, barking at the heels of the parents, ignored their accomplishments. The most maddening thing was that the younger generation made the same discoveries we had made. Even worse, they presented their old new ideas as if no one had ever entertained them before.

And as we got to talking about the old days when we were young, we sank back into time, literally living again the days that were gone, found ourselves twenty years back in time, until someone began to wonder if time really existed.

Our philosopher enlightened us. "Kant has already worked that out. Time is only our way of conceiving the present."

"What did I tell you! I've had the same idea, because when I remember little incidents that happened forty-five years ago, they're as vivid as if they happened yesterday, and what happened to me as a child seems just as close to me as what I experienced a year ago."

And then we began to wonder if that held true for everyone. A septuagenarian, the only one in our group whom we regarded as an old man, remarked that he still didn't feel old. (He had recently remarried and had a baby in the cra-

dle.) This choice bit of information made us all feel like mere
boys, and we began talking and carrying on like youngsters.

I couldn't help notice when we first met that my friends
hadn't changed much, and that had surprised me. But I had
also observed that they didn't laugh as readily as they used
to and that they were a little guarded. They had come to
realize the power of the spoken word. It wasn't that life had
softened their opinions, but discretion had taught them that
they would sooner or later have to eat their own words. Moreover, they had discovered that a man's register consisted of
more than one note and that the whole chromatic scale had
to be employed to approximate one's view of another person.
But right now it was different. The barriers were down. No
one bothered to tailor his words very carefully, no one had
any respect for the opinions of others. We fell back into our
old ways, let the pieces fall where they may, and we had
a good time.

Then there came a pause. . . . Several pauses. . . . Then
the room became uncomfortably quiet. The ones who had
done most of the talking had the uneasy feeling that they
had said too much. They sensed that new ties had been
formed silently by everyone there during the intervening ten
years and that new and undivined interests had sprung up to
separate old friends. Those who had talked so freely had run
aground on hidden reefs of thought or unwittingly opened
old wounds. All of which they would have been aware of if
only they had seen the side glances and dirty looks with
which the others prepared to resist and defend themselves, or
seen the corners of their mouths curl to hide a suppressed
word.

When we rose from the table, it was as if the newly made
contacts had all been broken. The atmosphere changed
abruptly. Each one felt himself on the defensive and crawled
back into his shell. But something had to be said, and we
uttered phrases that were quite meaningless, as one could
tell by the fact that the looks didn't go with the words; the
smiles were warm but the eyes were cold.

So it turned out to be an insufferably long night. The party
split into groups and couples to talk, but all attempts to stir
up old memories failed. Someone was always asking the

wrong kind of question, out of pure ignorance, of course. For example: "How's your brother Herman getting along?" (No one really cared to know; it was only an attempt to make conversation.)—General embarrassment. "Why, thank you, he's pretty much the same. Can't see any improvement."

"Improvement? You mean he's been ill?"

"Yes, of course. . . . Didn't you know?"

Someone stepped in to save the man from having to explain that Herman was insane.

Or another example: "Haven't seen your wife. You keeping her under wraps, you sly dog?"

(She was in the process of getting a divorce.)

Still another example: "Your son must be a big boy now. Has he graduated yet?"

(The son was the black sheep of the family, a complete good-for-nothing.)

In a word, we had not kept up with each other. Our little gang had disintegrated. And we had all had our sad and bitter experiences; we were no longer kids, to say the least.

When we finally broke up outside the gate, we all wanted to get away as quickly as possible. In the old days, we would have kept the party going at some café. Reminiscing about the past when we were young and gay simply hadn't had the refreshing effect we had expected. The past turned out to be nothing more than mulch for the present, but the mulch had already withered, dried up, and begun to rot.

And we couldn't help but notice that no one spoke any more about the future, only about the past, for the very good reason that we were already in that future we used to think about and it was no longer possible to dream one up.

\*    \*    \*

Two weeks later I found myself sitting at the same table once again, in almost the same company, and in exactly the same place. But now we had had time to go home and prepare answers to all the allegations and pointed statements that we had out of politeness left unanswered the first time. We came armed, like men of war. Those who were lazy, tired, or more interested in good food than in a good fight drew in their guns, drifted off to a quiet lagoon, and left a wake of

silence after them. But the belligerent ones prepared to do battle. The old cause that once bound us together, a cause that
had never been clearly defined, had been betrayed, and everyone accused everyone else of apostasy and defection.

"Never! I've never been an atheist!" someone cried.

"Oh, come off it! Never been an atheist?!"

And we plunged into a discussion that should have taken
place twenty years before. But now we tried to fabricate
consciously all that had sprouted forth unconsciously during
those happy years when we were young and blooming. Our
memories proved unreliable; we had forgotten what we had
once said and done; we quoted ourselves and others incor-
rectly. The result was absolute chaos. As soon as the room
grew silent, someone went right back to the beginning, and
the talk went round and round in a circle. Talk. Embarrassed
silence. Talk.

When we broke up this time, it was with a definite feeling
that the past was dead, that each of us had come of age and
had earned the right to leave the hothouse of public life and
to grow freely out on his own piece of land, without the
need for gardeners or pruning shears.

In general, that's how one comes to live alone, and I suppose that's how it has always come about. Nevertheless, one
didn't stop keeping company just like that. Those who didn't
want to stop developing, who wanted to explore, discover
and conquer new worlds, got together in a little group and
used the restaurants as parlors. We had already tried to meet
at home, but we soon found out that the good friend who
invited us in had retailored his life and changed his style.
He had got himself a wife, and as usual this made for a tight
fit. When she was around, we had to talk about "something
else." And if we forgot and talked about things that interested
us, one of two things might happen. Either she took the chair
and dictatorially settled all questions, or else she rose, fled to
the nursery, and wouldn't be seen again until she sat down
to the table, where you would be sure to be treated like a
wretch and parasite and made to feel that you were taking
her man from her, from house and home, from household
duties and marriage responsibilities.

Not that that actually happened. Friendships usually came

to an end because the wives couldn't get along. They were always finding fault with each other.

So, as I said, we met in cafés. But the strange thing was that now we didn't like sitting there. We tried to convince ourselves that this was neutral territory for conversation since no one was the host and no one felt like a guest. But we couldn't help thinking about the poor wives. Sitting there at home all alone was someone who, if she had been truly alone and not married, could have been out enjoying herself, but who was now doomed to lonely evenings at home. And another factor: most of the customers in the café were not married. That put them on the other side of the fence, and, being homeless, they seemed to enjoy certain rights in the café. They behaved as if it were their home; made a lot of noise, burst into salvos of laughter, regarded the married men as intruders—in a word—made themselves a nuisance.

Being a widower, I thought I had a certain right to be in the café. But I must have been wrong. And when I lured a married man to it, I soon felt the hatred of his wife, who would stop inviting me to their home. Perhaps she did right; in marriage three's a crowd.

And if the husbands did show up, they were so anxious to talk about their domestic affairs I had to listen to their troubles with maids and children, school courses and exams until I was so completely drawn into their family trivialities that I felt I had gained nothing by becoming a widower.

If we finally did get around to the subject of discussion, the big question that brought us together, one person would hold forth while someone else would listen with lowered eyes waiting for his chance to speak in order that he might harangue us on his favorite topic, which had nothing to do with the previous speaker and often made no sense at all. Or else, in some diabolical way everybody would talk at once and nobody could understand a thing that was being said. The result was a Babylonian confusion ending with bickering and complete incomprehension.

"You don't understand what I'm saying!" was the usual cry of despair.

It was true. During the past years each one of us had added new shades of meaning to the terms he used and new values to old ideas. Furthermore, we didn't want to express those ideas that constituted our trade secrets, or those thoughts that we felt heralded the coming age, notions that each one of us guarded jealously.

Every night that I walked home from one of these café meetings I realized how worthless these little nights-out were. All one really wanted to do was listen to his own voice and convince the others he was right. After each session my mind felt as if it had been rooted in, plowed up, and planted with weeds that had to be raked out before anything good could grow there. But when I got home to the solitude and silence of my rooms, I became myself again, wrapped myself in my own spirit, my own atmosphere, which fit me like old, well-tailored clothes. After an hour of meditation, I would sink into sleep and be dissolved, released from all desires, needs, ambitions.

Little by little I cut down on my café meetings and practiced being alone, sometimes falling back into temptation, but always drawing back more cured than before—until I finally gave in to the pleasure of listening to the silence and hearing the new voices that come from there.

## II

That was how I gradually came to live alone, limiting my business with the outer world to what my work required, and handling most of that by telephone. I won't deny that it was difficult at first, and that the emptiness I felt around me clamored to be filled. By cutting off my connection with other people I seemed at first to lose strength, but at the same time my ego began, as it were, to crystallize, to harden around a kernel where all my experiences collected to be assimilated as nourishment for my soul. Moreover, I accustomed myself to making over for my own purposes everything I saw and heard, in the house, on the street, out in nature. And in referring everything I apprehended to the work that occupied me, I felt how my capital grew, the observations I made in my solitude being more valuable than those I made on people in the social world.

In some phases of my life I've had my own home. This time I rented two furnished rooms from a widow. It took a little time before I could learn to live with these unfamiliar pieces of furniture—not too long, however. The desk was the hardest to adjust to and make part of myself, because the recently deceased councilman to whom it had belonged must have sat there for a whole generation poring over his minutes. His cyanine-blue ink, a disgusting color that I hate, had left stains on the desk. His arm had worn out the varnish on the right side, and on the left side he had pasted down a round piece of oilcloth of the most horrible yellow-gray color for the desk lamp. A real pain to me. But I was determined to go along with whatever cropped up, and pretty soon I no longer noticed the ugly patch. The bed—it had always been my dream to die in my own bed—but although I can afford to, I don't want to start buying new things. Not to own anything is one way to be free. Owning nothing, wishing for nothing, that's how to make oneself invulnerable to the worst blows of fate. And then at the same time to have enough money so that you know you can buy whatever you feel like, that's true happiness. That's real independence.

A crazy collection of bad pictures hangs on the wall, including some lithographs and chromos. At first I hated them for being so ugly, but soon they began to attract my interest in a way I couldn't have suspected. Once as I was writing I ran out of ideas, a crucial scene wouldn't come to me, and in despair I glanced up at the wall. What caught my eye was a horrible colored print that some illustrated magazine once upon a time had offered as a subscription bonus. It showed a farmer standing on a ferry dock and holding a cow that was to cross over with him on the unseen ferry. The lone man gestured upward at the sky—his one and only cow—his worried expression. . . . I got my scene.

And there is also in these rooms an assortment of small objects such as are to be found only in a home, redolent with memories, made by friendly hands and not store-bought. Antimacassars, dustcovers, whatnots with glass and porcelain

objects. Among these is a big loving cup with an inscription
—"in appreciation from," etc., etc. All these little things radiate friendliness, appreciation, perhaps even love. And to tell
the truth, in just a few days I felt as if these rooms welcomed
me. All these things once belonged to somebody else and I
have inherited them from a dead man I never knew.

My landlady, who soon saw that I was not a very talkative
sort, was thoughtful and considerate. She always had my
room ready for me by the time I got back from my morning
walk, and we would greet each other only with a friendly nod
that said everything that needed to be said: "How are you?"
—"Fine, thank you."—"Everything all right with your room?"
—"Perfect."—"I'm glad to hear it."

However, after a week of this, she couldn't contain herself
any longer. She had to ask me if there was anything I needed;
all I had to do was mention it.

"No, thank you, there's nothing I need. Everything's
perfect."

"Hmm. I just thought that—I've always been led to believe
that gentlemen always found something to complain about."

"I got out of that habit long ago."

The old lady looked at me in an odd way, as if she had
heard otherwise.

"Well, now, what about the food?"

"The food? I haven't really noticed. It must be excellent."

And it was excellent. In fact, the treatment I received was
in every way exceptional. It was more than the ordinary routine boardinghouse treatment. I felt cared for and looked
after, something I had never experienced before.

The days flowed by calmly and peacefully, softly and
pleasantly, and though I was sometimes tempted to speak to
my landlady, especially when she looked worried and troubled, I always resisted the temptation—partly because I didn't
want to get involved in other people's problems and partly
because I respected her privacy. I wanted my relationship
with her to be an impersonal one, and I found it suited my
mood better to let her past remain hidden in the shadows.
If I were to hear the story of her life, the furniture in my
rooms would acquire a character different from the one I
had assigned to them, and that would be the end of the beau-

tiful patterns my imagination had woven. Chairs, tables, washbasin, bed would all become props in her personal drama, which might begin to haunt me. But now all these things were mine. I had covered them with the slipcovers of my spirit, and the set would only work for my play. My play!

\* \* \*

I've also made myself a few friends, of a nonintimate, impersonal sort, and I've acquired them in a way that didn't cost me much. It is on my morning walks that I have gotten to know certain people whom I really don't know, people I don't say hello to because they're not personal friends. The first person I meet is the army major. He's retired, living on a pension, and must therefore be at least fifty-five. He dresses in civvies. I know his name and I've heard stories about his younger days. I also know that he's not married. Being retired, as I said, he consequently has nothing to occupy himself with as he waits out his life. But he confronts his fate with courage—straight and tall, broad-chested, coat unbuttoned usually, rather jaunty looking. His hair is dark, his mustache black, his walk military—so military I always stretch myself when I meet him; and I feel younger when I realize that he's past fifty-five. The look in his eyes gives me the impression that he doesn't hate me, perhaps even likes me. And after some time, he becomes an old acquaintance whom I'd like to nod hello to. Still, there is definitely a great difference between us. He has served out his time and laid down his arms, while I'm still standing in the middle of the battlefield, fighting my way forward. So there is no point in his looking for sympathy from me as if we were birds of a feather. I don't want to get involved.—I may be gray around the temples, but I know that tomorrow morning my hair could be just as dark as his, if I wanted it to be. But I don't bother with it since I don't have any women to preen myself for. Besides, it seems to me that his hair lies altogether too flat and smooth not to arouse some doubts, while my wavy locks rise up above suspicion.

Then I have another acquaintance who has the advantage of being a complete stranger to me. He is certainly at least sixty, his hair and his full beard both completely gray. At the beginning of our acquaintanceship I thought there was something in the sullen and splenetic expression on his face that I recognized, certain features in his figure, and I approached him with compassion and sympathy. I felt that he had tasted the most bitter dregs, that he had swum against the current of life and gone down, that he was living in an era that had gradually and imperceptibly left him far behind. He couldn't give up the ideals of his youth because they were too dear to him, and all the while he regarded himself as being on the right road. Poor man! He alone is in step and all the world is out of step. What a tragedy!

But one day when I looked him in the eye, I saw that he hated me, perhaps because he read the look of pity I gave him. The unkindest cut of all. I even heard him snort as he passed by me.—Maybe, without my being aware of it, I did him or those close to him an injury. It's possible. Or perhaps I indirectly messed up his life. Or perhaps I once actually knew him. Who can tell? He hates me, and strangely enough, I feel I deserve his hatred. I don't want to look him in the eye any more. His eyes pierce through me and sting my conscience. It's also possible that we are born enemies, that class, race, breeding, points of view have raised a barrier between us, and that we instinctively sense this. I have learned from experience how to tell friend from enemy on the street. There are certain people, strangers to me, who radiate so much hostility I have to cross the street in order not to come too close to them. And in my lonely state this sensitivity is sharpened to such an extreme degree that merely hearing a person's voice on the street upsets me, if it affects me at all.

And then I have a third friend, who rides a horse. I nod at him, for I've known him since our college days, and I have a good idea of what his name is but can't spell it. I haven't spoken to him in thirty years, only nodded at him on the street, and sometimes been greeted with a smile of recognition—and a very good smile it is under that big mustache of his. He wears a uniform and with the passing years the stripes on his cap have become steadily more numerous and broader. Now, recently, when after a ten-year hiatus in our friendship I met him again on his horse, he was wearing so

many stripes I didn't want to risk saying hello for fear of
being snubbed. But I guess he understood what was in my
mind because he reined in his horse and called out, "Hello,
there! Don't you recognize me?"

Yes, I recognized him, and then we moved on, each going
his own way, and the nodded hellos have continued since
then. One morning I noticed a strange, half-distrustful smile
under his mustache. I didn't feel like interpreting it even to
myself, it seemed so improbable. He looked as if—I was only
letting my imagination work, of course—as if on the one hand
he thought I thought he was a snob, and on the other hand
as if he suspected me of being a snob. Me??

It is not unusual in this world that people who think too
little of themselves have the reputation of bearing the deadly
sin of pride engraved in their scutcheons.

*       *       *

Then there is an elderly lady who is taken for walks by
her two dogs. When they stop, she stops—and they stop at
every lamppost, every tree, every corner. Whenever I meet
her, I think Swedenborgian thoughts. I think of the misan-
thrope who was so alone he had to keep company with animals. I think of her as punished by her imagination. She
believes she is commanding these two unclean beasts, while
it is the animals who are forcing her to follow their every
whim and crotchet. I call her Queen of the World and Protectress of the Universe because that is how she looks to me,
with her head thrown back and her eyes looking down.

Finally there is my tithe woman. I look upon her as occult.
She doesn't show up very often, but she's always there when
I've just acquired a goodly sum of money or when some danger is in the offing. I have never believed in "encounters" or
that kind of superstition. Never avoided an old hag, never spit
after a cat, and I've never given a kick in the pants to a
friend who was about to embark on a risky enterprise but
have instead wished him well from the bottom of my heart
and clapped him on the shoulder. Only recently I did just
that to a sophisticated actor friend of mine. His eyes flashing
with rage, he spun around and hissed at me, "Don't say that!
It's bad luck!" I replied, "No, the good wishes of a friend

can't bring bad luck, even if they can't do much good."—He didn't change his mind; he was superstitious like all unbelievers. The unbelievers, you see, believe everything—but backwards. If they have had a beautiful dream, it means something bad. And if they dream of vermin, for instance, that means money. I, on the contrary, pay no attention to insignificant dreams; but if I have a dream that forces itself on me, then I interpret it straightforwardly, directly, head on. A nightmare is a warning to me and a beautiful dream is an encouragement or a consolation. This is logical and scientific, because if I'm pure inside, I see pure, and vice versa. My inner being is mirrored in my dreams and so I can use them as I use a shaving mirror: to see what I'm doing and to avoid cutting myself. The same applies to certain "incidents" in waking life—but not all. For example, there are always bits of paper lying in the street yet not all of them catch my attention. However, if one of them does, I give it my careful consideration, and if there is something written or printed on it that has some connection with what is preoccupying me, then I regard it as an expression of my innermost unborn thoughts. And am I not right in thinking so? For if there did not exist this bridge of thought between my inner self and the outer thing, a transfer could never take place. Not that I believe that anyone is putting out bits of papers just for my sake, although there are those who believe only in the palpable and the physical and look only for material causes.

To get back to the old woman. I call her occult because I can't explain why she shows up just when she's supposed to. She reminds me of a fishwife in the market when I was a youngster, or the woman who sat out-of-doors in the candy booth. Her clothes are ash-colored, but holeless and spotless. She doesn't know who I am. Calls me Guv'nor, probably because I was a bit portly three years ago when our acquaintance started. Her thanks and blessings follow me down the road a piece, and I love to hear that "Bless you"—a sound so soft and gentle compared to the harshness of "Damn you." It seems to make me feel good the whole day.

After we had known each other for a year, I once gave her a large bill, and I expected to see in her face that idiotic, almost evil look you can see in some beggars when you give them too much—as if they thought you were crazy or had pulled the wrong bill from your pocket. If you give a young hooligan a silver coin, he always runs away laughing as if he expected you to chase after him and take the silver coin back and hand him a penny instead. But my old woman grabbed my hand in such a strong grip I couldn't get away, and with a voice filled with infinite wisdom and knowledge of human nature, she asked, nodding yes to her own question, "Oh, Guv'nor, you've been poor, haven't you?"—"Yes, just as poor as you, and maybe will be again!"—She understood that. I wondered if she had known better times, but I never wanted to ask.

That is pretty much the company I keep outside the house, and for three years they've been my associates.

But I had also started keeping company inside the house. Living as I do four flights up, I have four families with all their histories disposed in layers beneath me, including the family in the basement. I don't know any of them, don't know how they look, don't think I've even met them on the stairs. All I see is the name plates on their doors. I can tell pretty much what their political sentiments are by the newspapers stuck in their door handles. Wall to wall with me there lives in the next house a singer who sings beautifully for me. And she has a girl friend who comes to play Beethoven for me. These are my best neighbors, and I am tempted at times to make their acquaintance to thank them for all the bright and happy moments they have given me. Still, I resist the temptation because I feel certain that the best part of our relationship would be over once we started exchanging banalities. Sometimes the girls are quiet for several days on end and then my place seems dark and gloomy. However, I also have a happy fellow for a neighbor who lives, I think, in the house next door on one of the lower floors. He plays pieces apparently from operettas, which I don't recognize but which are so irresistibly funny and so harmlessly indecent I have to laugh even in the midst of my most somber thoughts.

As contrast and dark shadow to these bright and pleasant people is my nearest neighbor, who lives on the floor below. He owns a dog. His dog is a huge, red, crazy, galloping animal that barks and yelps in the stairway. His master, who looks upon the house as his and the rest of us housebreakers, lets this monster watchdog guard the stairs. If I should come home late at night and go groping up the stairs and should my foot touch some soft hairy object, then the peace of night is broken. In the blackness I see two phosphorescent beads shooting off sparks, and the whole sounding shell of the spiral stairway is filled with noise—a noise that results in a door being opened and a man stepping out to crush and annihilate me—me, the injured party—with the look of fury in his eyes. I certainly don't say I'm sorry, but still I always feel I'm the guilty party. Arraigned against the dog owners all the rest of mankind is guilty.

I have never understood how a person can devote his affection and solicitude to animals when there are fellow creatures he might better devote himself to—especially such an unclean animal as the dog whose whole existence consists in dirtying things. And this dog owner has a wife and grown daughter who share with him an emotional life centered on that animal. They often have dog soirées in which they gather around the dining-room table—I can hear precisely where they are sitting without having to listen—to discuss the monster. The one who can't talk howls his answers, which makes the whole family roar with contentment and pride.

Sometimes the barking awakens me in the middle of the night. I can imagine how happy the family must be to know that they possess a beast so alert, keen, and watchful that it can even sense through walls and closed windows the coming of the lavatory man and his cart. Does concern for the unhappy people whose peace and sleep is broken ruffle the happiness of the dog owners? Not a chance. For the priceless gift of blessed sleep, which comes so dear to some of us, for that they have no consideration. I sometimes ask myself how thick is the skin of those who through the silence of the night do not feel the curses hurled down on their heads by the rest of us who lie tossing sleeplessly in bed. Don't they feel this perfectly justifiable hatred penetrating ceilings, floors, and walls to damn and curse them?

Once long ago I had the nerve to complain about dogs

barking in a house filled with people. The dog owner parried by reminding me of children screaming in my house! He compared an unclean and pernicious animal to a child in pain or discomfort. Since then I have never complained. Yet in order to be at peace with myself and to reconcile myself with my fellow man—for hating is a torture to me—I have tried to find some explanation for this passion for animals, which surpasses comparable feelings for human beings. But I confess I can't explain it. And like everything I can't explain, it has a sinister effect on me.—If I were to philosophize using Swedenborg's method, I would settle for this: obsession as a form of punishment.—Enough said for the time being. The unfortunate merit our sympathy.

*     *     *

There is a balcony to my apartment and from it I have a magnificent view of fields, water, and woods shimmering in the distance out towards the seacoast. But if I lie on my sofa, all I see is sky and clouds. It is as if I were in a balloon, floating high above the earth. But then my ears begin to be pestered by a great many little sounds. My downstairs neighbor telephones and I can hear by his accent that he is from the province of Västergötland. A sick child is crying on one of the lower floors. And on the street two persons have stopped to talk under my balcony. Now I perk up my ears and listen —a writer has the prerogative of listening, at least to what is said in the street.

"Well, don't you see, there was simply no way of making a go of it."

"Has he closed up for good?"

"Certainly has."

(I understood right away they were talking about the grocery store on the street floor that closed for lack of business.)

"No, there are too many stores here—and he got off to a bad start. . . . The first day he took in thirty cents, the next day somebody came in to consult the city directory, and the third day he sold some postage stamps! I tell you, there are too many stores! I've got to be going. I'll see you."

"Goodbye. Going to the bank?"

"No, I'm going down to the customs office. . . ."

These were the curtain lines in a tragic drama I was a witness to during the last three months, a drama that was acted out in my building.

To the left of the entrance to my building they began to set up a grocery business. They painted and gilded, shellacked and varnished, while the young owner of the shop would step to the edge of the sidewalk now and then to contemplate the beautiful sight. He looked like he might be a good salesman, full of vigor, though perhaps there was something lightweight about him. Still, he looked hopeful and unafraid, especially when he showed up with his intended.

I watched the shelves and bins rise up against the walls. Soon the counter with its scales was ready, and a telephone was nailed to the wall. I remember the telephone in particular because it sang such a melancholy, wailing song in my wall. I didn't wish to complain since I was, and am, trying to get rid of that habit. Then they began constructing something inside the store, a *pan coupé* with an arcade. It looked theatrical in the bad sense, the false perspective designed to create the illusion of something magnificent.

They began filling the shelves with an endless amount of goods, with famous labels and without. That took a whole month. In the meantime a huge sign was painted on the colossal windowpane, and after three days of painting, I read in Gothic letters: *Östermalm Grocery*.

Now this whole section of town is Östermalm, and when I read that sign I thought of Sophocles' words:

> The gifts of the gods are crowned with one:
> Prudence. Therefore man takes care
> Not to affront the Almighty. Pride,
> Paying with burning sores for its rash deeds,
> Learns at the latter end of life
> The value of prudence.

How unwise of the young man! When Östermalm has at least two hundred groceries, to go and trumpet himself as owning the real, the one and only Östermalm store! A rather shabby trick betraying a disregard for the rights of others, who will now bite you in the heel.[1] Overreaching, overbearing, and overcredulous! Anyway, the newly married grocery man opened shop. The window displays were indeed magnificent, yet I trembled at what fate had in store for him. He must have invested all his life savings, or all the money he had inherited, or else he had borrowed on ninety-day notes.

The first few days passed just as the stranger under my balcony described them. On the sixth day I went in to buy something, and I noticed that the clerk was hanging around the door. This struck me as a tactical blunder. A customer wants to slip unhindered into a store, for one thing, and for another, it indicated there were no customers inside. And it also gave me to understand that the owner was away—out with his wife, of course, perhaps on a pleasure trip.

At any rate, I stepped in and was amazed at the expensive mise-en-scène, which indicated to me that the owner must have worked in the theater.

When the dates were to be weighed, they were grasped not with bare fingers but with two sheets of tissue paper—the good old traditional way. A good sign. The groceries I bought were excellent, and I became a steady customer.

A few days later the owner had returned and was standing at the counter. He was a modern soul: I saw that right away when he didn't try to strike up a conversation—that was old-fashioned. But his eyes spoke—respect, confidence, honesty. So far, so good. But he couldn't keep himself from putting on an act. He was called to the telephone, said excuse me and pardon me a thousand times and went to the telephone. Now, unfortunately for him, I've written plays and studied the arts of gesture and dialogue. So I could tell by his face that he wasn't talking to anyone on the phone, and I could hear from his lines in the pretended dialogue that it was all an act.

"Yes.—Yes, of course.—Yes, yes.—Right!—Certainly! Absolutely, just as you want it!" (He rung off.)

He was supposed to be taking an order but transitions and shades of tone were lacking. Though it was all really

[1] The verses quoted above are from *Antigone* and apply to Creon, but the reference to being bitten in the heel indicate that Strindberg had Philoctetes in mind.—EDITOR.

quite innocent, I didn't like being his fool and I didn't like waiting around while he played games. My mood became critical. I began reading the labels, especially the brand names. Though I was not a connoisseur of wines, I remembered from a long way back that if it said *Cruse et fils* on the bottle it was a genuine French wine. And that was the name I saw on a label. Amazed at finding Bordeaux wine in a grocery store, I broke down and bought a bottle at an incredibly low price.

Back home I made a couple of discoveries. I didn't get mad, mind you, but I never shopped at that grocery again. The dates that had been excellent before were now mixed in with others that were woody. And the wine may have been Cruse's—Robinson Crusoe's perhaps but definitely not *Cruse et fils*.

From that day on I never saw anyone enter the store. And now comes the tragic part of the story—a young man full of youth and vitality eager to work but doomed to idleness and consequently to defeat—the struggle against the inevitable that each day came closer. His high spirits began to break down and give way to a nervous defiance. I could see his face through the window, ghost-like, always on the watch for customers. After a time, he began to hide. It was terribly moving to see him from the front row, standing behind his theatrical arcade, apprehensive, afraid of everything, even of the approach of a customer, afraid that the customer would only want to look at the city directory. That provided the cruelest moment, because he had to smile and put on a show of being pleasant and friendly. On one of the first days of business he had caught the clerk contemptuously tossing the directory across the counter at a dignified elderly gentleman. Knowing a little more about people than the clerk, the owner had rebuked him with a reminder that customers are drawn in by postage stamps and directories. But he himself had not yet learned that good products are the best advertisement and that tricks don't fool anyone.

The dénouement approached. I suffered with him through all his agony. Thought of his wife, the end of the fiscal quarter, the rent coming due, the promissory notes. Finally, when I could no longer bring myself to go past his window, I took another way. But I couldn't escape him because his telephone wire sang such a sorrowful tune in my wall, even at night. That was when I heard the dirges, the long sighing, gasping songs of a life finished before it really got started. Of his hopes, of his despair, of not being able to begin again —and always of his patiently waiting wife and the unborn child.

That he himself was to blame didn't help matters any. Besides, it was doubtful that he really was to blame. All these little tricks that are part of business had been drummed into him by his bosses and employers; he didn't see that there was anything wrong in them. Imprudence! The cause lay in that, but not the blame.

Sometimes I asked myself how I got involved in all this. Perhaps because one has to share other people's sufferings, and share them precisely when one seeks through solitude to avoid them.

And so the story of the merchant reached its appointed end. It was actually a relief to see the doors close. But when the doors opened again and one saw the drawers and cases being emptied, the shelves stripped bare, and the whole great variety of goods, most of which were spoiled, carried out, it was like watching an autopsy. Since I knew one of the men on the job, I walked into the backroom behind the arcade. Here was where he had fought his battle. To pass the time and escape the curse of pure idleness he had written out piles of imaginary bills. They still lay there and were made out to Prince Hohenlohe, Félix Faure, even the Prince of Wales was included—he had purchased 200 kilos of Russian marmalade and one case of curry.

I personally was very much interested in observing how the man's mind had linked together Félix Faure's *Russian Journey* with the Indo-British kitchen of the Prince of Wales.

There was also a pack of advertisements he had written out, announcing "first-class" caviar, "first-class" coffee—everything first-class. But the advertisements were never printed.

I understood how he had sat at his desk and been forced to put on this act in front of his clerk. Poor man! But life is long and full of ups and downs, and this man will some day be on top again.

# III

This is ultimately what it is like to be alone: you spin yourself into the silk of your soul, you become a pupa and await the metamorphosis, which is certain to come. While waiting, you live on your past experiences and telepathically you live the lives of others. Death and resurrection; being reared and trained for something new and strange.

I am finally sole master of yourself. I don't have to put up with anyone's petty peeves and silly whims. My soul begins to grow in its newly won freedom and I experience an extraordinary sense of inner peace, of quiet happiness, of security and independence.

Living with someone, which is supposed to be an education of sorts, strikes me now as I think back on it as a co-education in sin. To anyone with a strong sense of beauty, looking at things that are not beautiful, hour after hour and day after day, is a form of torture that can give one a martyr complex. Having to shut your eyes to injustices out of regard for your wife and others teaches you to be a hypocrite. Constantly withholding your real opinions out of this regard makes you a coward. Taking the blame in order to bring peace to the house for things you did not do is a form of slow but steady self-debasement. Never hearing a word of encouragement saps you of your strength and self-assurance. And having to bear the consequences of the mistakes of others gives one a grudge against the whole world.

The worst of it is that you are not in control of your own reputation, even if you have every intention of doing the right thing. What good does it do for me to try to remain spotless if my marriage partner goes around slinging mud at me? At least half the shame is mine, if not all, which is the usual case. Marriage makes one feel insecure and unsafe. It puts one on public view, makes you dependent on someone else's whims. Those who did not dare to stab me in the back when I stood alone had an easy job of sticking a knife into

my heart when I let my wife carry it about the streets and
parks.

Another virtue of living alone is that I can determine my
own spiritual diet. Now I don't have to see enemies at my
table or have to listen in silence to abuse hurled at the things
I cherish. Within my own doors I am not forced to listen to
music I abhor. I'm spared the sight of newspapers lying
around with caricatures of my friends and myself. I'm freed
from having to read books I despise and from attending exhibits of pictures I disdain. In a word, I am master of my own
soul in those cases where one has some right to be master. I
am free to choose my own likes and dislikes. I have never
been a tyrant; I have only wanted to avoid being tyrannized,
and that's what tyrannical people won't stand for. On the
contrary, I have always hated tyrants, and for that the tyrants cannot forgive me.

I have always wanted to move onward and upward. That
is why I have had the higher court on my side against those
who wanted to drag me back and hold me down. And that
is why I have come to live alone.

*     *     *

Living in solitude you must first of all come to terms with
yourself and with your past. A long and hard task, a complete education in self-conquest. But there is no more re-
warding study than that of getting to know yourself, if such
a thing is possible. You have to use the mirror now and then,
especially a hand mirror, for otherwise you cannot see how
you look from the back.

I began the process of coming to terms with myself ten
years ago when I made the acquaintance of Balzac. While I
was reading his fifty volumes, I did not notice what was taking place within me. Not until I had gone through them all
did I realize what had happened. I had found myself, and I
could make a synthesis out of all the hitherto unresolved an-
titheses of my life. And by looking at people through his
spectacles I had also learned to view life with both eyes,
whereas I had formerly looked at life with one eye, as through
a monocle. And Balzac, that great magician, had not only
taught me that by resigning oneself, by submitting to fate or

providence, one can save oneself from the pains of the hardest blows, but he had also led me slyly into a kind of religion that I should like to call a confessionless Christianity. During my wanderings under Balzac's guiding hand, through his human comedy, where I got to know four thousand persons (a German has counted them!), I felt I was living another life, larger and richer than my own. By the time I had reached the end it appeared to me that I had lived two lives. Being in his world gave me a new slant on my own, and after a series of relapses and crises I finally ended up reconciled in a way to suffering. For I had at the same time discovered that sorrow and affliction had burned up the sweepings of my soul, purified my feelings and instincts, and even endowed my soul, which had been ripped free of the tortured and harassed body, with greater potentialities. As a result I accepted the bitter dregs of life as medicine. I considered it my duty to suffer everything—except degradation and subjection.

But solitude also makes one sensitive. Where before I had armed myself against suffering by being hardhearted, I now became more sensitive to the pains of others, an absolute prey to outside influences—not bad ones, however. Those only frighten me and make me withdraw even more. At such times I seek out the more secluded and remote streets where I meet only common people who do not recognize me. There is a special route that I call *via dolorosa,* which I take when my mood seems darker than usual. It takes in the city line at the north and looks like a one-sided avenue with a row of houses on one side and the woods on the other. Now in order to reach it I have to take a little side street that has a particular attraction for me, although I can't explain why. At the foot of the narrow street and dominating it is a huge church, which both elevates my spirit and casts shadows on it—but without managing to lure me in. I never go to church, since . . . well, I don't know why. Down to the right is the parish office where I asked to have the banns published once long ago. But up here on the north end stands a house just at the point where the street opens out into the fields and farmlands. It is as big as a palace, stands at the edge of the drop-off and commands a view of the water and the bays. I've wanted to live there, and I've imagined that someone lives there now who once had an influence on my life, or is having it right now. I can see the house from my apartment, and I stare at it every day when the sun shines on it or whenever the lights are turned on in it in the evening. In the meantime, whenever I walk past it I always seem to receive some kind and sympathetic message from it, and I feel as if I were waiting to be allowed to withdraw to it to find peace there.

So I march on to the avenue into which all the side streets debouch, and each one of them brings to life a memory from my past. Since the avenue I'm walking on runs along a high ridge, the side streets all run downhill from it, many of them making a bend on their way, thus forming a steep hill that resembles the globe of the earth. If I stand on the sidewalk on the ridge and look at someone coming up the hill, I see first a head sticking up from the ground, then the shoulders and then the whole body. This takes about half a minute, and I find it mysterious and fascinating.

I look down each side street as I pass by, and down each one of them can be seen in the distance either the south part of town or the palace or the city between the bridges [the old town in Stockholm]. And each time I look down I am plagued by the memories each street arouses. Down there at the bottom of this crooked tube known as ———— Street lies a house I went in and out of a generation ago as fate wove its net for me. . . . Opposite it is another house where twenty years later I lived under similar conditions—only just the reverse and doubly painful. Down there in the next street I lived through that period of life which for other people is usually the most beautiful. It was for me too, I must say, but at the same time it was the ugliest of all. And the passing years cover it with a varnish that does not bring out the beauty; rather the ugly spots spread out and devour the little beauty that once was there. Paintings feel the toll of time and the colors change and not to their advantage; white especially has a tendency to turn a dirty yellow. The "pietists" say that that is the way it is supposed to be in order that at the Great Parting we may take our leave without any regrets and go our way, happy to turn our backs on the whole affair. When I have gone some distance along the avenue past the big new houses, they grow fewer and fewer. The knobs of rocks begin to stick up, a tobacco field spreads out before me. A gentleman farmer has had his slaughterhouse shack neatly sliced through by a bend in the lane. And there stands a tobacco shed that I remember from—1859. I used to play in it. In a little cottage, which no longer exists, there lived a cleaning woman who had formerly been a nursery maid in my parents' home—and from the roof of that shed her eight-year-old son had fallen to the ground and hurt himself badly. We used to come out here to hire her for the spring cleaning at Easter and the winter cleaning at Christmas. . . . And I used to prefer to take these back streets to school in order to avoid Queen Street. There were trees and flowering plants, cows grazing, hens cackling; it was farm country then. . . . And I sank back into time, back to hideous childhood, when life lay before me, strange and frightening, when everything oppressed and constrained me. . . . Now all I have to do to put all this behind me is turn on my heels. And I do. But I still have time to see in the distance the tops of the linden trees that line the long street of my childhood days and the cloud-like contours of the pines out near the city cemetery.

I have turned my back on it now, and as I look down the avenue toward the morning sun rising over the hills purple in the distance, out near the seacoast, then I forget in a second all the concerns of my childhood, which is so snarled up with other people's concerns it isn't really my own, whereas my own real life begins out there near the seacoast.

That corner near the tobacco shed holds a terror for me. Yet sometimes it exerts a marvelous drawing power, as does everything painful. It's like going to look at caged wild animals that you know can't get at you. And that single moment of pleasure when I spin on my heel and turn my back on the whole thing is so intense that I treat myself to it occasionally. In that second I put thirty-three years behind me and I feel happy to be standing there. It was always my longing as a child "to be old." It occurs to me now that I had an intuition then of what lay ahead of me, which also occurs to me now as having been predetermined and unavoidable. My life couldn't have turned out any other way.

When Minerva and Venus met me at the crossroads of youth, it was not a matter of choosing. I followed both, hand in hand, as I suppose we all have done, and probably are supposed to.

In any event, as I walk on now with the sun in my face, I soon come to a spruce woods on the left. It was there, I recall, that I walked twenty years ago and looked at the city below me. I had been outlawed then, proscribed. For I had profaned the mysteries, like Alcibiades, and had knocked down the idols. I remember how desolate and lonely I felt. I knew I didn't have a friend, and the whole town lay below like an army massed against me alone. I saw the campfires, heard the alarm bells, and I knew they would starve me out. I know now that I did the right thing. But I took a malicious pleasure then in the conflagration I had started, and that was wrong. If only I had had a spark of pity for those I hurt! If! But that would be expecting too much of a young man who had never known any pity from the others!

Now as I look back on it, that walk in the woods years ago seems sublime, majestic. And if I didn't go down to defeat then, it was not because of my own strength, for I do not believe in that.

*     *     *

For three weeks straight I had not spoken to a soul. My voice had closed up shop, so to speak, and had lost its resonance and audibility. I became aware of this when I addressed the maid. She didn't understand what I said and I had to repeat it several times. Then I began feeling restless; my solitude seemed like an exile. I got to thinking that people didn't want to associate with me because I had rejected them. So one evening I went out. Sat down in a streetcar just to get the feeling of being in the same room with other people. Trying to make out from their eyes whether or not they hated me, all I could read was indifference. I listened to their talk as if I were at a party and had a right to participate in the conversation, at least as a listener. When the car became crowded, it was a pleasant sensation to feel my elbow making contact with a human being.

I have never hated human beings. The opposite would be

closer to the truth. But I have been afraid of them, ever since the day I was born. My sociableness has always been so great that I could enjoy the company of anybody and everybody, and I formerly regarded being alone as a form of punishment, which it probably is. When I have asked friends of mine who have been in prison precisely what the punishment consisted in, they have invariably answered: being solitary. This time in my life I have indeed sought to be alone but I made a tacit condition: that I would have the right to look up my acquaintances when I felt like it. Then why don't I? Something stops me. I feel like a beggar as I climb the steps, and I turn around when I get to the doorbell. And when I get home, I feel content, especially when I run through in my mind all the things I believe I would have had to hear as soon as I stepped into those rooms. Since my thoughts do not run in tandem with anyone else's, I am jarred and upset by virtually everything that is said; an innocent word can stab me like an insult.

I believe fate intended me to be alone and that it is all for the best. I want to believe it, anyway, for otherwise my situation would be intolerable. Yet, when I'm alone my head becomes overcharged now and then and threatens to explode. That's why I have to keep myself under strict observation. I try to keep my inventory of thoughts balanced between what comes in and what goes out. Every day I have to get rid of some stock by writing and take in something new by reading. If I write all day, I feel completely despondent and empty in the evening. I feel that I have nothing more to say, that I'm finished, done for. But if I read the whole day, I get so charged up I want to explode.

Furthermore I have to pick the right hours for sleeping and waking. Too much sleep exhausts me like a Chinese torture; too little sleep excites me to the point of hysteria.

I can make the days pass without any trouble; it is the evenings that are difficult. Feeling my intelligence flicker out each night is as distressing as feeling myself decay spiritually and bodily.

In the morning, when I rise from bed after a sober evening and good night's sleep, life is a positive pleasure. It's like rising from the dead. My soul is regenerated, and my powers, knitted together by sleep, appear to be redoubled. It is then that I imagine myself changing the world order, commanding the fates of nations, declaring war, deposing dynasties. When I read the papers and learn from the foreign telegrams what is happening in the world, I feel myself right in the center of things. I am a "contemporary," and I sense that in my small way I have been involved in shaping the present through my work in the past. After that I turn to read about my own country and finally about my own city.

Since yesterday the world has moved forward. Laws have been changed, trade routes opened, thrones upset, systems of government altered. People have died, been born, have gotten married.

Since yesterday the world has changed, and a new world has come with a new sun and a new day. I feel renewed and reborn.

Though I burn with the desire to get down to work, I must first go out for my walk. When I reach the street door, I know immediately which way I'll take. Not only do the sun, the clouds, and the temperature tell me, but some inner sense acts as a barometer and thermometer to inform me how I stand with the world.

I can choose one of three ways. The smiling way out to the Deer Park, the crowded Strand and the city streets, or the lonely *via dolorosa* I just described. I soon sense which way I am to go. If I feel at peace with myself, the air caresses me and I look for company.

Then I walk the streets crowded with people and sense that I am on friendly terms with all of them. But if something is not quite right, I see only enemies looking scornfully at me. Sometimes the hatred emanating from them is so strong I have to turn back. If I resort to the countryside near Brunnsviken or the oak hills around Rosendal, it may happen that nature is in tune with me and I with it. My heart sings. I have a claim on this countryside. I have become part of it and made it serve as a backdrop to my character. Of course, the countryside has its moods too, and there are mornings when we don't get along. Then everything changes. The triumphal arches of the birch trees turn into whipping rods; the bewitching leafy rooms formed by the hazel bushes can't conceal the all-too-eloquent hazelwood canes; the oak trees stretch their bony arms threateningly over my head, and I feel as if a horse collar had been slipped around my neck. This lack of harmony between me and my countryside makes me so tense I want to break loose and run away. And when I turn around and see the southern horizon with the magnificent skyline of the city, I feel as if I were in a foreign country, a tourist looking at it for the first time, abandoned and alone like a stranger who doesn't have a friend within those walls.

It is when I get home and sit down at my desk, that I really live. And the energy that has flowed into me during my morning walk either through the alternating current of disharmony and tension or through the direct current of harmony and peace is now released to serve my different aims. I live, and I live multifariously the lives of all the people I depict—am happy with the happy ones, bad with the bad ones, good with the good. I shed my own character and talk through the mouths of children, of women, of old men. I am king and pauper. I am the highest of the high—the tyrant—and I am the lowest and most despised—the persecuted hater of tyrants. I share all opinions, I confess all religions, I live in all ages, and I myself have ceased to exist. In this state I am indescribably happy.

But when it ends around noon, when I am finished writing for the day, my own existence becomes doubly distressing. I feel more and more as if death were approaching with the coming of evening. The night stretches out before me. After a day's work other people usually find some amusement in talking to each other, but not I. The silence wraps itself around me. I try to read and cannot. I pace the floor and wait for the hands of the clock to reach ten. Finally they do.

When I free my body of its clothes with all their buttons and elastics and snaps and clasps, my soul breathes more deeply and feels free and easy. And when after my Oriental ablutions I have gone to bed, my whole universe stretches itself and relaxes. The will to live, the battle, the strife ceases; and the desire to sleep pretty much resembles the yearning for death.

But I first take half an hour for meditation, that is to say, I read in some prayerbook or other chosen to fit the mood

I am in. Sometimes I choose a Catholic book. That brings
with it a breath of apostolic, traditional Christianity. It is like
Latin and Greek: it returns us to the roots of our ancestry. For
our—my—culture begins with Catholic Christianity. With the
Roman Catholic manual in my hand I feel like a Roman
citizen, a citizen of the European nation, and the inserted
Latin verses remind me that I am an educated, cultured man.
I *am not* a Catholic and never have been because I cannot
tie myself down to any one creed. So sometimes I take an
old Lutheran manual with a passage for each day of the
year, and I use it as a scourge. It was written in the seventeenth century when life was miserable here on earth, and
consequently it is terribly rigorous and stern, preaching that
suffering is a blessing and the gift of grace. Very, very seldom
do I find a good kind word in it. It can bring one to despair,
which makes me fight against it. It isn't true, I say to myself.
It's a temptation to waste one's strength. Catholicism has
taught me that the Tempter appears in his ugliest role when
he seeks to bring one to despair and to rob one of hope. But
to the Catholic hope is a virtue; for to believe that God is
good is the core of religion. To ascribe evil to God is satanism.

Sometimes I resort to a strange book from the eighteenth
century, the century of enlightenment. It is an anonymous
work, and I cannot say whether it was written by a Catholic,
a Lutheran, or a Calvinist, for it contains the Christian philosophy of a man who knew the world and who knew people,
and who was also a learned man and a poet. He usually
gives me just the thought I need for the day or the hour. And
if for a second I rise up and object to the unjust and unreasonable demands that he makes of a poor mortal, he is sure
to raise the same objections himself. He is what I call a reasonable fellow who sees with both eyes and apportions right
and wrong on both sides. Reminds me somewhat of Jacob
Boehme, who found that every question can be answered
with both a yes and a no.

On really important occasions I must resort to the Bible.
I possess several Bibles from different periods, which say different things to me, as if they possessed different voltages for
influencing me. One, in black cordovan, printed in Schwabach
black letter in the seventeenth century, emanates incredible

power. It once belonged to a family of clergymen whose family tree is inscribed on the inside covers. Hate and anger are accumulated in this book; it does nothing but anathematize and pronounce punishment; no matter how I turn the pages I am always confronted by the maledictions of David and Jeremiah on their enemies. And I do not want to read those for they strike me as unchristian. When Jeremiah prays: "Deliver up their children to the famine, and pour out their blood by the force of the sword; and let their wives be bereaved of their children, and be widows; and let their men be put to death," and so on—this is not fit for a Christian to read. I can well understand that one might pray for protection against enemies that seek to drag one down when one is striving to mount higher, or against enemies who out of sheer malice take the bread from one's mouth. And I can also understand how one might offer thanks to God when the enemy is slain, for people everywhere have always sung a Te Deum after a victory. But to pray for and call down a specific punishment on my opponents, that I cannot bring myself to do; and I might say that what may have befitted Jeremiah or David once upon a time does not suit me now.

And then I have another Bible, in half-leather and with gold lettering, from the eighteenth century. Naturally it contains the same words as the other Bible, but the material is presented in a different manner. This book looks like a novel and always presents its best side. Even the paper is brighter, the typography gayer. I can speak to this book as Moses spoke to Jehovah. Moses dared to make some rather surly remonstrances. For example, when his people began to murmur and grumble again, and Moses was fed up with it all, he turned to the Lord and said almost reproachfully: "Have I conceived all this people? Have I begotten them that thou shouldest say unto me, Carry them in thy bosom, as a nursing father beareth the suckling child? . . . Whence should I have flesh to give unto all this people? . . . I am not able to bear all this people alone, because it is too heavy for me. And if thou deal thus with me, kill me, I pray thee, out of hand. . . ." Jehovah replies in a not unfriendly manner to Moses' objections and proposes to help him by distributing the burden of leadership among the seventy oldest. This is

not the implacable, vindictive God of the Old Testament.
Not that this worries me; I know that there are times when
I feel closer to the Old Testament than to the New. And
one thing is certain: for us born into the Christian faith, the
Bible has the power to educate, whether because our forefathers deposited psychic energies in it at the same time they
drew from it or for some other reason is hard to say. It is a
fact that sanctuaries, temples, and holy books do indeed possess this power of serving as storage batteries, though only
for believers. Belief is my individual starting battery without
which I cannot make the dumb and silent parchment speak.
Belief is my countercurrent that creates energy through induction; belief is a collector, and it must perforce be a conductor, otherwise it could receive nothing; belief is the
rheostat that lowers resistance and permits the connection to
be made.

That is why holy books do not speak to unbelievers. The
unbeliever is sterile. His spirit has been so thoroughly pas-
teurized that nothing can grow in it. He is a negative number,
an imaginary quantity, the obverse, the parasite that does not
support itself but lives off its host. He cannot have an independent existence for he must have something positive to
be negative against.

Ultimately there come moments for me when only something in the nature of Buddhism helps. Only very rarely does
one get what one wishes for, so what good does it do to
wish? Wish for nothing, ask nothing of people and of life and
you will always feel that you have received more than you
could have asked for. And you know from experience that
after you got what you wished for, it wasn't so much the
thing itself that made you happy as it was the fact that your
wish came true.

There are times when some being inside me asks: "Do you
really believe all this?" I immediately silence the questioner,
for I know that belief is only a state of soul and not an act
of the intellect, and I know that this state is salutary and
instructive.

Nevertheless, it sometimes happens that I flare up against
the unreasonable demands, the altogether too rigorous law,
the inhuman punishments, and then I put aside my devo-

tional manuals for a while. But I soon go back to them, admonished by a voice calling to me from the primeval past: "I am the Lord your God, which brought you forth out of the land of Egypt, that ye should not be their bondmen; and I have broken the bands of your yoke, and made you go upright." And then my rebellion dies. What an ungrateful, cowardly wretch I would be if I were to deny my deliverer before the world.

## IV

Spring is coming again for the nth time. (After reaching a certain age one is reluctant to use figures.) But spring comes in a different way now than it did a number of years ago. The transformation used to begin when the streets of ice were chopped up, around Easter time. One could see every layer that had been deposited by the winter months, like stratums in a geological bed. Nowadays the streets of ice are not allowed to build up. Sleighs and sleigh bells and networks of tracks have become quite scarce. One might get the idea that the climate, like the age, has become Central European. Formerly, when the waterways were closed in the fall and there were no railroads, one found oneself quarantined in town, provisioned with salted food. And the coming of spring meant awaking to a new, fresh life. Now the icebreakers and the railroads have equalized the seasons, and there are flowers, fruit, and vegetables the whole year round.

Formerly one took out the inner windows early in spring, and the noise from the street would burst suddenly into the room, making one feel that one had regained contact with the outer world. The muffled quiet inside the house ceased, and one was awakened to a new life, not least by the increased light that was let in. Now the double windows stay in throughout the year. But in compensation the windows are not weather-stripped and may be opened at any time one feels like it during the winter.

With the seasons evened out this way, spring slips up on one without putting on a big show—and consequently is greeted without any particular enthusiasm.

I welcomed this particular spring rather matter-of-factly and without any great expectations.—"So it's spring. That means it will soon be fall again!"—I sat on my balcony and looked at the clouds. They tell me that spring has come. They gather in greater masses then, they are thicker and more clean-cut in outline. And catching a glimpse through a cloud ice-hole, one sees that the sky is nearly blue-black. And then in the distance I have the edge of a forest to look at— mostly pine and spruce—dark green, almost black, and spiny. To me it's the most characteristic aspect of Swedish nature. I point to it and say, "That's Sweden." At times this line of woods can look like a city skyline with its infinite number of chimneys, spires, pinnacles, peaks, and gables. Today, how- ever, it just looks like a woods to me. Since the wind is blow- ing, I am certain that this whole clump of slender trees is moving and stirring, but, being two or three miles away, I can't actually see. I get my binoculars and then I see the whole contour of the spruce woods moving like the waves on the horizon of the ocean—which gives me great pleasure, es- pecially since I feel I have made a little discovery. My heart soars off in that direction, for I know that the sea lies some- where behind the woods. I know that hepatica and anemone are growing at the foot of those trees, and I get more pleasure from seeing them in my imagination than from seeing them in reality. I long ago grew apart from that nature which comprises the mineral kingdom, the plant kingdom, and the animal world. What interests me is human nature and hu- man destinies.

Formerly I could lose myself in contemplating a blossoming orchard. I still think it's pretty, but not as pretty as I used to. I might try to explain this change in me by saying that I have a growing intimation that these are only faulty copies of more nearly perfect original images. Therefore I have no strong longing for the country, although I do notice a slight aversion towards the city, no doubt the result of a desire for change.

So I wander in my streets, where the faces of the people awaken memories and give me food for thought. And when

I pass by the shop windows I see objects from all the lands in the world, objects wrought or elaborated by the hand of man. I am put in touch with all of mankind and provided with a whole world of impressions, colors, shapes, and all kinds of associations.

In the morning when the rooms in the ground-floor apartments are being cleaned and aired, the windows stand open. I pass by and glance in; naturally I don't stand there looking, but in that one moment I have surveyed an unfamiliar room and got a whiff of someone's life story. This morning, for example, I cast a glance into one of the older houses through a sliding windowpane and beyond an aspidistra, that ugly Japanese plant of the lily family that doesn't blossom in the light but puts forth blossoms directly from its root just below the earth level, blossoms that look like star-shaped bits of flesh. Once past this plant, my eye glided over a writing desk, with its useful but tiresome tools, into a corner of the room where a white, square tile stove was standing. It was an old one, and the tiles, each funereally edged in black, resembled dirty fingernails. It had large doors on the Dutch oven and it stood in a corner that was made dark by the fantastically gloomy wallpaper. My first impression was of the 1870s and the dark rooms of that era, but I also had a vague sense of discomfort evoked by this moderately well-to-do middle-class home, by people who lived strict and difficult lives and who tortured themselves and each other. And then I recalled an old house, which I would never have remembered if that window had not been open. The lives of certain people long forgotten came back to mind, and I saw them in a new and interesting light. Now for the first time I understood these people, so many years afterward, understood the tragedy of their lives, which I formerly held myself aloof from since it seemed so trivial and unpleasant. When I got home, I sketched out a new play. And all this I had got from an open shutter!

If I go out in the evenings when darkness has fallen and the lights are burning, the circle of acquaintances I peep in on becomes larger because I can look into the upper apartments also. I study the furniture and the fixtures, and am provided with scenes from family life. People who don't pull down their shades are predisposed to exhibit themselves and I don't have to be tactful or discreet. Besides, I take snapshot impressions and afterwards work out what I've seen.

And so one evening I walked by a beautiful corner apartment with large windows. . . . I saw furniture from the 60s crossed with curtains from the 70s, portieres from the 80s and bric-a-brac from the 90s. In the window stood an alabaster urn, yellowed like ivory by the breathing and sighing of people, by wine fumes and tobacco smoke, an urn without use or purpose, which someone finally had turned into a repository for calling cards—a funeral urn made to adorn a grave and now containing the names of all the friends who had come and gone, of all the relatives living and dead, of engaged couples and married couples, of those christened and those buried. Many portraits hung on the walls, from all ages and epochs, heroes in armour, wise men in wigs, ecclesiastics in clerical collars. In one corner stood a game table in front of a divan, and four strange creatures sat around it playing cards. They said nothing; their lips didn't move. Three of them were as old as time, but the fourth was of middle age or thereabouts. He must have been the man of the house. In the center of the room sat a young woman, her back to those at the card table, her head bent over her crocheting. She was obviously working away at it but she took no interest in it—simply making the time pass, stitch by stitch, measuring out the seconds with her needle. Then she held her crochet work up and looked at it as if she were telling time on a clock. But she looked beyond her crochet clock and into the future—and her glance sped out through the window, past the funeral urn, and the rays from her eyes met mine out there in the darkness, though she couldn't see me. I thought that I knew her, that she was speaking to me with her eyes, though of course she wasn't. Then one of the mummies at the table said something. The woman replied with a movement of her neck, without turning around. And then as if her thoughts had been interrupted, or as if she had momentarily given herself away, she dipped her head lower than before and let her second hand go ticking away. Never have I seen boredom, tedium, weariness with life so epitomized as in that room.

The face of the man at the card table changed expression continuously. He seemed to be uneasy, as if waiting for something, and the mummies shared his uneasiness. Every once in a while they would cast a glance at the clock on the wall, whose longer hand was approaching the hour. Probably they were waiting for someone, someone who would drive away their boredom, bring something new into that room, give them a shaking up, perhaps even turn their lives upside down. As if on tenterhooks with the fear that that might happen they were afraid to devote themselves to the game. They played their cards tentatively, as if they expected to be interrupted at any moment. But no pauses in their play, no expression, no gestures. They moved like mannequins.

What was meant to happen happened. "What luck!" I said to myself as the portiere moved and a maid in a white cap came in to announce someone. A spark of life flew from person to person in that room, and the young woman turned halfway around as she rose to her feet. At the same instant the clock on the wall struck the hour so loudly that I heard it out on the sidewalk, and I saw the minute hand jump to twelve.

At that moment a passerby bumped against me. I came to so suddenly that I literally felt I had been thrown out into the street, out of that room where I had been in spirit for a long two minutes, living a fragment of the lives of these people. I continued on my way, a little ashamed. I considered turning back to see the rest of the story, but changed my mind when I thought to myself, "I already know the end; I've been in the same situation more than once!"

*　　*　　*

Spring comes, very much like it used to in bygone days, but still it isn't the same. Formerly the first sign was a lark on the parade grounds, but now there aren't any larks on that migratory stop, so the chaffinch in Humlegården and the starlings in Fågelbacken are now the heralds. But one thing hasn't changed: April is still moving time. I have always thought it was horrible to see furniture and household goods out on the sidewalk. Homeless people forced to lay their very entrails open to public gaze. They blush with shame. That's why one never sees the owner standing nearby watching his property. He would rather let strangers take charge of his things, which in the harsh light of day reveal all their defects. This sofa with the table standing in front of it was tolerable enough in the soft light of a room but out in the sun the stains and tears are exposed to view. And the fact that the fourth leg was loose didn't matter inside, but here on the sidewalk it has fallen completely off.

If any face is to be seen behind one of the cartloads, it is a face filled with worry, agitation, anxiety. But moving and traveling is meant to be a part of life. Pulling up roots, getting shaken up, being turned inside out, setting out again on a new phase of life. Sitting in my peace and quiet, I, who have never done anything but travel and move from place to place, recalled my impressions of a roving life, and these gathered and coalesced into a poem that I called "Ahasuerus."

## AHASVERUS

Ahasverus, upp och vandra!
Tag din ränsel och din stav;
ej ditt öde liknar andra,
ty dig väntar ingen grav.
Vagga fick du och en början,
men du får ej något slut,
evigt skall du trampa sörjan,
många skor få nöta ut.
Me'n du väntat på Messias,
tiden gått dig helt förbi;
tror du än du skall befrias,
hoppas du på amnesti?
Eller vill du som Elias
levande förlossad bli?
Ut på stigar, ut på vägar
ut ur dina varma rum;
läggs för fäfot dina tegar,
störtat som Kapernaum
är ditt hus, och hemmet härjat;
maka, barn sitt avsked sagt;
intet efter branden bärgat,
tomt och tilja öde lagt.

(Ahasuerus, up and wander!/Take your knapsack and your staff;/your destiny is not like that of others,/there is no grave awaiting you./You had a cradle and a beginning,/but you will have no end,/you must tramp through the sludge for eternity, /and wear out many shoes./While you waited for the Messiah,/time has passed you by;/do you still believe you shall be delivered,/do you still hope for an amnesty?/Or do you wish to be redeemed/in the flesh as Elijah was?/Out, out on the paths, out to the roads/out from your warm rooms;/your fields lie unplanted,/razed like Capernaum/is your house, your home devastated;/wife and children have bidden farewell;/ nothing salvaged after the fires,/land and house lie in ruins.)

> Spring upp på tåget med ränsel och stav
> men se dig icke tillbaka.
> Välsigna honom som tog och gav
> och lärt dig konsten försaka!
> Där står ingen frände och ingen vän
> att vinka dig lycka på färden!
> Vad gör det! Dess lättare sen
> att göra språnget ut i den kalla världen!

(Climb aboard the train with your knapsack and staff/and do not look back./Bless him who gives and takes/for teaching you the art of doing without!/No familiar face, no friend is there/to wish you luck on your journey!/What does it matter! It is so much easier/to take the plunge into the cold world!)

> Och tåget rycks loss från bangårdens kä,
> en rullande länga med hus av trä,
> en vandrande by med folk och fä.—
> Där är post och värdshus och magasiner,
> och sovrum bakom de tjocka gardiner.
> Nu rycker den fram som en stad på hjul,
> oemotståndligt! Den går genom väggar,
> den slinker igenom berg som ormen i skjul,
> den går på vattnet, och eldhästen gnägger;
> den tar ett landskap med sjumilasteg;
> ett konungarike är närsgårdsväg—.

Men landet tar slut, man står vid havet—
Nu Ahasverus släpper du land,
och allt som förr dig vid livet band
det ligger bak synkretsen djupt begravet.

(And the train pulls away from the station's quay,/a rolling
range of wooden houses,/a traveling city with people and
animals.—/There is a post office and a restaurant and shops,/
and bedrooms behind the thick curtains./Now it moves forward, a whole city on wheels,/irresistible! It moves through
walls,/it crawls through mountains like a snake into its den,/
it walks on water, and the fire horse neighs;/it covers the
country with seven-league steps;/a whole kingdom is merely
a step next door.—/But the land comes to an end, one stands
on the seacoast./Now Ahasuerus, you cut loose from the land,
/and everything that formerly held you close to life/lies
deeply buried behind the horizon.)

*

Se skyarna hur tunga de gå
och sjöarna de svallande,
de stigande, de fallande,
där foten intet fäste kan få
och ingen vila mer du kan nå.
Ej dag, ej natt, ej sovande, ej vakande;
än upp, än ner, än hit och än dit,
allt under sus och gnissel och knakande,
i rep och timmer, bultar och nit.
Tortyr för kropp, tortyr för själ,
ett pinoredskap på vattnet flytande.
Bekänn din skuld och tänk på ditt väl,
när du hör bränningens rytande!
Då är ej långt till räddande strand,
du tror! Men skeppar fruktar för land,
och lägger bogen rätt ut i sjöarna;
han flyr den sökta frälsande hand
och vänder rygg till de lugna öarna;
ty falsk är sjön, men falskare kust!
När medvind blåser med liv och lust
då har du att vänta den hårdaste dust.—

(Look at the clouds how heavily they move/and the swelling seas,/the rising and falling seas,/on which your foot can find no hold/and you can never reach a place to rest./Neither day nor night, neither sleeping nor waking;/now up, now down, hither and thither,/under the constant moaning and squeaking and creaking/of ropes and timbers, of bolts and rivets./Torture for the body, torture for the soul,/an instrument of torture floating on the water./Confess your guilt, consider your weal,/when you hear the roar of the breaking surf!/It cannot be far to a safe shore,/you think! But the skipper is afraid of running aground,/and points the bow toward the high seas;/he flees the sought-for hand that saves/and turns his back on the peaceful isles;/for the sea may be false, but the coast is even falser!/When the wind is with you and blowing hard/then you may expect the hardest blows.—)

> Till havs! Lägg ut på det gröngråa fältet,
> där skeppet plöjer och regnmolnet sår,
> men intet växer i plogens spår
> och ingen bor under himlatältet.
> I dag det liknar en presenning syd
> till värn mot regnet som alltjämt ökar.
> En ann skulle mena den är till skydd
> för himlens blå emot ångarnas rökar,
> mot jordens damn och flugornas prickar,
> eller som skärm mot de ondas blickar.

(To sea! Put out onto the gray-green fields,/where the ship plows and the rain clouds sow,/where nothing grows in the plow's furrows/and no one lives under heaven's tent./Today it resembles a tarpaulin made/as protection against the rain, ever-increasing./But others might hold that it was made to protect/the blue of heaven against the smoke of steamships, /against the dust of earth, the pricks of flies,/or as a shield against evil looks.)

*

> Ahasverus står i stäven,
> spanar mot den gråa vägg,
> ögat dävet, knuten näven,
> munnen vass i vitnat skägg.—

Inga syner ser han hägra,
minnena ha slocknat ut,
hoppet självt det synes vägra;
leva måste han i nu't,
detta nu som är en plåga,
utan mening, utan mål,
svarslöst som en galen fråga,
dött som flintan utan stål.
Ut i gråa intet stirrar
vandrarn, fängslad på ett däck,
mattslö ner i djupet stirrar,
känner sig som dränkt i säck.

(Ahasuerus stands in the bow,/gazing at the gray wall,/his eye moist, his hand knotted into a fist,/his mouth a sharp slit in a beard turned white.—/No mirages loom before him,/memories have all died out,/hope itself seems to deny him;/he must live in the present,/this present that is a torture,/without meaning, without purpose,/as unanswerable as a senseless question,/as dead and useless as a flint without its steel./Out into the gray nothingness stares/the wanderer, imprisoned on a deck,/stares dully, listlessly down into the depths,/feels as if he had been sacked and drowned.)

# V

After many setbacks spring finally arrives, and what a feast it is to walk under the linden trees that first morning when the leaves have just come out and to let the soft green filtered light fall gently on my eyes. The spring air is perfectly still, friendly, caressing. The fine, dry sand beneath one's feet suggests a fresh, clean new world. The new grass covers last year's leaves, dirt, and litter as the snow does in autumn. The tree skeletons begin to flesh out until finally a high backdrop of deciduous trees stands like a green bank of clouds over the shoreline of the bay. Formerly driven by the cold and the wind, I can now take my time, walk slowly, and even sit on a bench. The edge of the water under the elm trees is dotted with benches. There sits the yellow man, my unknown enemy, coat unbuttoned and reading a newspaper. Today I could tell, precisely by looking at the name of the paper he was reading, that we are indeed enemies. And I could also tell from the look in his eyes when he raised them over the edge of the paper that he had read something about me that made him feel good, and he was thinking either that I had already read the poisonous item or would soon do so. But there he was mistaken; I never touch that paper.

The major has lost weight and the approach of summer seems to make him uneasy. It probably doesn't make any difference to him where he spends it, but he has to get out of town in order not to be left entirely out of his class and made to feel like a member of the proletariat. This morning he stood out on a little point of land apparently counting the small waves that lapped the stones. He waved his cane in the air for no good reason, just to do something. Suddenly from the other side of the bay a trumpet signal sounded. He started—and then he saw over on the drill field a company of cavalry popping up from behind a rise, helmets first and horse ears. And then the cavalry charged, making the ground thunder. Shouting, yelling, clattering, the orderly mass rolled forward. The Major lived every second of it. I could see by his bandy legs that he had been in the cavalry. And perhaps this was his regiment—from which he was now discharged, benched. That's life, yes indeed.

My occult old woman is the same summer or winter, but this past winter has had its effect on her and she has taken to using a cane. Moreover she now puts in an appearance and joins the party just once a month, like the Queen of the World with her dogs.

But with the coming of the sun and the spring some new walkers and wanderers have penetrated into our circle who I feel do not belong there. The conception of property rights is so elastic that I had come to feel that *my* morning walk through this scenery belonged to me alone. I can't help looking askance at these strangers, if I look at them at all. In my introspective mood I don't wish to make contact with people by exchanging glances. However, people expect this kind of familiarity and speak indignantly of anyone "who won't look at people." Although they assume they have the right to peer into those they meet, I have never been able to understand where they acquired that right. I consider it a kind of trespassing, an invasion of my personality, at least an intrusion. Even when I was young, I made a sharp distinction between those who returned a look and those who did not. Now it strikes me that exchanging glances on the street with some stranger signifies: "Let's be friends, and no more!" But with people who look brazenly at me, I find myself incapable of entering into a friendly alliance. I prefer neutrality, or, if necessary, a war-like basis. Friends always acquire some influence over me, and that I don't want.

This encroachment on my privacy takes place only during the spring. Come summer, the strangers have gone off to the country, and the streets and lanes are just as lonely and empty as in the winter.

And now the longed for summer has arrived. It's an accomplished fact, and I have become indifferent to it. For I live in my work, looking ahead, sometimes looking behind me, at my memories, which I can treat like a child's building blocks. I can make all sorts of things with them, and the same memory can serve in all sorts of ways in a single dream structure of the imagination, turning up different colored sides. And since the number of arrangements is myriad, I get a sense of infinity as I play this game.

I don't have any special longing for the country, but sometimes I get the feeling that I have been negligent in not taking a walk in the woods or a swim in the sea. Also, I feel strangely ashamed at being in the city, since a summer vacation is one of the prerogatives of that class of society to which others assign me—I personally count myself as outside society. And furthermore, I have the feeling of being deserted and abandoned, knowing that all my friends have left town. It's true I didn't look them up when they were here, but I felt their presence. I could transmit my thoughts to them at a certain address, and now I've lost track of them.

Sitting at my desk I can see between the window curtains a bay of the Baltic Sea, and on the far side of it the gray-black cliffs, rounded and eroded; below them at the water's edge, the white line of beach; above them, the black forest of fir trees. Sometimes I am seized with a longing to go out there. All I have to do is take up telescope and without moving from my spot, I find myself transported there. I pick my way over the rocks on the beach, where yellow and purple loosestrife grow under the alder trees among old fence posts, reeds, and straw washed clean by the waves. In a crevice of the cliff the ferns on top of the lichen and moss force the sweetroot to spread like ivy. A few junipers are reconnoitering on the edge of the cliff, and behind them I can look deep into the forest of firs, especially if the sun is low. Then I see bright green chambers with soft liverwort and a light undergrowth of aspen and birch.

Sometimes I see some life moving, although not very often. A raven pecking around—or pretending to peck at something, for it looks very self-conscious and mannered, even though it doesn't know it's being watched. Obviously it's preening and showing off for one of its own kind.

A white sloop comes gliding by. Someone is sitting at the helm behind the mainsail, but all I can see is elbows and knees. Behind the foresail sits a woman. The boat slides effortlessly, and the sight of the wake behind it evokes for me the sound of the soothing ripple, ceaselessly slipping past and ceaselessly recurring. Therein lies the secret pleasure in sailing, apart from the thrill of controlling the helm and contending with the wind and the waves.

One day I captured a whole little dramatic scene in my telescope. The stony beach there in the distance had never been tramped on by a mortal (in my telescope); it was my private property, my retreat, my summer home. But one day I saw a punt make its appearance from the right side of the glass. The boat was occupied by a ten-year-old girl, in a bright dress and red tennis cap. I think my first words were, "What are you doing here?" But the improbability of the situation held my attention.

The girl pulled into shore neatly, drew up the oars, and climbed back into the boat to fetch a shiny object at the stern. My curiosity was aroused; I couldn't make out what it was she had picked up. I gave the telescope a twist and saw she was holding a little ax in her hand. . . . An ax in a child's hand? Now how could those two things go together? Some secret was eluding me, something sinister, unpleasant. First the girl walked along the beach, apparently looking for something, as one does when one walks along beaches, hoping to find some strange object that the inscrutable sea has cast up. . . . Now, I said to myself, she'll start throwing stones into the water: children can't look at stones and water without throwing the former into the latter. Why is that? There's a secret reason for that too, no doubt. . . . Now what did I say? She was throwing stones! And she started up the cliff! . . . And of course she would eat sweetroot, for she was a city girl and had gone to school in town. (The country children never eat sweetroot, which the city children call licorice.) . . . No, she went right on past the clump of ferns, which proved (?) she was a country child. . . . She went up towards the juniper bushes, and then I understood: she was going to cut juniper twigs for Sunday. Right enough, for today was Saturday. . . . But no, she took only a few whacks at a juniper bush, leaving a branch hanging limply, and then moved on. . . . I had it! she was cutting wood for a little picnic fire! . . . No, she climbed still higher and reached the edge of the woods. She stopped and seemed to be considering the length of the lower branches, which were especially thick with bright green needles. . . . Suddenly she jerked her head and her eyes followed some object in the air. Must have been a bird that flew up because she moved her neck with the same staccato movements one observes in the flight of the wagtail, a series of repeated falls.

Now she began to reveal what she was really up to. She grabbed a branch with her left hand and began chopping off little twigs, small, small twigs. But why spruce twigs? They're for funerals, and the child was not dressed in mourning.—Objection: the child is not necessarily related to the deceased.—Sustained.—The twigs were too small to be used for making brooms or for spreading on the front porch; and on the cottage floors the folks around here use only juniper cuttings. . . . Maybe she was from Dalarna where they use spruce instead? . . . Never mind, something else was happening now. Three yards away from the girl the lower branches of a large spruce moved upwards. A cow stuck its head through and mooed—I could see its open mouth and stretched neck. The girl stopped dead in her tracks, her whole body frozen with fear. She couldn't run she was so frightened. She strode forward: her fear caused a reversal of current and turned into courage. Ax raised high in her hand she approached the cow, who, after a moment's hesitation, resentful that her friendly gesture had not been appreciated, turned and withdrew to her hiding place.

For a second I had been so scared I reached out to defend the child. But now the danger was over, and I put away the telescope, observing to myself how difficult it was to be left in peace. Imagine, in the quiet of one's home to be drawn into faraway melodramas! And I couldn't stop worrying and wondering about those spruce twigs. What on earth were they for?

*    *    *

My neighbors in the apartment house have moved to the country, and the building seems cold and empty. I feel as if all the tension and all the life had gone from it. These vectors of force that exist in every family in the shapes of man, wife, children, and servants, these components of energy have gone and left only an empty diagram behind them. And the house, which always seemed to me an electric generator that I could plug into, has had a power failure. I stop dead. My contact with people is broken off. I miss all the little sounds from the different apartments that used to stimulate me. Even the dog who woke me up for my nocturnal meditations or aroused my wrath, got me good and mad, healthy mad, has gone and left me desolate. The singer is silent, and I can no longer hear Beethoven. Nor do the telephone wires in the wall sing to me, and when I climb up and down the stairway I hear my steps echoing through the empty rooms. Every day is as quiet as a Sunday, and in place of the sounds I used to hear I hear a ringing in my ears. I pick up my own thoughts as spoken words. I seem to be in telepathic contact with all my distant kith and kin, all my friends and enemies. I carry on long, orderly conversations with them, or repeat the old debates and arguments held at dinner parties or in restaurants. I oppose their silly ideas, I vigorously defend my own point of view, and I'm so much more clever and fluent than when someone is actually listening. Life becomes richer —and easier. Less wearing, less irritating, less embittering.

Sometimes this imaginary colloquy is built up to the point where I find myself arguing with the whole country. I sense how they respond to my latest book, which is still in manuscript. I hear how they discuss me near and far. Of course, I know that I am right and am only surprised that they don't realize it. I apprise them of a newly discovered fact; they deny it, or reject the source and cast doubt on the authority quoted, although they themselves usually cite the same authority. To me the situation is always one of conflict, of attack and hostility. I guess we are all enemies to one another, friends only when it pays us to fight together against a common enemy. That's the way the world is.

Yet, in spite of everything, this subjective inward life, however vivid it may be, leaves me at times longing for reality. My senses grow rusty and want to be put to use. I want to hear, above all, to see; otherwise my senses will dispense with the operator and begin to run themselves, out of an old habit.

This time my wish had not even been expressed before it was fulfilled. The drill field below my windows began to fill up with troops. First came the infantry. Men with metal pipes containing a gas-producing element, which, when ignited, expelled pieces of lead. They looked like streaks split at the bottom. Next there appeared variable combinations of people and four-footed animals—the cavalry. When a single rider came galloping along, the horse made the same movement as a boat in the waves. The rider was the helmsman—only he steered with the sheets in his left hand. And when the whole troop came parading down in closed ranks, there was created a mighty parallelogram of forces exerting several hundred horsepower even at a distance.

The artillery, however, makes the strongest impression, especially when they are running in competition. The ground shakes so that my ceiling lamp sways and trembles. Later when they unlimber, put the guns in position and fire, the ringing in my ears stops automatically. Before I got used to it, I felt like suing them for assault and battery, but after a few days' firing, I found the explosions rather salubrious. They kept me from dozing off into the eternal silence. And at the discreet distance that I keep the war games look like a play staged especially for me.

*    *    *

Though the afternoons and evenings keep growing longer and longer, I know from experience that it's no use going out for a walk. The streets and the parks are filled with the sad faces of those who are stuck in the city and can't go out into the country. Now when the more fortunate souls have evacuated the best parts of town, the poor people from the suburbs come in and take over the empty places. This gives the city an appearance of a town caught in an uprising or an invasion; and since beauty generally goes where the money is, it's not a pretty spectacle.

One Sunday afternoon when I felt I was on the same footing as the less fortunate souls, I decided to cut loose, to take a ride and look at the people.

I hailed a cab at Newbridge and climbed in. The cabman seemed sober, but there was something strange about his face that did little to calm and reassure me. As he drove down the Strand, I noticed a river of humanity flowing past on the left side, while I kept looking out over the water to the right, over the islands and bays to the hazy hills in the distance.

All of a sudden something right ahead of us caught the cabbie's attention and mine. A huge bedraggled beggar's dog, with hair so matted that he looked like a fat wolf pretending to be a sheep, low forehead, nasty, evil eyes, and so dirty that it was impossible to tell what color he actually was, started to run after the front wheel and attempted to leap up on to the cabbie's seat. He finally made it only to be kicked off by the driver.

"What on earth is that?" I asked, astonished not only at the monster's agility but also at the strangeness of the whole incident.

The driver muttered a few words from which I gathered that it was not his dog. But when he began whipping the horse, the dog made another attack and tried to leap into the carriage with me while we were going at full speed. At the same time I noticed a commotion among the streaming mob, and when I turned in that direction I discovered a parade of humanlike creatures following the struggle between the cabman and the dog, and obviously sympathizing with the dog. When I looked more closely at these creatures I found that the vast majority were cripples, crutches and canes mingling with crooked legs and broken backs—dwarfs with the backs of giants, and giants with the legs of dwarfs, faces without noses, and club feet without toes. All the misery and wretchedness that had been in hiding during the winter had now swarmed out into the sun to make its way into the country. I have seen such humanoids rendered in Ensor's masked mummeries and in Gluck's *Orpheus in the Underworld*, and I thought then that they were merely fantastic exaggerations. Not that they frightened me now; I could explain their appearance and behavior. Nevertheless it was disturbing to see all those unfortunates parading by on the town's finest street. And I could feel their perfectly justifiable hatred squirted like venom over me, the man in the carriage, while the dog was the embodiment of all their collected feelings. I was their friend, but they were my enemies! Strange.

As we rode into the Deer Park, this stream of life met a countercurrent. But the two currents flowed through and past one without so much as a glance at the clothes and faces of the other group. Deep inside they knew that they were all alike. But they looked at me. Now that I had two files to pass between, I was forced to look at one or the other. I felt ill at ease and depressed, alone and lost, and had a sudden longing to see a familiar face. I wanted to be reassured with a glance of friendship or recognition. But no such luck.

As we passed by the Hasselbacken Restaurant, I let part of me run up the steps to peep into the garden where I was almost certain someone I knew would be sitting.

Now we were getting near the plain of the Deer Park, and I had a premonition that I was bound to meet someone I knew or recognized, bound to! I couldn't say exactly why, but it must have had some connection with a sinister tragedy that occurred in my youth, a tragedy that utterly destroyed a family and left its mark on the lives of the children. I can't say precisely how I associated this tragic drama with the Deer Park plain, but the connecting link must have been a barrel organ and "the banner on a pole"[1] picturing a murder under horrible circumstances in which the murdered man was actually innocent but the shadow of guilt, not to say the guilt itself, fell on him.

What happened now? Well, the man in question, that is, the son, now gray-haired, unmarried, highly respected, came walking along with his white-haired mother on his arm! Thirty-five years of inner torment and undeserved suffering for someone else had given their faces that peculiar pallor of death. But what were these rich and respected people doing in this crowd? Perhaps they were being pulled by that force which draws like to like. Perhaps they found some solace in seeing others who had suffered just as much and just as undeservedly.

The fact that I had a premonition I would see them has its secret causes buried deep in the soul, causes no less strong and effective for all that.

On the plain, new forms of wretchedness appeared. Children on bicycles, eight, ten years old, with evil faces; little girls, old for their age, with traces of potential beauty distorted by corruption. Even where there was a pretty face, there was some fault that marred it, a wrong proportion, a nose too big, a gaping tooth, bulging, frog-like eyes encroaching on the forehead.

Farther on the crowd began to thin out, and small groups of picnickers had deployed themselves in the grass. But I was struck by the fact that they were groups of three, with two men and one woman in each—the first act of a pastoral drama that would end tragically with the knife.

Hereabouts the cab driver began to talk to me and to treat me to his stories. It wasn't that he was being too familiar that bothered me; but he disturbed my thoughts, and that irked me. And when his comments on the various ladies riding by led my thoughts into channels I didn't want to explore, I felt he was a torturing spirit, and asked him to take me home.

[1] See **Strindberg**, *The Son of a Servant*, Doubleday Anchor Books, p. 187.—EDITOR.

More disappointed than hurt by my order, he turned around in the next intersection. At the same moment another cab cut in front of us. There were two drunk women in it, demimondes. The cabby tried to pass them but the crowded road prevented him. So I had to ride behind these two women, and when the traffic forced them to stop, I had to stop too. It looked as if I were chasing them. The ladies found this extremely amusing, and so did the people in the street.

I ran this gauntlet all the way into town until I finally got off at my front door, feeling as if I had been released from a bad dream.

"Better to be alone," I said to myself, and that was the last time I went out in the afternoon that summer. Keeping oneself company is best; still, one has to be on guard against the bad.

\* \* \*

Consequently I stayed in the house, enjoyed my peace; imagined that I was beyond the storms of life; wished I were a little bit older so that I would not feel life's temptations; and believed that the worst was behind me.

And then one morning as I was having my coffee the maid came to me and said, "Your son was here, but I said you were still in bed."

"My son?"

"That's what he said."

"That's impossible! What did he look like?"

"He was tall, and . . . well, he gave his name and said he would come again."

"How old was he?"

"Young—seventeen, eighteen."

I was struck dumb with apprehension, and the girl left. So it wasn't all over! The past was rising from its grave. Though it was piled with dirt and the grass on it was old, the past was not dead. My son who went off to America with respectable people when he was nine years old, and who I thought had made a career for himself. What had happened? Some accident, naturally—or several.

What would it be like to see him again? That terrifying moment of recognition, when you seek in vain for the familiar features of the child's face, those features that you helped shape from the cradle on, as you sought to make him as good as possible. In front of your child you always tried to show your best side, and for that reason you tried to catch the reflections of your better nature in that pliable and impressionable child's face, which you loved as a better version of yourself. Now I was to see it again, deformed and distorted. The growing adolescent is ugly, disproportioned, showing forth in terrible mixture both the angel in the child and the waking animal in the young man; filled with intimations of passion and conflict; fear of what is to come and remorse over what he had already experienced—and always that constant, restless sneering at everything; hatred of everything that is above him and represses him; which means hatred of the older generation and of those who are better off. And, above all, a distrust of life itself that had just transformed him from an innocuous child to a predatory man. I knew all this from my own experience and remembered how disgusting I was as an adolescent when all I thought of, however I tried not to, was food, liquor, and the coarsest pleasures. . . . It wasn't necessary to remind me of this again; I already knew it, and I felt I could not be blamed for the way nature had arranged things. And, wiser than my own parents, I had never demanded anything from my son in return. I had brought him up to be a free and independent man and taught him from the first that he had certain rights as well as certain responsibilities to life, himself, and his fellow man. But I knew that he would come to me to make extravagant demands stretching back to infinity, although his claims on me ceased when he was fifteen.[2] And he would grin and sneer when I spoke of his responsibilities, I knew that too—from my own experience.

If it was only a question of money, I wouldn't mind. But he would make demands on my person, even though he despised my company. He would lay claim on the apartment, which wasn't mine, my friends, whom I missed, my relatives,

[2] According to Swedish law a father was compelled to contribute to the support of his children, whether illegitimate or in the custody of a wife from whom he was divorced, until they were fifteen.
—Editor.

whom he thought I possessed, my name, with which to establish his credit.

I knew he would find me boring and that he would bring home ideas from a strange land with an entirely different outlook, with different manners and attitudes; that he would treat me like an old fossil who didn't understand anything at all—since I was neither an engineer nor an electrician.

And what about his character and his propensities? How had they developed during these years? Experience has indeed taught me that one remains throughout life pretty much the same as one was born. No matter how he was rigged up, every human being that I had observed sailing through life from childhood on was as a rule still the same man at fifty, with a very few changes. It's true that many of them had suppressed some of their more glaring faults, unsuitable for social life; some had acquired a polish that concealed their worst side; but at bottom they were the same as they had been. In the case of the exceptions, certain traits had grown and spread, sometimes moving from virtue into vice. I remember one fellow whose firmness and tenacity had turned into stubbornness, whose sense of order had hardened into pedantry, whose thriftiness had taken root as stinginess, whose love for civilized men had been converted into hatred of the uncivilized. But I also remembered a man whose bigotry had been slowly distilled into piety, whose hate had turned to forbearance, and whose obstinacy had become firmness and strength. . . .

After brooding for a while, I went out for my morning stroll, not in order to put aside painful thoughts but to face them and to accommodate myself to the inevitable. I considered every possible course that the meeting with my son might take. But when I came to the questions about what had happened from the time of our separation until now, I trembled and wanted to turn tail and run away. However, experience had also taught me that one's back is the most vulnerable side and that the chest is protected with a shield of bones, evidently meant for defense. So I decided to stand my ground and bear the blows.

Steeling my nerves and emotions, and adopting the dry and matter-of-fact attitude of a man of the world, I drew up my program. I would find a room for him in a boardinghouse, after having bought him some clothes. Find out what he wanted to be. Get him a job immediately. Above all, treat him as a respectable stranger who would be kept at a distance by the absence of any confidences on my part. To protect myself against any invasion of my privacy I would pretend that the past didn't exist. I wouldn't give him any advice, and I'd leave him completely free to do as he pleased —he certainly wouldn't be likely to take my advice anyway.

Done! And done with!

My mind made up, I headed back home. Yet I was fully aware that a change had taken place in my life, a change so radical that the streets, the country, and the town took on a different appearance for me. When I had got halfway across the bridge and was looking up the avenue, the shape of a young man came within range of my vision. I shall never forget that moment. He was tall and gangling, walking hesitantly as if looking or waiting for something. I saw him stare at me. Just as he seemed to recognize me, a shiver coursed through his body, and then I saw how he pulled himself together, stood up straight, and crossed the avenue, headed straight for me. I grouped my forces for defense, heard myself clear my throat to summon up a light, pleasant tone of voice in which to say, "Hello, my boy!"

Now we were only a stone's throw from each other, I saw how *déclassé* he looked. Just what I was most afraid of: he had come down in the world. The hat on his head wasn't his: it didn't fit him. His trousers hung loosely: the baggy knees were too low. His whole appearance was shabby and out-at-elbow. Decay and corruption inside and out. Like a waiter out of a job. Now I could make out his face, thin and unpleasantly bony. And I could see his eyes, large blue eyes, in sunken blue-white sockets. It was he!

This down-and-out, up-and-growing boy had once been my little angel, whose very smile could make me throw out the ape theory and the origin of the species, who used to be dressed like a little prince and who once did in fact play with a real little princess down in Germany. . . .

Like a sharp blow I felt the whole rottenness of life. But

without a vestige of self-reproach, for it was not I who had abandoned him.

We were only a few steps apart!—A doubt sprang up. Was it he? And in the same second I decided to pass by leaving it up to him to give a sign of recognition.

One. Two! Three!!—

He went past!

"Was it he, or wasn't it?" I asked myself as I headed for home, certain that he would show up no matter what the circumstances.

Safe at home, I called in the maid to get more information from her and especially to find out if the man she had seen could have been the one I had passed. But it was impossible to settle the matter, and I was kept in suspense all morning. At one moment I would be hoping that he would come right away and put an end to the affair. The next moment I thought the situation had been so completely exhausted that nothing more could happen.

Lunch was over. The afternoon passed. And as it did, I got a new slant on the matter that made it even worse. He had assumed that I didn't want to say hello to him, that was it! I had frightened him and he had crawled away like a dog—was wandering dazedly in a bewildering town in a strange country—had taken up with bad company—perhaps fallen into despair. Where and how could I find him now? The police!

That's how my thoughts went round and round torturing me. I don't know why, since it was not I who had been in charge of his bringing-up.[3] And I felt as if an evil power had forced me into this situation to put the blame on me.

[3] When Strindberg was divorced from his first wife in 1892, the custody of the three children was given to the mother. The episode of the surprise return of the narrator's son from America was based on a real incident. Strindberg was upset in December 1900 by the news that his son Hans was about to visit him from Finland. The news turned out to be untrue. It was at about this time that Strindberg's attitude toward the children of his first marriage changed from fatherly solicitude, accompanied by remorse at not having been able to provide adequately for their upbringing, to stepfatherly coldness. He accused them and their mother Siri of blackmailing him and of begging rather than working for a living.—EDITOR.

Evening finally came. Then the maid entered with a calling card—on which was printed—the name of—my nephew!

When I was wrapped in my solitude again, I felt relieved that the anxious moments I had gone through had resolved themselves into projections of my imagination, which for me had had the same effect as the real thing. Still, these imaginings of mine had forced themselves upon me so importunately and so irresistibly that I felt there must have been some solid reason for their existence. Perhaps, I said to myself, perhaps my son in a faraway land was a prey to similar sensations. Perhaps he was in need, longed for me, "saw" me on some street just as I had "seen" him, and was torn by the same doubts. . . .

With that, I stopped worrying that particular bone and buried the incident away among other experiences I had had. But I didn't write it off as some kind of joke. Not at all. I kept it as a precious memory.

The evening was gloomy but peaceful. I couldn't work. I paced the room and kept glancing at the hour hand of the clock. Finally it got to be nine. Now I looked forward with dread to the last long hour that remained. It seemed as long as eternity itself, and I knew of no way of shortening it. I hadn't chosen to be alone; solitude had been forced on me; and I hated it as a prison. I wanted to break out, I wanted to cry out, I wanted some release, an eruption, I wanted to hear music, something magnificent, overwhelming, music by someone who had suffered all his life, I wanted to hear Beethoven, and I began to rouse in my inner ear the sleeping notes of the last movement of the Moonlight Sonata, which has become for me the most sublime expression of humanity's yearning for liberation and deliverance, of a sublimity that words cannot approach.

Twilight had fallen. The window was open. Standing in the light the flowers on the dining-room table, silent, still, fragrant, reminded me that it was summer.

Then I heard, distinctly, as clearly as if it came from the next room, that mighty allegro—of the Moonlight Sonata—unroll like a gigantic fresco—I saw and heard at the same time. Not knowing whether it was a delusion or not, I felt a shudder run down my back, the tremor that comes from suddenly confronting the unknown. The music came, you see, from my unknown benefactors in the house next door—and they were in the country! Of course, they could have returned on some errand. No matter. The music was being played for me, and I accepted it gratefully, feeling now I had company in my solitude and was joined to other poor human creatures who shared my mood.

Now if I confess to you that the same allegro was repeated three times during that long hour, the incident appears even more inexplicable. But that was precisely why it gave me even greater pleasure. And the fact that no other piece was played I interpreted as a special sign of grace.

Finally the clock struck ten, and blessed sleep put an end to a day that I shall long remember.

## VI

Summer has crept forward to the first of August. The street lamps are turned on, and I welcome them. They mean autumn and autumn means some progress has been made and that's the main thing. Something has been put behind and something lies ahead. The city begins to change its appearance. Now and then one can see a familiar face, which is comforting and reassuring. I even find the opportunity of saying a few words, something new for me, so new that the register of my voice has for lack of use been lowered and acquired a dull, husky ring. I feel it belongs to someone else.

The shooting on the parade grounds has ceased; my neighbors have returned from the country and settled in; the dog is back at his barking, day and night, and the family has started giving soirées once again, at which the chief entertainment consists in throwing a bone across the dining room floor and having the dog go after it, barking sharply as he chases it and growling when the family tries to take it away from him.

The telephone is at work again, and the piano playing pursues its appointed course. Everything is the same as it was. Everything returns—except the major, whose obituary I read in this morning's paper. I miss him as a member of my circle, but I can't begrudge him his death as he was having a miserable time of it ever since he had to lay down his arms and surrender to age and retirement.

The autumn days rush by, and life spurts ahead with the fresh winds that make breathing easier. Once again I take to walking abroad in the evenings, wrapping myself in the darkness that serves as an invisible cloak. This shortens the nights and deepens my sleep.

My habit of translating experiences into poetry provides a substitute for speech and functions as a safety valve for the excess of impressions that force themselves on me. What I experience in my solitude acquires a touch of premeditated design, and much of what happens seems to have been staged especially and exclusively for me. For instance, one night I witnessed a fire in the town, and at the same time I heard the howling of the wolves from the Skansen Zoo. These two threads were knotted together in my imagination, and combined with the appropriate warp they wove themselves into a poem.

## VARGARNE TJUTA[1]

Vargarne tjuta på Skansen,
isarna råma på sjön,
furorna knaka i backen,
tyngda av första snön.

(The wolves are howling in Skansen,/the ice floes are roaring on the sea,/the pine branches creak on the hillside,/ under the weight of the first snow.)

Vargarne tjuta i kölden,
hundarne svara från stan;
solen gick ner efter middan,
natten börjar på dan.

[1] "Vargarne tjuta" ("The Wolves Are Howling")—this poem was inspired by the great fire that broke out in Stockholm December 30, 1900.–EDITOR.

(The wolves are howling in the cold,/the dogs answer from the town;/the sun went down right after noon,/the night begins in the middle of the day.)

> Vargarne tjuta i mörkret,
> gatornas lyktor sitt ljus
> sända som norrsken i höjden
> över de hopar av hus.

(The wolves are howling in the dark,/the street lamps spread their glow/like the northern lights high above/the huddled houses.)

> Vargarne tjuta i gropen,
> nu de fått blodad tand,
> längta till fjäll och urskog,
> när de se norrskensbrand.

(The wolves are howling in their pits,/now that they have tasted blood,/and long for the plateaus and the forests deep,/when they see the fire of the northern lights.)

> Vargarne tjuta på berget,
> tjuta sig hesa av hat,
> mänskorna gav dem för frihet
> tukthus och celibat.

(The wolves are howling on the mountain,/howling themselves hoarse with hate,/man took their freedom and gave them/a prison and the life of a celibate.)

Vinden vilar, stillhet råder, stadens tornur slagit tolv!
Tysta slädarna på föret glida som på bonat golv.
Sista spårvagnsklockan klingat, ingen hund på gatan hörs,
staden sover, lyktor släckas, ej en kvist på träden rörs;
nattens himmel svart som sammet välver sig oändligt djup.
Högt Orion svärdet svänger, Karlavagnen står på stup.
Eldarna i spisen slocknat, blott i fjärran står en rök;
ur en skorstensobelisk den stiger som utur ett jättekök;
det är bagarn, som om natten reder oss ett dagligt bröd.—
Röken stiger, blåvit, lodrätt; men—just nu den färgas röd.
Det är eld!
Det är eld! Det är eld! Det är eld!

(The wind is still, silence reigns, the clock in the city tower
    has struck twelve!
Silently the sleighs glide by as if on polished floors.
The bell of the last streetcar has clanged, no dog is heard in
    the streets,
the city sleeps, the lamps are out, not a tree branch is
    trembling;
the heaven of night, dark as velvet, arches up to infinite
    heights.
Orion swings his sword on high, Charles's Wain teeters on
    two wheels.
The fires in the stoves have died out, only in the distance is
    there smoke;
from a chimney obelisk it rises as if from a giant kitchen;
it's the baker who through the night prepares us our daily
    bread.—
The smoke rises, bluish white, straight up; but—now it's
    turning red.
                                Fire!
                        Fire! Fire! Fire!)


Och ett rödglödgat klot stiger upp som en måne i fyllet;
och det glödande rött går i vitt och i gult och slår ut som en
    solros ur hyllet.
Är det soln, som går upp bland de kolsvarta moln utur
    husmassors hav?
där vart tak är en kam på en våg, som är svart lik en grav.
Nu står himlen i brand, varje torn och kupol uti stan,
varje spira och stång, varje gränd, varje prång stå så ljust som
    på dan!
Varje kabel och tråd utav koppar blir röd som på harpan de
    lågstämda basar.
På fasaderna ses varje ruta i eld, och de snötäckta skorstenar
    lysa som kasar.
Varken sol eller måne det är! Ingen lusteld beställd!
            Det är eld! Det är eld! Det är eld!


(A red-hot orb rises up like the moon at its full;
and the glowing red changes to white and to yellow and
    blossoms like a sunflower.

Is it the sun, rising behind the pitch-black clouds over the sea
of massed houses?
where each roof is the crest of a wave, as black as the grave.
Now the sky is aflame, and every tower and cupola in town,
every spire and pole, every alley, every nook is as bright as
at day!
Every cable, every copper wire turns red as the bass strings
on a harp.
On the house fronts every pane is afire, and the snow-covered
chimneys shine like beacons.
But it's neither the moon nor the sun! No bonfire this!
It's a fire! It's a fire! It's a fire!)

Men på berget som nyss uti nattmörker låg, där är ljust, där
är liv.
Ifrån vargarnes gropar där stiger ett tjut som de stuckits med
kniv,
utav hat, utav hämnd; det är mordbrännarlust, det är mör-
darefröjd,
då ett skallande skratt ifrån rävkulan går, man är glad, man
är hemsk, man är nöjd.
Och i björnarnes bur, där dansas på häl vid ett grymt som av
slaktade svin,
men i lodjurets gryt är det tyst och man ser blott ett tan-
draders skinande grin.

(But Skansen hill, which only a moment ago lay in the darkness of night, is bright and humming with life.
From the wolf pits comes a cry as if they had been stuck
with knives,
a cry of hate, of revenge; the incendiary's joy, the murderer's
lust,
in a howling laugh that comes from the foxholes. They are
happy, savage, satisfied.
And the bears in their cage are dancing and grunting as if a
pig had been slaughtered,
only in the lynx's lair is there silence, and all one sees is a
shining row of smiling teeth.)

Och sälarne ropa sitt ve! Ve över staden!
Rop som av drunknande på havet.

Och alla hundarne tjuta i kör;
gläfsa, vinsla och skälla,
rycka i kedjorna, kedjorna,
sjunga, gråta och gnälla
som osaliges andar!
De hava medlidande, endast de, hundarna,
med sina vänner mänskorna,—
vilken sympati!

(And the seals bark out their cry of woe! Woe over the
city!/The cry of a man drowning at sea./And all the dogs
howl in chorus;/yapping, yelling, barking,/pulling at their
chains, their chains,/whining, crying, moaning/like the souls
of the damned!/They take pity, only they, the dogs,/take
pity on their human friends,—/such commiseration!)

Nu vaknar älgarne, nordanskogens furstar,
de samla och reda sina långa skänklar,
sträcka ett trav i en begränsad volt
inom kättens stängsel.
Törna mot gärdselstängerna
som sparv mot ruta;
böla oförståendes,
undrande om det är dag igen.—
En ny dag, som all de andra,
lika dödande lång
utan annat synligt ändamål
än att följas av en natt.—

(Now the elk wake up, the sovereigns of the northern
woods,/collect themselves and unbend their long legs,/
stretch, trot, turn about/as much as their pen will allow./
Knock against the fence/like a sparrow against a windowpane;/mooing their confusion,/wondering if it is day again.
—/A new day, but like all the others,/as deadly long and
boring/with no other apparent purpose/than to lead us into
night.)

Då blir det liv i fågelvärlden;
örnarne skrika och flaxa,
fresta de nötta vingarna,
pröva en lönlös höjdflykt,

stöta huvet mot järnstänger,
bita i galler, klösa, klänga,
tills de falla på mullen,
och bli liggande lama,
med släpande vingar som på knä—
knäböjande, bönfallande
om en nådestöt,
som återger dem åt luften
och friheten.

(Then the bird cage comes to life;/the eagles cry and flutter about,/trying out their rusty wings,/making a vain attempt to fly high,/hitting their heads against the iron rods,/bite the bars, claw, climb,/till they fall to earth,/and lie there lame,/wings drooping, as if they were on their knees—/kneeling, imploring/for the *coup de grâce*/that would return them to the air/and to their freedom.)

Falkarne vissla och ila
som fjädrade pilar—hit och dit;
vråkarne jämra sig
som sjuka barn.—
De tama vildgässen vaknat
och sätta an med spända halsar
ett ackord av vallhjonslurar.—

(The hawks whistle and flash/like feathered shafts—hither and thither;/the buzzards whimper/like sick children.—/The tame wild geese are awake/and with stretched necks strike up/a chord of alpenhorns.—)

Svanorna simma stumma,
snappa mellan isflaken
efter de speglande eldflammorna,
som ila likt guldfiskar
på dammens yta;
stanna stilla och sticka huvena
ner i det svarta vattnet—
de vita svanorna—
bita sig fast i botten
för att slippa se på
hur himlen brinner opp.

(The swans glide mutely,/snapping between the ice-bits/at the reflected flames,/that flash like goldfish/on the surface of the pond;/stop dead and stick their heads/into the black water—/the white swans—/biting fast to the bottom/in order not to see/the heavens burning up.)

> Det mörknar åter, brandkårsluren
> har vigt in tystnad över stad och land;
> ett rökmoln sträckes över stadskonturen
> som bilden av en svart ofantlig hand.

(Darkness returns, the horns of the fire brigade/have consecrated to silence town and country;/a cloud of smoke reaches out over the skyline/like some vast black hand.)

By means of books I limit my circle of friends to the impersonal. Balzac, whose fifty volumes I have read over and over during the last ten years, has become an intimate whom I never tire of. It's true that he has never created what is called a work of art—at least it would not be called that at the present time when art is confused with literature. Balzac is always artless. One is never aware of the structure of his works and I have never noticed any particular style. He does not play with words, indulge in metaphors and similes, which belong to "poetry" anyway. But on the other hand he has so strong a sense of design that the subject matter is always clearly present without a word being wasted. He disdains all showy effects and works directly with the simplest means, like a storyteller among friends, sometimes narrating an incident, sometimes introducing characters who narrate, sometimes commenting on the action and explaining it. And to him everything forms part of history, contemporary history. He reveals every person, no matter how small, in the light of the present, but at the same time gives him a past history and shows his development under this or that form of government, thus widening the perspective and furnishing a background for each figure. I am astonished when I read how Balzac was misunderstood by the critics of his time. This believing, trusting, tolerant man is described in my schoolbooks as a merciless physiologist and materialist, and so on. An even greater paradox is that the physiologist Zola hailed Balzac as his great teacher and master. Who can make sense of that? But the same thing holds true for my other literary friend, Goethe, who has of late been used for every conceivable purpose, and mostly in an idiotic effort to resurrect the pagan world. Goethe passed through many stages on life's way. Through Rousseau, Kant, Schelling, Spinoza, he reached his own position, which might be called the philosophy of enlightenment. He had solved all the problems; everything was so clear and simple that a child could understand it. And then came the moment when the pantheistic explanations of the inexplicable began to fail him. To the seventy-year-old Goethe everything appeared remarkably, extraordinarily incomprehensible. The mystic in him stepped forward and even Swedenborg was called in for advice. But all in vain: the Faust of Part Two had to bow down before the All Powerful, reconcile himself with life, turn into a philanthropist (and swamp reclaimer), become half a socialist, and be apotheosized with all of the apparatus that goes with the Catholic Church's doctrine of the four last things.

The Faust of Part One, who emerges from his wrestling match with God as victorious Saul, becomes in Part Two a defeated Paul. This is my Goethe! But though there is a Goethe for everyone, I cannot understand where one finds the pagan Goethe, unless it be in a few mischievous verse fragments in which he takes a whack at the clergy. Or in his "Prometheus" in which the chained son of the gods can just as well stand for the crucified son, who scoffs at the impotence of the rejected Zeus.

No, it is the whole of Goethe's life and all the creative writing rising from it that appeals to me. While he was still growing up, an older friend of the poet gave him this key to his creativity: "What you are striving to do, the goal of your work, is to render a poetic image of reality. The others seek to realize their so-called poetic dreams, their imaginative fancies, but they create only nonsense."

Goethe quotes this in *Aus meinem Leben*, and in another place in the same book he himself says: "Such was the beginning of that course from which I have never in my life been able to deviate; I mean, the transformation of whatever delighted or distressed me, or otherwise preoccupied me, into a poem or image, and in that way to deal with myself, in order both to rectify my conception of the outer world and to bring peace and order to my inner life. No one needed a talent for this more than I, possessing a temperament that constantly drove me from one extreme to another. Everything that I have published comprises the fragments of one great confession, which this little book is a bold attempt to complete."

One of the pleasures I get from reading Goethe comes from his light touch. It is as if he could not take life altogether seriously, either because it lacked full reality or was not worth our rage and our tears. Also the temerity with which he approaches the gods in heaven, who are friends and relatives to him. And his contempt for forms and conventions, plus the fact that his mind was not closed to new ideas, that he was continually developing and renewing himself. This kept him always young, always in the vanguard, always ahead of his time.

Always, now as well as in the past, Goethe has been set up as Schiller's opposite, and the two of them are used to form an either/or, just as is the case with Rousseau and Voltaire. I don't find it necessary to choose between them; I have room for both since they complement each other. I cannot in so many words list the differences between them, not even formal differences. Schiller has a greater sense of form, especially in the drama, and his wings carry him to the same sublime heights as Goethe. Their development was the result of collaboration, for they influenced each other. That is why the pedestal at Weimar has room for the two of them. And if they reach their hands out to each other, I can see no cause why they should be separated.

*　*　*

It's winter again. The sky is gray, and the light comes from below, from the white snow on the ground. My solitude is in perfect harmony with the apparent death of nature, although being alone sometimes oppresses me too much. I long to see someone. But living alone has made me too sensitive, as if my skin had been stripped from my soul. I am so spoiled from being complete master of my thoughts and emotions that I can scarcely endure contact with another person. Any stranger who comes near me seems to cut off my air. He brings with him his own spiritual atmosphere, which infiltrates mine. However, one evening just as I found myself yearning for some company, the girl came in with a calling card. I was ready to receive anyone, even the most unsympathetic soul. The sight of the calling card delighted me, but when I read it I glowered. It was no one I knew. Never mind, I said to myself, it's a human being anyway. "Show him in."

After a moment a young man entered, very pale, quite nondescript in appearance, so much so that I couldn't tell what class he belonged to, especially since his suit hung so loosely on him. He was very withdrawn and self-conscious; kept on the defensive, alert and watchful. After a few polite formalities, which put a chill on our meeting, as far as I was concerned, he came directly to the point and asked me for a bit of financial help. I told him that I was reluctant to help utter strangers, since I had often helped the wrong person. At this moment I noticed a red scar on his forehead over his left eye; for a second it appeared blood red, and in that moment he seemed a monster to me. But in the next instant I was seized with pity for him in his deep despair, and realizing that I was in a somewhat similar position what with a winter's night ahead of me, I changed my mind. Not to prolong his suffering, I handed him the amount he asked for and asked him to sit down.

As he put the money in his pocket he seemed more surprised than grateful, and he looked as if he wanted to leave now that he had finished his business. To start a conversation I asked him where he came from. He stared at me, startled, and stammered, "I—I thought you recognized my name." He said this with a touch of arrogance that repulsed me, but when I confessed my ignorance, he spoke out calmly and with dignity.

"I have just been released," he said, "from prison."

"Prison?" (This was beginning to be interesting: I was at work on a crime story.)

"Yes. I took twenty crowns that didn't belong to me. My boss decided to overlook the matter, and it was all forgotten.

Until I decided to write for another paper—I'm a reporter, you see—write against the religious dissenters. And then it was all brought up again, and I was sent up."

A delicate situation. I felt as if I had been challenged to express my opinion. Since I didn't want to, I parried and side-stepped the issue.

"Now don't tell me that in these 'enlightened times' a man is going to be prevented from getting a job because he's been in pris—"

My last word was clipped off by the flash of anger on his face.

To help give him a new start in life I suggested that he should write for a certain people's newspaper, whose editor I knew was above sharing the cruel prejudice that will not allow a man who has served his sentence to return to society.

When he heard the name of the paper, he snorted contemptuously and protested, "That's the paper I'm opposed to."

This struck me as being very perverse. I thought that in his present circumstances he would seize on any means that might restore him. But not knowing the whole situation and not wanting to waste time on explanations, I once again went round about, motivated by a very human desire to get something in return for my money. Adopting an urbane conversational tone, I said, "You know, I've often wondered how hard prison really is. What's the actual punishment?"

I could tell he thought I was being too inquisitive. I must have hurt him.

To help him out I didn't wait for his answer but answered myself. "It's the lonesomeness, isn't it?" (I struck myself with that blow!—as often happens when one has to keep talking.)

He picked up the conversational ball very slowly and deliberately and tossed it back. "Yes, that's true. I've never gotten used to being alone. It's always seemed to me to be a punishment inflicted on those who are bad in one way or another."

(I had reached out a helping hand and look what I got in return! Bitten by the dog I was petting. Though he probably didn't realize that.)

A pause followed, and I could tell that he had cut himself

with his last remark and was sorry he had said it. He hadn't been thinking of me when he pronounced judgment on the prisoner in solitary confinement.

Now the conversation had run aground and we had to find some way of floating it free. Since I was really in the enviable position, I decided to get him off the hook by demeaning myself in such a way that he would leave feeling that he had received something besides money. But I hadn't sized him up properly. I probably assumed that he regarded himself as a martyr, the innocent victim of an unscrupulous newspaper editor.

Yes, that was it. He had already forgiven himself and settled his account on the first installment. The real crime had been committed when the other person brought charges. Yet something in the air must have told the young man that he could not count on any support from me. The whole situation seemed to have arisen from a misunderstanding. He had thought I would be another type of person, and perhaps he was now aware that he had started off on the wrong foot and that it was too late to change.

So I attempted a different approach and pretending to have noticed his downheartedness and his shyness, I spoke what I thought were words of wisdom from the mouth of an enlightened man.

"You mustn't let yourself become despondent because you've been in—(I avoided the word). Modern society has progressed so far that it considers a crime for which the culprit has been punished—(he sneered cynically)—as paid for, stricken from the record. Not long ago I was sitting with my friends at the Hotel Rydberg, and in the group was a former friend of mine who had done time—two years—in Långholmen Prison. (I deliberately used plain language.) And he was guilty of embezzlement on a grand scale."

I paused to observe the change that I expected to take place in him—a sigh of relief, his face lighting up. But he seemed only more hurt and angry because I had dared to compare him, the innocent and injured, to a confirmed criminal. But I caught a glint of curiosity in his eye, and when my brusque silence compelled him to speak, he asked, chopping his words, "What was his name?"

"It wouldn't be right to say, if you can't guess who it was. But the point is that he wrote down his impressions of prison life and had them published, without trying to excuse himself for the inexcusable things he had done. And by doing that he has regained his former position and held on to his old friends."

That hit him in the solar plexus, though it was meant as a pat on the shoulder. He got up. And so did I since there was nothing further to add. He bade farewell politely. But when I saw him from the back, and noticed his drooping shoulders and his dragging legs, I began to fear for him. I could see he belonged to those who appear to be composed of two mismatched halves.

After he had left I thought to myself, "Maybe he made the whole thing up."

But when I looked at his card, on which he had written his address, it struck me that I had recently seen that handwriting on an anonymous letter. I pulled out the drawer where I keep letters and began to look for it. Now there's something one should never do. While I was looking for his, all the other letters in my desk filed past me, and my mind and heart got as many sharp stabs and pricks as there were letter writers.

After going through them three times, certain that that style of handwriting was there somewhere, I stopped hunting. The distinct impression had been formed in me: "You are not to snoop around in this man's life. But you are to give him more money without further ado. You know best why!"

My apartment had undergone a change. The stranger had brought an oppressive atmosphere into it and I had to get out. There must have been strong stuff in that soul. I had to move the chair he had occupied in order not to see him still sitting there.

Then I went out into the fresh air, after I had opened the window—not to get rid of a physical odor but to rid the room of an intangible impression.

\*       \*       \*

Some old streets have absolutely no atmosphere, while others have a lot even though they are new. The newer part of Knight Street is steeped in romance, not to say mysticism. No people are to be seen on it, no store-fronts with doors open. It's elegant, distinguished, closed tight, deserted, although the apartment houses there hold the destinies of so many people. The fact that the cross streets are named after the bigwigs of the Thirty Years' War reinforces the impression of ancient history mingling pleasantly with the present. Turning the corner at Banér Street, one sees to the west a hill with Count Magnus Street twisting in at the right and closing off the view with a shadowy bend in which one can imagine all sorts of things.

If one comes back from the west, down the old part of Knight Street, and looks down Count Magnus Street, the bend appears very sharp, and the gloomy, castle-like houses there with their portals and overhanging towers tell of destinies on a larger scale. Magnates and statesmen live there, influencing the fates of nations and dynasties. But right above, up Count Magnus Street stands an old house preserved from the beginning of the previous century. I like to walk by this house, for that is where I lived during my stormy youth. There I drew up plans for my campaigns, plans that were later carried out successfully, and that is where I wrote my first important poem. But the memory of it is far from bright and cheery. Poverty, humiliation, squalor, and quarreling left their dirty fingerprints on it.

This evening, without knowing why, I had a longing to see this house once again. And when I came upon it, I saw it had not changed much—only cleaned up and with newly painted window heads. I recognized the long, narrow, tunnel-like entry way with the gutters on each side and the street door itself with an iron rod supporting one half of it, and the notices for pressing and ironing, hand laundry, shoe repairing. . . .

As I was standing there lost in my thoughts, a man came up behind me with quick, firm steps. He put his hand on my neck, as only the oldest of friends would do, and said, "Trying to talk yourself into coming up to see yourself?"

He was a young man, a composer, with whom I had worked in the past and whom I knew very well.

Without further ado, I followed him into the house and

up, up the wooden stairs, and, right enough, we stopped on the third floor in front of my door.

We walked in, he turned on the lights, and I drifted back thirty years in time. There was my old bachelor apartment, with the same wallpaper; only the furniture was new.

When we had made ourselves comfortable, I felt as if he were visiting me and not vice versa. However, there was a grand piano in the room, and so I immediately turned the talk to music. Now, like most musicians, my friend was so preoccupied with music that he could scarcely discuss anything else, nor did he want to. He knew practically nothing of what was going on in the world. If one mentioned words like parliament, cabinet, Boer War, strike, or suffrage, he wouldn't open his mouth. Not, however, because he was in the least embarrassed by his ignorance or disconcerted by the choice of subject: it simply did not exist for him. And even when he talked about music, he spoke in nothing but generalities and never expressed any opinions. With him everything existed only as notes, bars, and rhythms; he used words only to express the basic necessities of life.

I knew what he was like, and I only had to point at the open piano to get him to sit down and play for me. And when he began to fill the little room with music, I felt as if I had entered a magic circle in which my present being was wiped out and my former self of the 1870s sprang to life.

I saw myself lying on a sofa bed that stood where I had been sitting a moment ago, in front of a closed-off door. And it was night . . . and I was awakened by my neighbor who was lying just on the other side of the door, restlessly tossing in his sofa, sometimes sighing heavily, sometimes moaning. Being young, unafraid, and selfish, I was only interested in getting back to sleep. . . . It was only twelve o'clock and I dismissed the sounds from my mind by telling myself my neighbor had come home drunk. At one o'clock I was jolted awake by a cry of distress I thought had come from me, for I had been having a bad dream. Not a sound came from the room next door, absolutely not a sound. But I felt something distinctly unpleasant emanating from there. A cold draft, a feeling that I was being observed, as if someone in there were listening or peeping through the keyhole to see what I was up to.

I couldn't get back to sleep. I kept fighting against something disturbing, something awful. At times I found myself wishing that I could hear some sound from there, but though there was only one foot between us, I could hear nothing, no sound of breathing, not even the rustling of the sheets.

Finally morning came. I got up and went out. Upon my return home, I found out that my neighbor, who was a bricklayer, had died during the night. I had been lying next to a corpse.

(All the while this scene was passing through my mind, my friend was playing, and I continued undisturbed to think about the past.)

The next day I heard the preparations being made for the shrouding and burial—the clatter and rumble of the coffin in the stairway, the washing of the corpse, the slow, soft speech of the old women.

As long as the sun was up, I found it all merely interesting and could joke about it with people who came to call. But when night fell and I was alone, the mysterious cold aura that corpses give off entered my room, a coldness that is not a lowering of temperature or an absence of heat but a positive freezing coldness that can't be registered on the thermometer.

I couldn't stand it there, and I went out to a restaurant. There they poked so much fun at me for being afraid of the dark that I talked myself out of my earlier decision to sleep somewhere else and went home, feeling rather tipsy. I shook and trembled as I got into my bed next to that corpse, but I managed to crawl under the covers. Far be it from me to say how, but that dead body still seemed to possess some qualities of life that put it in touch with me. A smell as of brass bored right through the door and right up my nostrils, depriving me of any sleep. A silence that only death knows reigned throughout the house, and the bricklayer seemed to exert a greater influence on the living when dead than when alive. After a while I could hear through the thin walls and floors the whisperings and mumblings of sleepless people until well past midnight. Then, contrary to custom, the house became absolutely silent. Not even the policeman who used to come through on his beat was heard from.

The clocks struck one. Two. I jumped from bed, jolted by a banging that came from the dead man's room. Three bangs! Three! My first thought was that the man had been in a state of suspended animation but I didn't want to take the chance of being involved in any spirit scenes. I grabbed a fistful of clothes and dashed down to the next floor where an acquaintance of mine lived. He let me in with a few appropriate jokes and I slept on his sofa cot until morning came.

That was the first time I had given much thought to the common everyday phenomenon of death, which is so simple but which nevertheless has a profound and secret effect on even the most lighthearted of souls.

(My friend at the piano, probably influenced by my thoughts, had kept himself to dark and somber music. But at this point he switched over to something very light.)

The masses of tone seemed to crowd me out of the room, and feeling an impulse to throw myself out through the window, I turned my head and let my glance go out behind the neck of the piano player. Since there was no roller curtain, my glance shot out across the street into an apartment in the house opposite, which was somewhat lower, so that I found myself at the supper table of a small family.

There was a young girl, of dark complexion, slim, plain, moving around a dining-room table at which a four-year-old boy sat. On the table was a vase with chrysanthemums, two large white ones and one bright yellow. I stretched my neck and saw that the table was set and that the boy was about to eat his supper. The young lady tied a napkin under his chin, and in doing so, she lowered her head so far that the back of her neck came into full view, a small neck, slender as a flower stem. Her charming little head with its luxuriant hair bent forward like a flower bud over the child, sheltering it, protecting it. At the same time the little boy made the sweetest motions with his head, first bobbing backward to make room for the bib, and then bobbing forward to shove the stiff bib down with his chin in such a way that his mouth opened and revealed his little white milk teeth.

The woman could not have been his mother, for she looked too young; or his sister, for she was too old. But she was related somehow, I could see that.

The room was furnished simply but neatly. A number of portraits hung on the walls and on the tile stove, breathing the spirit of family love. And hand-woven antimacassars lay on the furniture.

Now the young girl sat down at the table—not to eat, fortunately for me, for it isn't very nice to watch others when you're not participating yourself. She sat down to keep the boy company and to coax him to eat. The little man wasn't in a very good mood, but Aunty (so I had already begun to think of her) soon got him to laugh. I could see by the movements of her mouth that she was singing to him. It struck me as very mysterious that I was seeing her sing but not hearing her, all the while my pianist played along. I felt that he was accompanying her, or should be. I was in both rooms at the same time, but mostly in the room across the street, and I formed a bridge between the two. The three chrysanthemums seemed to take part in the scene, too. For a moment I smelled their health-giving, wound-healing camphoric odor blending with the chaste fragrance of iris from her hair, and together they formed a haze over the table that caused the food to vanish, and the child seemed to open his mouth only to inhale this perfume and to glance with laughing eyes at his beautiful dinner partner. The white glass of milk on a white tablecloth, the white china, the white chrysanthemums, the white tile stove and the white faces— everything was white in there. And pure shining white was the motherliness of this young girl toward this boy she had not given birth to, as she untied the bib, wiped his mouth, and kissed him. . . .

At the same time my pianist turned to face the window, and now I heard that he was playing for her. I realized that he had seen her—and known the whole time that she was there.

I felt unwanted and superfluous, so I indicated I would be leaving. But he kept me there for a while, and we ended the evening by agreeing to collaborate again on a new work.

# VII

I returned to my piano player both because I found my youth again and because we collaborated on a work. The fact that I also stole many moments of pleasure in listening to his music was no larceny on my part since he was playing for her and not for me.

I saw almost the same scene repeated in her rooms on many evenings. Everything was pretty much the same: the child, the bib, the glass of milk. Only the flowers in the vase changed—always three chrysanthemums, however, with the third one changing color while the two white ones provided the basic tone. When I asked myself what it was that made the young girl radiate so much charm and joy, I found that it was due more to her movements than to her figure. Her rhythmical motions seemed to keep time to his music. One might say that he composed to her tempo, her dancing steps and swaying walk, and set to music the fluttering of her arms and the dipping of her neck.

We never talked about her, even pretended not to see her; but we lived with her. And I noticed one day that she had worked herself into the music for my poems—which I surely would not have objected to if she really had fitted in with my somber thoughts. But this she didn't do. Her soul moved in three-quarter time and the music always turned into a waltz. I didn't want to say anything for I knew that the magic spell would be broken with the first spoken word. And if it came to a choice between her and me, he would have thrown me away like an old rag.

*    *    *

Winter crept forward in a rather pleasant fashion, since I was no longer alone and my wanderings were no longer aimless. Moreover, I felt I was also enjoying a bit of family life since I was involving myself, at a distance, with a woman and child.

Spring came early; it was here in March. One evening as

I was sitting at my desk and writing, my piano player was announced and in he came. By the glow of the lamp I saw this mild little man looking like the cat that swallowed the canary, and he had something in his hand that he wanted to give to me.

It was a card on which stood two names, a man's and a woman's. He was engaged. Since by this time we scarcely found it necessary to use words with each other, I answered with a smile and spoke one word: chrysanthemum, with a rising inflection. He answered with a nod.

It all seemed absolutely natural to me, as if I had always known about it. We didn't waste words on it, but talked a little about our project and then he left.

I wasn't plagued with curiosity for I knew the answers to all the questions that could be asked. How did they meet? In the usual fashion, of course. Who was she? His fiancée. When did they intend to get married? In the summer, when else? Besides, what did it matter to me? Nevertheless I was afraid that he would now break off our collaboration, which was going very smoothly, and that our evening get-togethers would soon come to an end. That was only to be expected after the great event—although as he was on his way out, he told me that he was always home to me up to seven-thirty, and that if he was not at home, I should just walk in and wait for him—the key was in the cabinet in the hall.

I let three evenings go by, and on the fourth I ventured out at about six-thirty to see if he might be in. Halfway up his stairs, I realized that I had forgotten to see if his lights were on, as I usually did. At his door I groped in vain for the key. Then I took it from the cabinet, just as I used to thirty years ago, and put it in, exactly as in former times, and walked into my room.

It was a strange moment. I tumbled straight down into my youth, felt again all the formless fears of the unknown future oppressing me, ready to pounce on me, knew again that self-intoxicated feeling of surging high hopes and of happiness enjoyed in anticipation, alternating moods of confidence and despondency, overestimating my powers and failing to recognize my abilities.

I sat down without turning on the lights. The street light,

the same one that had shone on my misery, cast a meager light and threw on the wall the shadow made by the cross of the window frames.

There I sat. Everything was behind me, everything! It was all over. The battles, the victory, the defeat, the bitter and the sweet. And so what? Was I old and tired? No. The battle raged as savagely as ever, on a bigger scale and for greater objectives, always forward, forward. And if my enemies had lain ahead of me in the old days, now they lay both behind and ahead of me. I had only been resting up for the next advance. And as I sat there on that sofa in that room I felt just as young and just as ready for a fight as I had a generation ago. Only now the objective was different; the old mileposts lay far behind me. Those who had stayed behind wanted to hold me back too, of course. But I couldn't wait. And so I would have to go my own way alone, reconnoitering the wastelands, seeking new ways and breaking new paths, sometimes mocked by mirages, forced to turn back, but no farther back than the crossroads, and then onwards once again.

I had forgotten about the curtainless window, and when I did think of it and rose to take a look, I saw in the house across the way exactly what I expected to see.

He was sitting at the chrysanthemum table and she was sitting opposite, and both were busy with the child, who belonged to neither of them. It was her sister's son, a widow's only child. The fact that their first love sprang up with a child as its center gave an unselfish aspect to their relationship. Their feelings for each other, joining in the love of an innocent child, were ennobled. And I felt that he had been given an assurance of happiness in the motherly feelings she displayed.

Sometimes they forgot about the child and looked only at each other with that indescribable bliss that comes when two lonely people meet and know that from then on they will fight the loneliness together. For that matter they did not seem to be thinking at all, either about the past or the present. They lived only in the present, basking in the pleasure of each other's company. "Sitting at a table and looking at each other as long as life lasts!"

Glad that I had reached this point in life where I could smile at the happiness of others without any sense of regret or loss and without any imaginary apprehensions or misgivings, I walked out of the torture room of my youth and headed home to my solitude, my work, and my struggles.

# ANCHOR BOOKS

## DRAMA

## Drama (continued)

FIVE COMEDIES OF ARISTOPHANES, A57

FIVE PLAYS OF STRINDBERG—Elizabeth Sprigge, trans., A219

GHOSTS AND THREE OTHER PLAYS: *A Doll's House; An Enemy of the People; Rosmersholm*—Henrik Ibsen; trans. by Michael Meyer, A215e

GOETHE'S FAUST with the original German on facing pages—Walter Kaufmann, trans., A328

GREEK TRAGEDY—H. D. F. Kitto, A38

HAMLET AND OEDIPUS—Ernest Jones, A31

HEDDA GABLER AND THREE OTHER PLAYS—Henrik Ibsen, Michael Meyer, trans., A215c

THE HUMAN IMAGE IN DRAMATIC LITERATURE—Francis Fergusson, A124

THE IDEA OF A THEATER—Francis Fergusson, A4

THE IMMEDIATE EXPERIENCE—Robert Warshow, A410

INFERNO, ALONE and Other Writings—August Strindberg, trans. by Evert Sprinchorn, A492c

MADMAN'S DEFENSE—August Strindberg, trans. by Evert Sprinchorn, A492b

THE MODERN THEATRE, Vol. I: Buchner, *Woyzeck*; Verga, *Cavalleria Rusticana*; Becque, *Woman of Paris*; Brecht, *The Three Penny Opera*; Giraudoux, *Electra*—Eric Bentley, ed., A48a

THE MODERN THEATRE, Vol. II: Musset, *Fantasio*; Ostrovsky, *The Diary of a Scoundrel*; Schnitzler, *La Ronde*; Yeats, *Purgatory*; Brecht, *Mother Courage*—Eric Bentley, ed., A48b

THE MODERN THEATRE, Vol. III: Gogol, *Gamblers*; Labiche and Marc-Michel, *An Italian Straw Hat*; Conrad, *One More Day*; Giraudoux, *Judith*; Anouilh, *Thieves' Carnival*—Eric Bentley, ed., A48c

THE MODERN THEATRE, Vol. IV: From the American Drama—Swerling, Burrows, & Loesser, *Guys and Dolls*; Fitch, *Captain Jinks of the Horse Marines*; Mitchell, *The New York Idea*; Wilder, *Pullman Car Hiawatha*; Saroyan, *The Man with the Heart in the Highlands*—Eric Bentley, ed., A48d

THE MODERN THEATRE, Vol. V: Buchner, *Danton's Death*; Gogol, *The Marriage*; Ghelderode, *Escurial*; Anouilh, *Medea*; O'Casey, *Cock-a-Doodle Dandy*—Eric Bentley, ed., A48c

THE MODERN THEATRE, Vol. VI: Musset, *Lorenzaccio*; Wedekind, *Spring's Awakening*; Sternheim, *The Underpants*; Beerbohm, *A Social Success*; Brecht, *The Measures Taken*—Eric Bentley, ed., A48f

## MUSIC

# ANCHOR BOOKS

## LITERARY ESSAYS AND CRITICISM

## Literary Essays and Criticism (continued)